AMERICAN TEENAGER

Ward Of The Court

By: JIMMY MAXWELL

JIMMY MAXWELL

badass productions

This is a work of non-fiction.
However, many of the names have been changed to protect
the innocent, and the guilty alike.

Published by Badass Publications

First published in the United States by
Badass Publications

First Edition

ISBN-10:
ISBN-13: 978-0-9971632-9-2

JIMMYMAXWELL.NET
BADASSPUBLICATIONS.COM

DEDICATION

This book is dedicated to Maxine Fullerton.

A nice lady with a sweet soul.

–Rest in Peace–

June 6, 1980

JIMMY MAXWELL

Contents

ACKNOWLEDGEMENTS

Thanks to my wife Karin Lisbeth Maxwell, my rock, my strength, my moon and my stars. Who without I couldn't do what I do. I would also thank my beta readers/copy editors Red Beard and Shaggy. We do the best with what we got, don't we fellas.

I'd also like to put a word in for the people at Crystell Publications. They put in the footwork scanning, typesetting, and creating this book's cover and interior design. If you need help publishing a manuscript, I suggest contacting them at: CrystellPublications.com

FOREWARD

This book is non-fiction...or as close to it as my memory and my very limited research resources allowed. Having said that I must clarify that, other than Mrs. Fullerton's, all of the staff members' names from the Helena reformatory have been changed and many of the inmates names as well. Also, I often blended two or three personalities of guards and extras together so as not to bog the reader down trying to keep up with a lot of different characters. The side stories I filled in from knowledge that I gained directly from the individual I was writing about or indirectly by other means. I did the best I could considering that I am still incarcerated and wrote and edited this with nothing more than a Brother type writer and the help of a few friends. Be watching for a revised second edition of *American Kidd: End of Innocence* to be re-released soon, and the new story I am working on called *American Bad Boy: Coming of Age*. I hope that you the reader enjoy these books. I wrote them with aspirations of building a solid foundation for my future on the wasted ruins of my self-destructive past. Please know though I am not trying to glorify, nor advocate violence or criminal activity. My wish is, actually, that people see my mistakes and strive not to repeat them.

Sincerely, Jimmy Maxwell

PROLOGUE

El Paso, Texas
1978

Blood. Bright red, arterial blood. It was everywhere. So much I could smell it, thick and coppery in my nostrils. I was in shock. The whole thing happened so fast. Less than ten minutes was all it took to paint the walls red.

I had just gotten home. Something was wrong, that was obvious soon as I stepped through the door; the living room was trashed. I grabbed a butcher knife from the kitchen on my way down the hall to investigate the noises coming from the back bedroom. It sounded like one person. I was supposed to be watching my friends' trailer house while they were out of town. Rick and Bud were tied in with a Juarez cartel and it probably wouldn't go over well if I were to let their house get robbed while they were gone. I was focusing so hard on that thought and what was in front of me that I was caught completely off guard when another thief stepped out and grabbed me from behind, pinning my arms to my sides.

"The kid's back," the man holding me hollered over my shoulder alerting the guy in the back room. His breath and body odor stunk so bad it assaulted my sinuses like something dead and decomposing in the dump.

The one in the back came out wearing one of Rick's shirts over his stained and filthy one. He was holding a pair of Rick's boots in one hand, and a big claw-hammer in the other. Presumably what they had used to spring the lock on the back door that was hanging open. They were just bums. Nevertheless, they evoked terror in my soul when the menacing-looking transient marched up the hallway and hooked the claw of the hammer in my orbital socket, and threatened to gouge out my eyes if I didn't tell them where the money and drugs were. I knew without a doubt that I was face to face with death.

The man said they had been watching us from their camp across the levee for weeks and knew there was a big drug operation running out of the trailer. The men also seemed to know I was alone.

Up until then, that was the closest I had ever come to true evil. I was scared and lashed out from a place of pure fear and survival instinct. No heroics, nor cockiness to it. The tidal wave of blood that soaked and squished in the carpet after I'd gotten the kitchen knife turned around in my hand and stuck bone-deep beneath the groin of the smelly robber holding me, was mind-numbing, and frightened me almost as much as the men had. It was just as shocking and unexpected to my friends who came home in time to catch the would-be robbers before they could crawl away.

I thought they would be mad at me—but instead were full of compassion...and maybe...respect. The look in my friend's eyes when he told me they would deal with the clean up, I just needed to get as far away from El Paso as possible, and that I didn't want to know what was going to become of what was left of the hoboes, told me all I would ever want to know.….

One month later, and 500 miles away.

A squad car pulled in across the street and my heart skipped a beat.

The cops had been asking around about me, but wouldn't say why. It baffled me how they could have found me so fast. I'd run as far as I could, all the way to Guymon, Oklahoma. I had nowhere else to go. If the killing of those two homicidal hoboes back in El Paso was what this was about I supposed it was better to know it now. I could not keep having a meltdown every time I saw a cop; I'd be shit house crazy by the time I turned sixteen. With nerves stretched tighter than a barbed-wire fence, I stepped out the front door and walked up on the two officers before they got out of their cruiser.

"I hear you're lookin for me. What for?"

The policeman driving stood and shut his car door. He was middle aged and overweight, but still looked formidable. As did his partner coming around to join us.

"You James Maxwell?"

I nodded. "Jimmy. Yeah."

He raised an eyebrow. "Well, son, we have a report that you're a runaway."

Runaway?

At first, relief washed over me, then from nowhere it changed to anger and my face flushed.

Runaway!

In my mind I was so far beyond being a runaway that the label made my blood run hot. Where were the cops when a kid actually needed them?

"I'll be damned if I am! My step-dad kicked me out over a year ago. Been on my own ever since." I puffed up my chest getting more confident. "I moved to Guymon to get a fresh start. Ask my grandmother, Jean Moyer, if you don't believe me."

"She is the one who reported you missing. It is my understanding that you have just turned fifteen."

"So what. That doesn't change anything," I said.

The heavy officer raised his hands. "Look, I'm not your enemy. I don't know what the law says about a situation like this, but we would like you to come down to the station so we can figure it out."

Still piqued but disarmed by the man's body language, I agreed, "Yeah. Why don't we do that." I got in and rode with them to the station.

Now that it was clear they weren't after me for what may or may not have happened back in El Paso, I was feeling more than a little galled that I was apparently in trouble...for what...surviving? Still too young and naive to know that going through police station doors from the outside, is a lot easier than coming back out of them again—we weren't to that point yet, where going in and not coming back out had become a lifelong affliction—I marched through the glass double-doors of the precinct feeling justified in my emancipated status and bitter that after all I'd been through, this was what the authorities cared about. The officers called in Judge Ogden, supposedly a family friend, the district attorney, and my grandmother.

My grandmother hadn't been trying to get me into trouble, and she didn't know the circumstances for which I left Texas. She was trying to do what she thought was best. Regardless, by the time I had my say, considering they did not know why I'd left El Paso either, and there was no specific law at the time requiring me to live with my grandparents, it was determined that as long as I maintained a job and valid residence they really couldn't do anything to me.

Of course, this all transpired with a knowing and slightly wicked glint in the prosecutor's eyes. Which is something I have subsequently come to know so well. He said before I left his office that my status was contingent on my staying out of trouble, and the moment I didn't they would load me up and send me off to Helena, a boys' home, where I would have to sit until I aged out at eighteen.

Well, as life went, I didn't do too bad. I lied about my age and with a fake ID I'd brought from Texas, got a job in the oil field working on a rig. My girlfriend, Tina, and I got a little place and bought a run-down Ford Galaxy 500.

Things were great, except I'd hooked-up with probably the most promiscuous girl in the panhandle. Tina was a couple years older than me and tended to sleep with adult men. So with what little pugilistic experience I had picked up my few years on earth I found myself battling it out with men who had no idea they were getting their asses handed to them by a fifteen year-old kid. Life is what it is I didn't say I was smart, but I was passionate about the things I believed in.

Whether it be work, love, fighting, or family.

A few months into my new life in Guymon it finally happened: Unable to take his frustrations out on me, my stepfather's anger found other outlets, such as my little brothers, and my mother.

The day I called home and found her crying because he had slapped her, was the day I got arrested for stealing tires from a used car lot. I needed fresh rubber on my Galaxy so I could make the eight-hour drive to El Paso to destroy the man. Realistically, when I was thirteen I may not have been able to handle my step-father. But at fifteen and oil field strong, I could have killed him with my bare hands, at the very least hospitalized him, settling a long standing score.

I don't know which one of us God was looking out for that day, but I was caught and taken into custody in the midst of the tire heist. That seemed to be what the D.A. was waiting for; to prove his point I guess.

True to the district attorney's word, the next thing I knew, I was on my way to the reformatory in Helena. *Hell* for short. It was said to be the roughest juvenile facility in the state at the time. And it's where I started my criminal education, my violent reputation, and my never—ending cycle of one reform school, jail, prison, and escape after another....

CHAPTER 1

HELENA

When the sheriff's deputy and his plain-clothed side-kick turned west down the long, ruler-straight avenue that led to the Helena Boys Home; I remember thinking that I had really screwed the pooch this time. Helena was going to be long-term compared to what I'd been through before. Judge Ogden had said nine months, but I knew that the system could potentially keep me until I aged-out at eighteen. Considering I was turning sixteen in a few days, that was bad news for me.

Nineteen seventy-nine was on its way into nineteen eighty; rap music was taking off with the Sugar Hill Gang's, *Rapper's Delight*, Steven King had come out with *Dead Zone*, and Iranian militants were holding multiple hostages in Tehran. Or, at least, that was what Paul Harvey was droning on about over the radio while we'd been making the three-and-a-half-hour trip from Guymon.

I'd been all eyes most of the ride, taking in the overcast gray-green landscape and squirming around in the back seat trying to get comfortable in my handcuffs and leg-shackles. Although, once we reached the small farming town of Helena, Oklahoma, and I heard the deputy's buddy—who was acting as navigator—say the facility we were looking for should be in sight soon...all of my attention became laser focused through the dirty front windshield, anxious to get a glimpse of what awaited me. There were buildings along the north and south sides of the road that led to the teenage prison, but I couldn't tell you what they were. Those structures we were rolling past registered as no more than blurry shadows dancing across my peripheral vision. Ghostly mirages made of wood, concrete, and steel funneling me towards a frightening and unknown future.

I didn't have long to wait. I spotted the complex of drab institutional red-brick buildings a quarter mile off. The front unit was spread out facing us at the end of the road; a three-story, stone beast anticipating its next sacrificial youth. The avenue we were on rolled right up to a guard shack, which squatted next to a tall, ornate, iron gate. As it came into full view I could see six or seven more, one-, two, and three-story buildings that were all connected by a matrix of sidewalks. The whole place was surrounded by a single twelve-foot-tall chain-link fence that had five strands of barbed wire strung across the top between angled spikes.

It had an ominous feel to it that turned my stomach to lead.

On top of everything else it appeared empty, almost haunted, there was not a single person, staff nor inmate on the compound. Of course it was mid-October, and Old Man Winter was on the porch pounding on the door. A nice day would show itself occasionally, but this was not one of them; it was cold and windy and I suppose intelligent people chose to stay inside. Regardless, the place appeared gloomy, and uninviting, just the way most probably think an institution for the unruly wayward teen should look.

Damn it, I thought, as we pulled into a parking space next to the gate house, *this is going to suck...big time.*

When the deputy opened the door to let me out, a blast of frigid air blew in. The county mounty straightened his cowboy hat and spit a mouthful of tobacco juice on the curb before he pulled me out by my handcuffs. They were handling me kind of rough for a guy who'd been out on bond the last several months and had turned himself in that morning at the courthouse. But, whatever. I followed him into the shack, taking short steps and dragging the chain of my leg-shackles between my ankles, our plain-clothed side-kick bringing up the rear.

We were met inside by two older men. The one sitting behind a desk was dressed in bib-overalls, his sweat stained ballcap laying beside him leaving his bald head pale while the rest of his face was the color of cured leather; farmer, I surmised. I was not sure what to make of that deduction but hoped I hadn't just walked into the town the movie *Deliverance* had been based on. I could almost hear the banjo music in my head. His compadre was cut from the same cloth, except he had stubbly gray hair and wore a long-sleeved button up shirt, jeans and cowboy boots. He was standing, leaning against the wall. His leathery face showed deep crow's feet around his eyes as he frowned at me.

"Howdy." The bald one stood up behind a worn wooden desk and reached to shake the deputies' hands. "Y'all have someone fer us?" When he spoke, I noticed he was missing a couple teeth and the ones he had were badly stained. I just knew at any moment he was going to look at me and yell "Squeal like a pig, boy!"

The deputy jerked his thumb towards me, "Yep. James Maxwell, from Texas County, Guymon Oklahoma." He moved up to the desk producing my court documents and I lost interest in what they were saying.

I shuffled over to the window so I could look over the grounds. From there I could see that the buildings all had white painted metal shutters covering their windows, horizontal slats instead of bars, but still effective for keeping people in. I also noticed the braces on top of the fence that held the strands of barbed wire were leant inward over the grounds, and the upper six-foot-wide section of the fence was a much tighter chain mesh than the lower half. I was wondering how many kids had tried to get away from here to warrant the extra security measures, when—

"That's designed so potential escape artists cannot get their fingers in between the links and climb, over." I turned and saw the gray-haired man staring at me.

"What?"

"I can see you are already looking for a way out. It's not going to happen here. Even if you made it off the grounds there is nothing but flat fields and well-armed farmers for fifteen miles in every direction."

He walked over to another window facing the south and waved his hand toward it for emphasis. Sure enough, two or three houses away the town ran out and there wasn't anything except flat, empty fields for at least a half-mile before I even saw a tree.

Although, I couldn't help but think: *Where there are trees, there are places to hide.* I kept the thought to myself and simply replied: "If I was planning on running off, I wouldn't have self-surrendered to these guys this morning. I'm just curious. I have never been in a place quite like this."

He stared at me for a minute, then finally grunted as if he was satisfied and pushed himself off the wall.

To be honest he wasn't all that far off the mark. I hadn't gotten to the point of actually plotting a breakout, or even deciding to, but I was already regretting showing up at the court house and turning myself over to Barney Fife and his trusty companion, Dudley Do-Right.

The man walked over to me and glanced through the glass I stood by. "That's where you're going first." He pointed up the sidewalk toward a big building that sat at the top of a slight rise. The beast I'd honed in on from the road. It was the mantle-piece of the complex. All the other structures were constructed behind and to its sides. From this close it looked like the offspring of an old Victorian manor and a state run psychiatric hospital. In the front was a fan-shaped spill of wide concrete steps, which led to an equally wide covered porch. The upper landing was framed by two, tall, white columns decorated with ornate capitals and bases. The building was a hundred and twenty feet from end to end and two-and-a-half stories tall with the lower office-floor windows ground level.

"That building is called Impala, it's our receiving and orientation unit. You'll live there four to six weeks before moving to one of the other buildings." He pointed north of Impala. "The building to the right of receiving holds Mustang on the first floor, and Cadillac on the second."

I glanced at him.

He read the question on my face. "They are all named after cars. The building behind Mustang is Thunderbird, and above that is Corvette"—he waved his hand to the left—"and over there is Camaro."

"I can see you are a cocky kid, probably think we're some backwoods yokels—you have that look. Self-surrender or not, we aren't going to put up with any shit from you. We have a place for trouble makers, and people who know just how to deal with them. Just so you know."

The deputy and his side-kick had finished processing me in, they retrieved their cuffs and shackles, then with a few parting words and a wave at the other men they left. I went to pick up my stuff, but Baldy informed me I wouldn't be getting my property; ie; soap, shampoo, toothbrush, shoes, etc. Which I was told I could bring, until I got through receiving.

"Bob, you want to walk him up to Impala?" the bald desk-jockey with the bad teeth asked the man who had been giving me the company speech.

"Sure, Hank. I'd be happy to check this gentleman in." Bob unlocked a door facing the compound and escorted me through it.

Despite the stoic face I presented, I could not remember feeling so lost and alone in a long time. I wondered what I was walking into and what kind of kids would be here. I'd already been through my fair share of tribulations over the course of my young life and I was confident I could handle myself in most circumstances, but as "Bob" walked me up that long cold sidewalk toward the menacing stone buildings that were full of troubled teens just like myself, my heart pounded in my chest like a boy who just woke up in a dark casket full of tarantulas. I tried to push the fear away, but there were too many unknowns ahead of me. In the end, I sucked it up and faked it the best I could.

When we got to the top of the steps I could see faces looking at me through the wrought-iron bars that covered the glass front door. Kids of all shapes, sizes, and colors, vying with each other trying to get a look at the newbie on his way in. I took a deep breath and squared my shoulders while the stooped, white-headed house parent—as the housing guards were called—ambled up from the inside and unlocked the door for Bob and me.

When we entered the foyer the first thing I noticed was the smell of antiseptic supplies and sweat. The building tender—another name for the unit guard—had ordered the residents to their cots before he'd let us in. I saw rows of beds separated by waist-high wooden partitions with a built-in desk and chest-of-drawers in each lining both the east and west walls of the place. The north wall held an office that doubled as a class room and the south end of the housing unit was where the bathroom and showers were. The floor was gray and white square tiles in a checkerboard pattern and the walls were pale yellow. There were faces in almost every alcove staring out at me from over and around their wooden barriers. A few had tough, bored looks etched in them; the sort of *'I don't give a fuck'* expression I myself was trying hard to carry off, but most just appeared as frightened and insecure as I felt on the inside.

After a few words with the aging key-man, who introduced himself as Mr. Green, Bob passed me off to him like I was a human baton in a relay race and left the same way we'd came in.

When the door was secured Mr. Green gave a nod and the kids began moving around. Most went to the TV area in the south wing, which was made of three plastic benches sitting horseshoe-shaped around an old black and white Magnavox. Several of the kids gathered around me as I followed the man to his desk. It was strategically located fifteen feet inside the door, where he had an equally good line of sight covering both ends of the building. There was a locked door to a stairwell behind the desk that I later learned led to the floor above—LTD; a unit for high-crimes, misfits, and trouble makers—and below to the administrative offices.

"Where are you from?" a short and stocky blond-haired boy asked. He was wearing jeans and a red-and-blue flannel shirt, which at least let me know we weren't going to be decked out in some sterile uniforms.

I told him my name and that I'd came from Guymon that morning. "What about you?"

"My name is Tracy Brunkin. I'm from the south side of Oklahoma City. You can call me TB if you want."

"TB stands for Tuberculosis. Is that really your nick name?" I said with a sly smile.

"Well...I thought it sounded cool. But now not so much." He laughed. "Just call me Tracy, or Tracy B." He indicated a tall kid with shoulder-length dark hair. "This here is Nathan Lentz, from Tulsa." Then pointing at a small Mexican... "And Niegro is from Broken Bow. I can vouch for these guys. Can't say much for the rest of these pussies."

"Who you callin' a pussy, white boy?" a tall, lanky, black kid said as he sauntered up.

I bristled at the intrusion, ready to get my first fight out of the way right off the bat. Standard procedure in any new lock-up. But Tracy B. laughed, before he announced: "...And Kilo here is the biggest pussy of them all!" Tracy dodged a half-hearted punch from Kilo. "Naw...really he's alright too—for a jungle bunny." This time Tracy caught a blow to the chest. He grunted and laughed.

"I got your jungle bunny, cracker," the black kid shot back, smiling also.

"We were in the Barry House together. Kilo backed me up against some gang bangers who were jumping me. He's a good dude." Tracy finished his speech while rubbing the spot where his black friend had hit him. Apparently the Barry House was what passed for juvenile hall in Oklahoma City.

Mr. Green shuffled around his desk and shooed most of the kids away, then told Nathan and Niegro that I was bunking between them on the north end, and had them show me where it was. They hung out while I made my bed. My two new friends were full of stories about why we were going to be stuck there, *in Hell*, as they called it until we turned eighteen. 'Didn't matter what the judge said, parole was a joke', they told me. That night I laid in my bed, tossing and turning between the rough sheets, thinking that there was no way I was going to stay there for two whole years!

Over the next few days I settled in. My birthday came and went with no more fanfare than a card from my grandmother. By default I started hanging with Tracy, Nathan, and Niegro.

Tracy was a car thief, he knew a lot about automobiles. His uncle, "Trouble", had a chop shop since before he could remember. Said he'd cut his baby teeth on the steering wheel of his first stolen car. He might have been a bit full of shit, but I had no doubts that he knew his business.

He told us he got sent down because, unbeknownst to him at the time, the Cadillac he stole belonged to the mayor of Oklahoma City. Apparently, the caddy had been passed down from his late father and was extremely sentimental. Needless to say, the police pulled out all the stops, beating the streets black and blue, trying to find it. He and his uncle had never seen so much heat come down over a car.

When the cops started kicking in doors and putting pressure on some of their associates in the "car business", Tracy's name was dropped. His Uncle Trouble told him to ditch the car somewhere and take the loss, so the mayor could get his ride back and the heat would have a chance to die down. Then maybe they could get back to business as usual.

While Tracy was on his way to park the Cadillac over on the northeast side of town, hoping to draw the heat off him and his family on the southwest side, the cops spotted him. They chased him right off the side of the overpass at I-35 and 44th Street. He survived, but the car was not so lucky.

The mayor wanted him certified as an adult. The D.A. however, said that even though the car was special, it was still just a car and not serious enough to justify adjudicating Tracy as an adult. Nevertheless, he did send Tracy on the first thing smoking to Helena.

I picked his brain about how to hot-wire different models and told him and the others about breaking out of the group home back in Texas with Jerry, Ben, and the girls. "We sure could have used you then," I admitted. I left out any reference to the would-be robbers and Rick and Bud's little weed empire, but I caught them up on my move to Guymon, along with what sent me to Helena; which seemed lame in comparison to some of the other's charges. However, they were pretty impressed that I had my own car, apartment, and a live-in girlfriend.

Niegro was seventeen. He was small and wiry, and had a bad habit of breaking into houses. He reminded me of some friends I had back in El Paso. "I can get into anywhere," he claimed, "but I really only steal to help my big sister. Since our parents died in a tornado a few years ago she's been working two jobs trying to take care of me and my two sisters. The judge said she couldn't keep me in line, that's why they sent me here." He looked frustrated and pulled on the end of a short wispy mustache he was cultivating. "I need to find a way out of here, so I can get home and help her."

"You couldn't go home. They'd find you," I pointed out. Even though I had begun thinking about the very same thing, myself. It was really a no-brainer if what they said was true and I was going to have to age-out, anyway.

"I only have to make it six months," Niegro said. "Then I turn eighteen, and they can't touch me."

I nodded as I stored that information in the back of my mind for future reference.

Nathan told us he was Jewish. He looked the part, I guess, he had dark thick eyebrows and dark hair. Although, that is where the similarities to the nice, business minded, religious folks that I stereotyped Jewish people to be...ended. His mom and dad were no holy-rollers. Nathan's pops was a Mongrel biker and his mom was a stripper. He'd grown up around drugs and partying since he was a small child. It should have been no surprise that he would be involved in some kind of illegal activity early in life. Eventually, he got busted selling weed to an undercover agent.

Nathan believed they were really after his dad. When they couldn't get close to his pops he thought they settled for him. Why they would "settle" for a sixteen year-old kid, over a gang affiliated drug dealing adult I wouldn't know, but Nate seemed to think he'd taken the hit for his dad, and wore that belief like a badge of honor.

"That was pretty solid of you," Tracy said. "I'll bet he is proud of you."

"Naw. He just thinks I'm stupid for selling to the dude. Although, Dad will kill that narc if he finds him."

"What's wrong with your chest?" I asked him. His sternum stuck out almost to a point.

He told us his dad's motorcycle fell over on him when he was seven and broke his ribs.

Niegro popped off. "Damn, does it still hurt? It looks like it hurts."

"Only when I laugh!" He slugged Niegro in the shoulder and busted out laughing, then grabbed his chest like he was in agony.

Nathan had a thousand funny stories and kept us in stitches. Though I learned he was really pretty bummed under it all. He worried about his mom; didn't like her working at a strip club. It was dangerous, amongst other more obvious things. Nathan would quietly relate his fears to me through our partition after the lights went out.

Kilo and Tracy had a pretty close bond forged out of adversity, so Kilo adopted us as well, and in turn, we adopted him back. He was only fifteen, but he'd been in a lot of trouble already and was lucky to still be handled by the courts as a juvenile. He had been caught trying to rob a convenience store with a pocket knife.

His mom's boyfriend sold heroin. Kilo knew where the dude kept his stash and would pinch a little every day or so. The man noticed his shit missing and set a trap, catching Kilo in the act. Threatened to beat him in the head with a tire iron if he didn't pay him "in full" by the end of the day. Instead of getting the money, Kilo got sent to Hotel Hell, with us.

We didn't know much about racism back then. The other black kids didn't seem to like Kilo that much, he fit in better with us than them.

When we got into a fight with four or five black gang-bangers from Lawton over control of the TV, Kilo rode with us. Nobody knew he was doing anything wrong. His help gave us the edge, and we beat down their whole clique. We came back to our side of the building whooping and hollering and slapping each other on the backs. Battle tested and solidified into an eclectic band of brothers.

A week later I got into it again. This time with a big white kid from Woodward, Oklahoma. He'd come in with a chip large as the state of Texas on his shoulder. We'd both worked the oil field and pretty soon we were arguing about who could run rods the fastest. It may sound stupid, but those things mattered to us at the time. It led to him jumping up and shoving me, and me three-piecing him before we ended-up rolling around on the floor until enough staff arrived to pull us apart.

This time I went to lock-up for a few days. Lock up was called "Dodge House"; a long, one-story, stone building. Inside was no more than a hallway with a half-dozen six-foot-wide brick cells lining each side. The rooms were plain and empty, except for a toilet and a cot. They were pale blue, and smelled like urine and dirty clothes. Light came through a small window at the top of the outer wall which you had to pull yourself up to the sill by your fingertips to see out of. It was while trying to scale the wall to get to the window that I realized I'd broken a bone in my hand. The one that connects the wrist to the little finger, I had done it before and knew it was called a boxer's fracture.

It took them a week after I got out of the hole to take me to the clinic where they set it, giving me a light-aluminum brace, and wrapping my hand and forearm with an Ace bandage. Leaving me, I thought, quite vulnerable.

We spent our days testing: I.Q. tests, educational and cognitive reasoning tests, medical test, drug and alcohol tests, every test you could think of, evaluating us for classes and special needs we would require as we were moved along the juvenile rehabilitation process. In the evenings, a couple of times a week, we were allowed to go to the gym to play basketball, lift weights, or just hang out and try to look tough.

One night after we'd come back from recreation Tracy asked me: "Have you had enough of this place yet, Jimmy?" We were sitting on the couches in the TV area. The light flashing from the screen in Tracy's eyes made him look like a mad scientist.

"I've been thinking about it. I didn't realize they could keep me longer than the judge said when I turned myself in."

Tracy brushed the shaggy blond bangs out of his eyes. "Well if you do I know how we can do it."—he leaned forward, lowering his voice even more—"I've already talk to Nathan and Niegro. They want to go too."

Flexing my injured hand I thought it through. The way things stood I knew I would eventually try anyway. And with the news I'd been getting from Guymon concerning Tina and our apartment... The sooner the better.

"There is no point in waiting. I'd just be wastin' time. What's your plan?"

He looked at me and grinned. "I found an unlocked window in the gym."

CHAPTER 2

ESCAPE

The sun was falling toward the horizon when the coach and our housing staff took us to recreation. The other units went earlier in the day. Since Impala was the new kids on the block we were always last. Considering what was on our minds, that suited us just fine. Our gym time would run a couple of hours. By then it would be dark and the majority of the little town of Helena would be tucked in for the evening, especially on such a chilly night.

We all wore our heaviest coats but Tracy was sure he could hot-wire something and get us out of the frigid temperature pretty quickly, so we weren't too worried about being stuck in it for long.

The recreation building was by far the best feature of the whole institution. It was a wide open-spaced three-story building that was split down the middle, north to south, by a wall and concrete bleachers that overlooked a full-sized basketball court and a boxing ring on its west side. The bleachers ran almost to the ceiling and had a flat tier on top where a weight machine and some free iron sat. In the east wing of the building, accessed by hallways that passed under either end of the bleachers was an Olympic-sized swimming pool. The staff usually wouldn't let us go back there, but it was in the north hallway that led to the swimming pool door where Tracy had found the unlocked window.

Inside the gym we tossed our coats on the floor under the open arch of the north hall, so when we were ready to make our move they would be close at hand. We didn't want to look suspicious dragging them around for an hour waiting on the sun to go all the way down. The four of us shared a conspiratorial glance and split up; Tracy and Niegro went upstairs to pretend to lift weights, and Nathan and I moseyed over to punch on the speed-bag.

From there I took a visual inventory of our surroundings. Most of the other kids were either cliqued-up on the steps of the bleachers or were playing basketball. There were a couple of lone stragglers, who just stood around trying to avoid everyone else. Kids like that were unpredictable and could walk up and foul shit up at the damndest times. One of them, a skinny fourteen-year-old, with shaggy, dirty-dishwater colored hair that hung over his eyes like a sheep dog, was hovering around our coats. He would have to move around. The kid didn't think anyone was watching and had his index finger embedded halfway up his nose.

I nudged Nathan with my elbow. "Look at Timmy over there. He's diggin' for gold!"

About that time Timmy pulled a juicy little nugget from his nostril. We sat and watched him study the green gob on the end of his finger.

Nathan leant in, "Bet he eats it."

"No way." The kid was weird, but I didn't think—

Timmy glanced around to see if anyone was looking. Then quick as you please stuck his finger in his mouth.

"And down the hatch she goes." Nate laughed, elbowing me in the ribs at the same time.

I cringed. "Oh, shit...that's gross!"

The coaches were sitting at a desk that was placed, more or less, to block the south hallway; I assumed because it didn't have a door they could lock to keep people from the pool, like the north hall did. Of the two staff members we had to concern ourselves with, the younger coach was much more attentive to what was going on than the older one, but nevertheless we knew one of them would always have to man the desk.

I settled in to work the bag with my good hand to pass the time.

"What are we going to do if Tracy can't get us a ride? It's as cold as Jack Frost's jingle balls outside and it's going to get even colder tonight."

I stopped the rhythm I had going with the speed bag. "Aww hell Nate, it ain't that cold. Besides, he'll get us a car, and if he don't...I don't know...we'll figure it out then."

I moved over and Nathan stepped up to the bag and hit it a couple of times. "I don't know how you do this shit?" he complained when the bag bounced back before he could get his other hand up.

"It's in the timings Dufus, not how hard you can hit it. So are you backing out, or what?"

"No man. I'm just sayin'. What about you...you're going to Guymon, totally the other direction than the rest of us?" Nathan gave up on the bag and we hopped up to sit on the edge of the boxing ring.

"I'm just going to get out of here first. Then I'll worry about getting to Guymon."

I heard a commotion and saw Kilo arguing with one of the Lawton bunch over who fouled who in their basketball game. The younger gym teacher got up from the desk and walked to the sidelines and the kids resumed the game.

Nathan and I talked about what he planned on doing when he got home and I told him more about my life in Guymon; my job in the oil field; my cheating-ass girlfriend; and the countless fights I had been in over her.

"You shouldn't even go to Guymon," he said. "Hell, come to Tulsa with me. There's a lot more room to hide in, and plenty of girls hanging around my dad's clubhouse."

"You're probably right. I'll think about it."

I glanced at the top of the stands and saw Tracy and Niegro staring down at me. Tracy shrugged with his palms up in a silent question, and with a quick glance around the room I located the staff members. The heavy-set older man was parked right where we knew he would be;

behind the desk. But the other guy was in-shape; pro-active; and moved around a lot; he was still hovering around the basketball court keeping an eye on Kilo and the rest of the players. However, he was currently pacing the south end of the court. If he stayed where he was I didn't see any reason we couldn't slip down the north hallway without being seen. I gave Tracy a nod.

They stood up and started working their way down the bleachers.

Nathan was looking at the floor and swinging his legs back and forth. I kicked him in the foot. "Come on. It's time to go." Jumping down from my seat I casually began making my way in the same direction. Nate followed.

I was just thinking about what to say to scare Timmy off without raising his suspicions when he saw us coming and slunk off on his own.

Tracy B. and Niegro were five or six steps from reaching the gym floor. With a peek over my shoulder to make sure the coach wasn't watching, I ducked around the wall into the hallway. I squatted down and dug all of our coats out of the pile. Nate stopped and kept watch at the entrance while Tracy and Niegro came around the corner, also.

The bleachers hid us from most of the gym. Someone would have to be coming through the front door, or standing by the north basketball goal to see down the hall. However, if either coach suspected someone was loitering around in that breezeway they would come running to shoo them back into the gym. We especially couldn't afford to be seen going out the window, we would need a head start to get over the fence and put some distance between us and the grounds.

The unlocked window Tracy had found was midway down the hall, and the sill was six feet above the floor. It was one of those wide, multi-paned frames that swung on a horizontal axis—when you pushed the bottom out, the top swung in. Once we were up the wall it would be as easy as rolling over the ledge and dropping to the ground.

Niegro was no slouch; the boy wanted to go home. He grinned at me when I handed him his coat then pushed right by Tracy and started climbing up the radiator pipes to the window sill. He pushed the bottom and it opened just like Tracy said it would.

Cold air came rushing in! I stared at Nate. He was still watching from the end of the passage way. He didn't look back, but waved his hand for us to go.

Tracy went next. He shrugged into his brown corduroy coat. When Nathan gave him the go ahead he jumped on the radiator pipes and scrambled up them. I felt another icy blast when he slid out into the night. Suddenly, Nathan was waving his hand frantically, indicating that 'the man' was on the move.

I was standing at the bottom of the window ready to make my break, but Tracy got hung up on his coat trying to hurry. He finally freed himself and disappeared. But before I could start my assent, Nate bent down as if to tie his shoe and gritted through his teeth: "He's right here don't open that window. He'll feel it."

The gym teacher yelled at a player on the court, almost from the end of the hall. I froze. When he came into view I stepped back against the wall trying to blend in with the shadows. I was reasonably sure that the coach could not see me unless he looked directly in my direction. Tracy and Niegro would be wondering what was holding us up, but there was nothing I could do about it. If I moved I would be seen.

I stood there two or three minutes with my heart pounding blood through my arteries, knowing the longer I took the less likely my friends were to still be waiting. However, I was determined to get out of there, also, be what it may.

Nate glanced back at me, he could see I was desperate to get to the window. He turned around and stepped out of the hall and yelled "Fuck you Kilo. You can't play ball to save your life!"

I heard Kilo yell something back and I lost sight of Nathan as he started down the side-lines. I leant out and saw the coach moving to intercept Nate. Once his attention was occupied with him and Kilo I tossed my coat up onto the ledge and sprang for the window. Using my left forearm in place of my hand I climbed awkwardly up the pipes to the window sill. With one last look to make sure the coach was still out of sight I cracked the sash letting in another gust of air, then spun around and slid out facing the outside brick wall. The frame automatically latched as it shut behind me. It's all or nothing now, I told myself, then dropped to the ground, scraping my hands and snagging my bandage on the rough masonry as I fell.

Crouching low in the shadows I put on my coat and repaired my wrap. It wasn't as windy as it seemed coming through the window, but it was still damn cold. I exhaled billowy clouds of frosty breath. I turned my collar up and looked around for my friends. They were nowhere to be found.

"Tracy...Niegro..." I whispered.

Nothing. Not a sound. I hesitated for a moment thinking about Nathan, but I knew he wasn't coming. He was taking one for the team. And Kilo...if he didn't know what Nate was doing, would know soon enough.

Holding onto a slim hope that I could catch up to the others I took off around the corner of the building.

"Pssst...Tracy...Niegro!" I called out louder as I cut between the gym and the visitors building. Still nothing.

There was no more time to spare wondering if they were still around. I jogged by the maintenance barn and past the automotive vo-tech. The shadows were dark next to the buildings, but the gate I was going for was lit up like home plate at Dodger's Stadium. There was no getting around it though, this little flaw in the fence system was the fastest and surest way over, especially for a guy with a broken paw.

Back here behind the auto shop the southern most fence had a double hung gate that allowed vehicles to be driven in and out of the garage. It was just as tall, and equipped with the same deterrents as the rest of the perimeter fence; however where the gate came together in the middle, there was only the latch, chain, and lock holding it shut. It appeared to only be a four-inch gap where the gate latched, but once up and standing on the chain and lock...it was just a matter of pushing one half of the gate forward while pulling the other half back to make room to slip through. Even with my left hand wrapped in an Ace bandage, getting past the fence took less time than going through the window.

On the other side of the gate I sprinted across the perimeter road and hurdled someone's adjacent chicken-wire property line. I tore through a garden and blew across a couple of nicely landscaped yards, heading south. Still subconsciously sticking to the direction I thought my two cohorts would be taking. The folly of that notion quickly caught up to me. I decided to follow my instincts and try to get beyond the first open fields that surrounded the institution before the alarm was raised and they became awash with floodlights—trapping me in town, or worse, out in the open trying to cross the flat unobscured landscape.

An older model blue pickup turned onto the street of the house I was behind, sending its headlight beams momentarily towards me. I laid flat on the ground, watching. It paused at the perimeter road I'd just crossed as if it might turn in. The truck had no state insignias on it but the driver had to be an employee. I breathed a sigh of relief when it flipped around and drove off the other way.

If I had any doubts, seeing that truck made up my mind. I turned toward Guymon—giving up any lingering hope of finding Niegro and Tracy, knowing west would be the last direction they would head—and started running as fast as I could for the nearest field.

Right before reaching open farmland something shocked me, and flipped me end-over-end into the air. "Oooomph!" I landed hard in a pile of sod. The front of my thighs ached. I rubbed them and climbed to my feet, silently cursing the asshole who had strung an electric wire across the back of his yard.

There was no time to mope. Shaking it off, I ran—stumbling over the rough, up-turned soil of the field. I kept my eyes open and wary for any more snares in my path, while puffing great white cotton balls of breath out of my lungs with every step. My only thought was of getting across that first field and putting a couple of fences and a few trees between myself and the search lights that would be flooding the expanse behind me very soon.

Nathan was torn, he thought, *There is no way Jimmy is going to make it out the window if I don't do something fast*. Escaping in the middle of winter was not his idea of a good time anyway. *Screw it*. Stepping out of the hallway he decided to take the hit for his friend.

"Fuck you Kilo. You can't play ball to save your life."

"Oh yeah? Well fuck you too, Nathan," Kilo shot back.

Nathan stormed up to the sideline.

Kilo was confused by Nate's sudden anger, but responded in kind, running up to get face to face with him. He gritted through his teeth. "What the fuck has gotten into you?"

Nathan was happy to see the coach already moving in to intercept him and Kilo. He whispered before the coach could get near enough to hear, "Just roll with it. I had to distract the police so Jimmy, Tracy, and Neigro could get out the window in the hallway."

With surprise, and what looked like hurt in his eyes, Kilo shoved Nate back a couple of steps. The younger coach was just close enough to jump in between them.

"What's going on here?"

Several of the ballplayers, mostly black, seemed to be standing with Kilo. There were only two random white guys behind Nathan.

The coach was looking at Nate and Kilo; then looked around at the others in the crowd. "Where are your friends, Lentz? Why were you standing over by that hallway? Something is going on here...I want a head count."

Nathan was stunned, thinking, *how could this guy snap so fast?* He obviously paid more attention than anyone gave him credit for.

Within minutes the man knew three kids were missing and called it in. Nate's heart sank when the horn went off. He just hoped that his friends had had enough time to get over the fence and away from town.

WOOOOoooow...WOOOOoooow...WOOOOoooow! As if I'd thought it into existence a short blast from a siren suddenly broke the cold, quiet of the night. With a look over my shoulder I could see several lights coming on shining through the fence back at the reformatory. "Damn that was fast," I gritted through clenched teeth. The blaring alarm only lasted a moment, but the silence afterward left my breathing and the blood pulsing through my veins to pound in my ears as loudly a bass drum in a marching band. The escape horn and the lights were enough to drive panic into my flight, and as my brain dumped copious amounts of adrenaline into my system I doubled my strides. I was young, fit, and fast, but after a hundred-and-fifty yards or so, even with the nitrous boost, I could feel the debilitation of my muscles as my strength quickly ebbed away. My eyes were stinging from the cold and moisture was streaming from their corners back to my ears. I squinted and ducked my head as I huffed and puffed my way across the last fifty yards of the furrowed field to the first fence line.

With no time nor energy to climb over the barbedwire property-line, I dropped to the ground and scooted under the bottom strand, snagging and tearing my down coat as I did. From there I dragged myself into the grassy ditch along the side of a dirt road.

My breath came in hitching gasps, while I desperately tried to mask the vapor trail coming out of my hot, overworked lungs. When I'd somewhat gained control of my breathing and my racing heart, I crawled up the side of the ditch and looked back at the boys home. I could smell the fresh, red Oklahoma dirt, and yellow, dry grass that was gripped between my fingers.

I'd made it farther than I thought. The detention center's fence was half a mile away now, but I could still see a lot of activity on the other side of it. Flood lights were slamming on one after another facing out into the fields, though they didn't come close to reaching me. Another dozen flashlight beams could be seen bouncing around, as personnel ran the grounds shining them in the dark corners trying to determine if we had made it off the property, or were still hiding somewhere inside of the fences. I didn't know how they'd gotten onto our departure so fast, but it was obvious they had seen something somewhere. So far, it didn't appear that they were on my trail yet.

Within minutes police vehicles arrived and began driving the perimeter road of the institution, pointing their spot lights into the yards and along the neighborhood streets. An unmarked SUV showed up and drove slowly around the farm buildings shining his lights out in the fields, thoroughly scanning every shadow his beams could reach.

Their next step would be to hit these county roads. They would want to cut us off and contain us inside a grid. I had to get past it. I had to move, I told myself—*NOW!*

Jumping up, I started running south down the dirt and gravel section-road I'd come out on. My legs hadn't had time to recover and I didn't make it a hundred yards before I had to slow to a walk. On top of my burning legs and lungs, my hand was hurting again. I assumed it was damaged when I'd ran into the electric fence.

I looked around—there was no way I could just stroll along this dirt lane or take off through another field—they would be coming down these roads soon, shining their spotlights across the flat horizons. I had to figure something out, and quick. The moon was up and I could see the darker shadows of a tree-line far to the south, and another to the west. But the search party would be all over the area before I could make it to them.

As I studied the situation I realized that my only cover, besides an occasional gnarled chinaberry tree along the side of the road, was the weeds and grass that had grown up under the bottom strand of the barbed-wire fences. It was not part of the fields nor the shoulders of the roads, so it never got plowed, or mowed, and stood a couple feet high in places. It was also ubiquitous to every fence-line I could see. With a spark of an idea I climbed over the wire into the nearest field and started walking along the inside of the barbed-barrier.

I'd not made it fifty yards when I glanced back and saw the first set of headlights coming my way. Searching the line I quickly found the tallest and densest patch of grass I could and laid on my back beside it. I had just moved the swaying foliage to hang over me when I heard the search car approaching from the north.

It came slowly rolling down the gravel road.

There was no doubt that it was members of the posse on the hunt. The car was equipped with spotlights on its side windows, and the occupants of the car would periodically stop and scan as far into the fields as their beams would reach.

They stopped and performed the ritual only twenty yards from me. I tried to become as small as I could, willing myself to blend in with the dirt and grass. When their searchlights came on my hope sank. I held my breath as the beams swung out across the frost encrusted fields.

Soon the car began moving again. I had a rock digging in my back and grass was tickling my face, but I stayed as still as a gravestone while the passenger shined his light over me. The car was so close that its acerbic exhaust fumes clawed at my nose. Then the light went out as abruptly as it came on and the car pulled forward. I let out a full breath for the first time since the vehicle approached. I tried to keep the vapor trail to a minimum but could still see it, ever so slightly.

Suddenly the passenger side spotlight came back on and the car stopped again. I clamped down on my nerves, my breath, and my beating heart all in the same instant. This time his light swung along the grassy line I was laying beside. My only reprieve was that they had pulled up fifteen yards past me.

Then with an explosion of feathers and grass a large pheasant burst from the weeds forty feet from me and took flight! *Flumph! Flumph! Flumph!*, its wings shook the air as it climbed into the sky. I tensed and fought the urge to look. The man must have rolled down his window, because I heard him and the driver laughing.

The light went out and the car moved on. This time they drove off quickly. I sat up letting go of the breath I'd been holding in and watched their red taillights disappear behind a cloud of dust.

I doubted that the institution and Helena's smalltown police force had enough manpower to double up on patrols, so I leaped up and started hoofing it along the inside of the wire in the same direction the car had driven. When I approached a crossroads, I would take my time and creep up to them in case a searcher had been stationed in what seemed like a strategic spot.

The night wore on and the land started getting rougher; farmers' fields gave way to cattle pastures that were cut up by arroyos and littered with patches of brush, scrub oak, and mesquite trees. And, of course, the occasional watering hole. With relief, I took to traveling cross-country.

When the deputy drove me to Helena from Guymon, I'd seen a sign right after we turned north off Highway 412 from Woodward, which said: Helena - 12 miles. Guymon was west—all the way out in the panhandle. The nearest highway where I might catch a ride was the four-twelve, a dozen miles south. All I had to do was continue moving southwest and eventually I would find my way home.

As the hours passed it was getting colder just like Nathan had predicted. I thought about him and Kilo. I wished Nate was with me, it would probably be easier to get to Tulsa than Guymon, and it wouldn't be near as lonely. That made me wonder about Tracy and Niegro; I hoped they had got a car and weren't freezing their asses off, too.

Tracy and Niegro were halfway to Oklahoma City by then. They had stopped in Enid long enough for Niegro to call his sister in Broken Bow and arrange for her to pick him up from Tracy's house.

"I wonder if Maxwell and Nate ever made it?" Niegro said as he lit a cigarette off the pop-out lighter in the truck they had stolen in Helena.

Tracy kept his eyes on the road and lit his own smoke from the end of Niegro's. "If they did I hope they were as lucky as us."

They had tried to wait, even tried to look for them, Tracy consoled himself. But, honestly, when he'd gotten hung-up coming over the window sill it had unnerved him. Niegro was already around the corner hiding in the shadows, anxiously bouncing from foot to foot. After a couple of minutes Tracy told Niegro, "Lets go."

"Are you sure? What about the others?"

"I don't want to leave them either, but there must be a problem, or they would have been right behind us. We can't afford to be inside the fences if they've got caught trying to get out."

With streams of frost billowing from Niegro's nostrils, he nodded. "You're right. Either something is wrong, or they've changed their minds."

With that they both ran down the side of the gym and around the automotive shop—up and over the flaw in the gate Niegro had noticed when he was looking into signing up for vo-tech.

On the other side of the fence they ran in an all out panic, tripping over short garden fences and plowing through flower beds.

"Stop." Tracy gasped at Niegro, he bent over putting his hands on his knees, "We need to go deeper into town so we can get a car. It's too cold out here."

A lot of the house lights were already off on the street they turned down. There were a few cars still roaming around, but not many. The street lights on the edge of town were widely spaced. Overall, it was quiet, and dark.

The first vehicle they came to was a blue, late model Ford pickup, sitting in a driveway. "Trucks like this are usually pretty easy to hotwire," Tracy whispered to Niegro.

There were a couple lights on in the house, but they were in the back. The truck was unlocked. Tracy B. climbed in the driver's side and stuck his head under the dash. Niegro crept in to the passenger seat. He thought it smelled like Lifesavers and rubber floor-mats. When the dome light came on he covered it with his hand and looked around in the diffused light. There were some papers and a stocking cap on the dash. A console of sorts was sitting in the floorboard across the front of the bench seat with a can of V-8 juice in the passenger's cup holder. The driver's cup holder held something else.

"I'll bet you five smokes I can get this truck started faster than you can, Tracy."

Tracy grunted. "What the fuck, I'm doing the best I can. It's been awhile."

"Well maybe these will help." Niegro jiggled a set of keys down in the foot well in front of Tracy's face.

Tracy sat up, red-faced and grinning. "Damn straight those will. Good job, Niegro."

Tracy grabbed them and stabbed the Ford key into the ignition. He hesitated. "I wonder if we should push it out of the driveway before I start it?"

"Stick it in neutral." Niegro found the switch for the dome-light and turned it off, then got out and put his shoulder to the door frame.

Tracy followed his example, but kept a hand on the steering wheel. Luckily the drive was graded down to the road, and after an initial struggle to get the wheels moving the truck began to roll. They were able to push the truck twenty feet down the road, puffing giant clouds of breath out of their overworked lungs, before jumping in and starting the engine.

Tracy pulled around and headed back toward the reformatory.

"What are you doing?" Niegro asked.

"I want to see if we can spot Jimmy and Nathan before we leave. We didn't wait very long for them and I feel a little guilty."

"Yeah? Me too," Niegro admitted. He put the stocking cap on and started digging around in the glove box.

As they drove up the cross street, their headlights shined across the yards they had just sprinted through when running from the gate. He stopped at the perimeter road that led behind the automotive shop. "Should we drive back there?"

"No. The cops might come to see what we are doing."

Tracy silently agreed and flipped a U-turn and drove back the way they had came, still looking for any signs of their friends.

He stopped at the end of the road, thinking about going back and looking along the streets again when the sirens went off, and lights down at the reformatory started coming on.

"Oh shit! *Something* has happened," Tracy said.

"Get out of here!" Niegro shouted. "They must have got caught already!"

Tracy knew it must be true. *Maybe it's for the best*, he thought, as he headed for the highway. *It is cold as a bitch out there. And I wouldn't want to be trapped out in it.*

The wind picked up and was blistering my face and cutting right through the denim of my jeans. I could not stop moving, even for a minute, without my body temperature dropping. I plodded along trying to keep it bearable.

Seven or eight miles into my trek I spotted the lights of a drilling rig. Hope blossomed in my cold soul. I circled around a pond, stopping long enough to drink a couple handfulls of dirty water, and climbed up a shallow ravine. Hugging the shadows, I ran from one mesquite or chinaberry tree to another and came up beside a wide fir next to the drill site. The sign on the side of one of the trucks said: 'Williams Drilling - Woodward, Oklahoma'.

Woodward! Hell yeah! From there, Guymon was only a hundred and twenty-five miles straight west down Highway 3. My heart beat faster. I was excited. If I could make it that far, my success would be almost assured.

I crouched watching the rig, getting more hypothermic by the second. I knew that drilling went on twenty-four hours a day, seven days a week. Normally it was divided in three, eight-hour shifts...occasionally into two, twelve-hour shifts. Either way this crew would be getting off in the next few hours.

All I could see were the regular rig hands; Driller, floor-hands, derrick man, etc. Most of them were wearing greasy coveralls, the exceptions who were in jeans and heavy coats I assumed were company men. I had been around the oil field enough to know that they each had the look of a roughneck, there were no state employees among them. Though, I remained cautious.

Finally, I decided the reward out weighed the risk. With visions of getting out of the cold and a good part of the way home, where I could surprise my friends with an unexpected appearance, I threw caution to the wind and climbed over the barbed-wire fence separating the cattleman's land from the well-head and went to ask for a ride.

I thought about my story as I climbed the metal stairs to the platform. Three men were inside the operations room. Two of them were older and obviously in charge. The third man was younger, in his early twenties. However, they all wore relatively clean warm-looking coats, jeans and boots. The older mens' hard hats were laying next to them on the control console, both of them had short dark hair, though the older of the two had gray streaks above his ears. The twenty-something year old had blond hair stucking out from under his metal cap. His hardhat was covered in different oil company stickers, a sign that said he was not new to the business. They were all leant over the panel of buttons and gauges. The younger man noticed me first and got the others attention.

It was at least one in the morning; it was a shock to see a raggedy kid materialize out of nowhere miles from the nearest town. They all stared at me with different expressions of surprise on their faces.

I looked pretty haggard, my face was blistered red from the cold and my shaggy brown hair was wild with bits of grass entwined in it from my several encounters with the ground while evading my pursuers. My blue coat was torn and had down feathers falling out of it. There were dirt and grass stains on the knees of my jeans, and a filthy bandage wrapping a metal plate which kept my hand stable, sticking out of my left sleeve.

"Erm...I noticed y'all were from Woodward. I was wondering if you would give me a ride when you change shifts?"

The forty-something-appearing roughneck with the gray running through his temples looked at me. He had deep weathered lines around his eyes and the corners of his mouth. I assumed he was the Driller, or possibly the Tool-Pusher. "Where the hell did you come from?"

The operations room was a lot warmer than the freezing wind-blown prairie I'd just crawled in from, but I still pushed my hands into the pockets of my coat and shrugged. "I was hitchhiking from Tulsa to Boise City. Three guys gave me a lift last night in Enid. They took the back roads, pulled over and tried to rob me. We fought and they jumped back in their car and left me. I've been walking for hours. I'm cold. I saw your lights. I used to work on a rig, and thought maybe you guys would help me at least get to Woodward."

"That's some crap ass luck," the other dark headed man, who appeared to be in his late thirties commented. He looked at the other men and stroked his black goatee, "I guess we can take you to Woodward. What do you think Bill?"

"Yeah sure." The man with the gray looked at his watch, "It will be another four hours before we pull out of here. You can wait in the doghouse until then."

"Thanks a lot. It's been a rough night."

"Tim, show our guest where the doghouse is," Bill pointed over his shoulder directing the younger man.

Tim led me out of the control room and along a catwalk, then back down a flight of stairs to a small trailer that was lined with lockers for the crew to store their day-clothes in. It was packed full of extra equipment also, hard-hats, zip-line for the derrick hand, and safety harnesses. It smelled like grease, oil, and paraffin. The young roughneck took off and I laid down on the long bench that ran up the middle of the room and closed my eyes. It wasn't heated and didn't have a door but it was out of the wind so I made the most of it.

I don't know if I dozed or not, but when I opened my eyes Tim was back. I was shivering so hard that my teeth were chattering.

"Listen," Tim said as he pulled the well-seasoned hard-hat off and ran his fingers back through his blond mop, "I heard Frank and Bill talking. They're thinking that you might be from one of the boys homes around here."

I stared at him with my hopes for a ride out of the danger-zone dropping with every word he spoke.

"I don't *think* they would call in on you, but you should know if anyone comes looking for you, they *will* turn you in. Anyway, I'm just letting you know..." He glanced out the door toward a newer model, four-door, maroon-colored Pontiac Catalina. "You should wait in the car. It's warmer in there and if someone does come, you'll be able to see them first."

I remained mute on the subject, but I acknowledged my appreciation and took him up on the offer.

"It's almost two, you have a few more hours to wait." The young roughneck nodded at the car again and left.

I got up and looked at the control room. The rig was makin' hole, the Driller and his protege were occupied. I didn't think Tim had told his bosses that he'd suggested I move to the car, so I crept over to it and climbed into the back seat without them seeing me. It was better to be safe than sorry.

The interior was red and smelled like cigarettes and stale beer, not entirely unpleasant. It was plush and warm as if it had been running not long before. *I might just make it yet*, I told myself. With that comforting thought I curled up in the seat pulling my coat tight to conserve heat and tried to sleep.

However, it's hard to sleep and listen at the same time. Tim had given me the heads-up; he didn't say the others would go out of their way to turn me in, but he didn't say they wouldn't either. I was acutely aware that people who are already in that sort of mind set are only one phone call, or in this case, radio call away from screwing up your whole day. So, I dozed, and jumped at every sound.

I laid there and thought about how my girlfriend, Tina, had repeatedly ran me through the rinse-cycle in the past. I decided Nathan was right, I didn't have anything to stay in Guymon for and shouldn't even try if I didn't want to get caught. Moving back to El Paso was probably my best bet. I was pretty sure Rick, Bud, and Company had already left and whatever was going to happen with that situation had already happened, or had blown over. They might have even left a way for me to find them. I was mulling those thoughts around when I heard an engine. Then a pair of headlight beams broke through the windshield and lit-up the scarlet interior like the inside of a plastic jack-o-lantern.

My heart jumped all the way up into my throat. I had to get a grip on my nerves before I got the gumption to peek over the front seat.

It was a white pickup with two men sitting in it. Painted right on the side door was a county sheriff's gold star.

CHAPTER 3

TORINO

The driver of the truck, a man with closely cropped hair and a cowboy hat, spoke briefly with his passenger before he exited the pickup wearing a brown jacket with a wool collar and a sheriff's badge embroidered on the breast pocket. The passenger, a man in civilian clothes and a John Deere cap, acknowledged him and watched as he walked around the front of the truck. The sheriff passed within twenty feet of me before climbing up the metal staircase on his way to the control room.

My time was short. As soon as he spoke with the driller my presence would be revealed. There was no choice, I had to run.

Without further hesitation I shoved the back passenger door open and made a break for the nearest fence-line. I glanced at the truck mid-flight and saw the pickup's passenger reaching for the horn. He beat on it with his hand. *Honk! Honk! Hoooooonk!*

I shot him the finger before tucking my arm close to my chest and diving over the top strand of barbed-wire. I landed on my upper back and rolled to my feet.

*Honk! Honk! Honk!...*the blowhard persisted. Someone, the sheriff, came running after me, yelling for me to "Stop!".

I ignored him and ran straight up the side of the hill as if I was a half-back going for the winning touchdown, dodging mesquite and fir trees that were growing along the slope. The top of the rise leveled onto a clear mesa fifty yards wide. By the time I was halfway across I could no longer hear my pursuers, but I kept running until the mesa abruptly ended.

It suddenly sloped twenty-five feet down to the valley floor. Just as I ran off the edge I caught sight of the upper portion of a tall fir tree sticking up from the darkness in front of me. With no time to stop...I leaped. I was airborne half a dozen yards before crashing through the upper limbs of the tree and catching the center mass of the narrowing trunk—breaking my fall. The pine branches were thick with needles and I pulled myself close to the trunk and worked my way around to the far side.

Moments later I heard men talking from the top of the plateau. I held still pressing my face against the rough bark; the bitter-sweet scent of pine stinging my eyes. Soon the voices faded, and so did my surge of adrenaline. Cold and fatigue were quickly seeping back into my muscles. Branches painfully poked me in the ribs, and sticky tree sap oozed between my fingers. It was too cold for ants or they would have, no doubt, been eating me alive. Moreover...I feared my hand was re-broken. It throbbed with every beat of my heart.

When I could not hold myself in the tree any longer, I half climbed, half fell out of it and tumbled the rest of the way down the hill. A cloud had blown across the night sky, blocking the light from the moon and stars, and it took a moment to reset my bearings.

My flight had taken me south from the oil rig, but I'd veered to the west trying to find somewhere to hide before pulling my flying squirrel act. Keeping the slope to my back I hoped would have me traveling in the right direction.

The topography rolled across the landscape like waves on the open sea. Though in places it was gouged and scarred with deep gorges and arroyos that resembled jagged claw marks across the plains. The land had very little vegetation; only dry pale grass, cactus, and the occasional mesquite bush.

When the clouds broke and let the moonlight illuminate the crest of the mesa again, I knew to an observant eye my silhouette would stand out on the horizon as clearly as a Baby Ruth floating in a swimming pool. I tried to stay low walking the plateau, but I was cold, tired, hungry, thirsty, and my hand hurt. Soon I gave up worrying about what my pursuers were up to and just plodded along, putting one foot in front of the other. I was beginning not to care whether I got caught or not.

I stepped over a patch of prickly cacti and right into a pile of cow shit. "Ugh!" I swore under my breath. There was a low outcropping of rock nearby. I sat on it and scraped my shoe with a weathered sliver of wood I found in the dirt. The whole while cursing my friends who were probably in a nice warm car, or truck, right about then. I was thinking about giving up my westerly trek to turn south for the highway, where I too might catch a warm ride, soon as possib—

VOICES!

There were two men speaking, but from the sounds I could tell there were three or four. They were west of me over a small hump in the landscape and moving in my direction. The men would be on me in seconds, their voices were getting louder and more distinct.

"...might have went further south. There ain't no way we're gonna find them out here on foot, Chett."

Recanting my earlier thought, I decided I did not want to be caught after all, and scanned the area desperately trying to find somewhere to hide. There was nothing behind me but open pastures.

"God dammit, Pete, we seen one of the little bastards just northeast of here. He's got to be somewhere close." His voice was accompanied by the crunch of boots in the dirt and the beams of at least three flashlights fanning out over a thirty yard span.

Panicked as a trapped badger I scrambled for what to do. Running back the way I had come would leave me exposed and they would probably hear me. Not to mention, if they were to the west of me, there were most likely others coming from the east as well trying to pinch me between them.

My eyes fell on a dark shadow on the ground. I noticed similar patches of darkness that, without much imagination, could have appeared to be cattle laying down hugging the prairie against the cold. Completely out of options, and out of time, I hustled over to the nearest shadow in a half crouch. It was a hollow in the earth no more than a foot and a half deep. Actually, it did look like an animal had used it as a windbreak at one time. As the men crested the knoll, I scooted into it and curled up, willing myself to be invisible.

The smell of the earth was strong—and so was my urge to flee. With my face pressing into the dirt, I lay holding my breath being as quiet and still as a chunk of petrified wood. I couldn't believe how near the men were. One was passing less than ten feet from me. Luckily the others were further south. They stopped talking and I was afraid somehow they could sense me nearby.

My hiding place was a joke. *What had I been thinking?* All it would take to reveal me laying there, would be the sweep of a flashlight. I imagined myself a stone, a log, a cow turd. Still, there was no way this was going to work. At any moment I would be caught. The slightest movement would blow my cover—if cover is what you could call it. I was making plans to jump up and run if the man came one step closer.

However, my shadow must have appeared the same as all the other dark patches peppered across the plateau—and, I can only assume, that the men never considered I might be hiding right in the middle of their path. Because they walked right by me never even swinging their lights in my direction.

I heard one of the search party members griping: "If it were me, I'd be hightailin' it straight for the highway. It's too cold to be trudgin' around out here on foot."

The closest one to me grunted some type of agreement and swore to beat the shit out of us for his misery, before turning and walking south with the rest of them.

I stayed frozen in place, afraid to move until my teeth started chattering again. There was no way for me to know if they had gone. The fear of capture had images plaguing my mind of the men hiding in ambush...ready to spring out and grab me as soon as I showed myself.

Fifteen minutes of turning that scenario over and over in my head was all I could stand. I got angry and shoved myself up off the ground ready to run, fight, or whatever depending on what awaited me. But laying there freezing my ass off, scared of every shadow, was no longer an option.

I crouched like a wild dog looking in the direction the men had walked. Nothing. Stealthily as possible, I sprinted the dozen or so feet to the summit of the small rise blocking my view and peered over, trying desperately to locate my pursuers' lights. Still nothing. No lights. No sound. No movement. I had a good field of view, I should have been able to see someone carrying a flashlight. They had vanished. *Where did they go? Where did they come from?* The mystery left me questioning my sanity. Finally, I concluded that I had laid in that hole, like a frightened rabbit, for longer than I thought. Nevertheless, I was happy I'd evaded them again.

The fact was, they now had a fresh sighting of their quarry, and the advantage I had when the posse had no idea which way I or the others had initially ran, was lost. I could now expect them to concentrate more resources in my southwesterly direction. On top of that Pete, Chett, or whomever had decided I was probably going for the highway—which was exactly what I was going to do. I was getting too cold not to. Regardless, what was to be, was a challenge I would face when the time came.

For the moment, to avoid overtaking the men between myself and the road, I forced myself to travel west a bit longer. As I walked I looked at my hand in the dim moonlight, and flexed my fingers. I decided maybe it wasn't re-broken after all. It hurt like there was a sixteen-penny nail driven through it, but my fingers moved. With renewed confidence I determined to make it to the highway and get a ride before anything else happened to it. Besides, I was so cold I was afraid my ears might freeze and break off if I didn't warm them up soon. I hiked across the remaining section of cattle land, jumping over gullies and weaving my way through gouges in the landscape, before again turning south.

Pastures gave way to farm land, then back and forth again. After a few miles I found my journey blocked by a fence-line running east and west. It was separating the flat furrowed field I'd been walking in from an encroaching forest, which seemed to be held at bay by the few strands of barbed-wire stretched in front of it. The leafless and barren trees loomed over the fence, like a crowd of ghoulish rubberneckers banished behind the crime-scene tape at a fatal accident.

The grove appeared to be overgrown and thick with dead falls, but if my sense of distance was on point, then my black, yellow-striped, asphalt ribbon to freedom would not be more than another mile or so straight through this swath of spooky looking woods.

With that thought motivating me I climbed over the fence and began plowing my way through the dense underbrush.

It was immediately obvious to me that taking a short-cut through this patch of trees was easier conceived than accomplished. The twisted and gnarled trunks of mesquite, chinaberry, scrub oak, and the occasional fir were so closely clustered that their limbs, and few remaining leaves overlapped, almost completely blocking any light from the moon and stars. The air was heavy and smelled of moss and mildew. Low hanging branches and twigs tore at my already tattered coat. My hair was long, just past my shoulders, and was also easily snagged by the pervasive brush. It was as if I fought blindly against a musty horde of grasping, bony claws.

That was not the worst of it. The timber from the cleared fields had been dragged and dumped into the surrounding thicket. Their rotting trunks and limbs were laying prostrate across the forest floor, and often stacked on top of one another like Chinese pick-up sticks, making it hard to find my footing.

Still, I struggled on, feeling my way from tree to tree and guarding my eyes in fear of poking one out on a sharp invisible twig. If I was careful with my steps I could usually find the ground, or a solid log to step on. It was harder than I had expected. On the bright side, I thought, if it was this difficult for me to get through this stretch of trees, then it would be just as frustrating for the people hunting me.

Fifty yards in I was coming to the conclusion that going this way had been a mistake, when I stumbled into a small open glade. There was a twenty foot circle of nothing but dead grass, and dry brown leaves. The gap in the canopy let the night's dim light through. It was a relief to be able to see again, even poorly.

I strolled to the southern edge of the little oasis looking for signs of the blacktop that I was so desperately striving to reach. The land to the south rolled into a sweeping depression, which allowed me to see the moon reflecting off the leafless tree tops. They reached for the light of the moon from the inky blackness below like a sea of broken bones for a quarter mile before the earth rose again. I neither saw nor heard anything to indicate I was near the highway. Disappointment seeped into my cold soul. I knew, however, if I kept going in that direction I would eventually find it.

I pulled my coat tighter around me and rested under one of the scrub oaks that bordered the pale patch of moonlit grass. There were no sounds of life, no bugs chirping, nor dogs barking in the distance; only the occasional rustle of the dry branches as the wind blew through them. I was not looking forward to entering the dark, oppressive woods again. A fit of shivering reminded me I needed to make it to the road before daybreak and it became too dangerous to hitchhike out in the open. That is, if I wanted to have some chance of getting out of the cold anytime soon.

The tangled forest swallowed me two steps after I left the moonlight and started down the hill. It was easy to imagine I was in the black bowels of a huge dead beast. Within a few steps I found it just as dark, overgrown, and hazardous with dead falls as it had been on my way in. I gave up and turned back to the clearing.

It occurred to me that I was probably safe where I was, and if I stayed put it might warm up, at least a little, when the sun rose. I would also be able to see.

However, stopping even long enough to rest let the cold seep into my bones and soon had me overcome with bouts of teeth jarring shivers. Not to mention, this particular patch of woods, with its twisted grasping limbs and tightly woven, light-blocking canopy was beginning to freak me out.

I was old enough to know there were no self-aware, evil forests, like in a Brothers Grimm fairy tale. It looked like one, though, and I was still young enough for what I knew not to matter if I let some spooky thought take root in my mind. As it was, every time fear began burrowing its way into my imagination, I struggled to reject it and think of something else. Moreover, I wasn't without ghosts of my own, and I was losing the battle. In the end, I decided it would be best to exit the forest and go around.

Soon I was trudging my way north, back the direction I had entered the grove from. I knew it was less than two hundred feet to the fence, but by the time I'd made it fifty I was brought to a halt. The debris on the ground seemed to be stacked higher than it was on my way in. My feet fell through twisted jumbles of dead branches and rotting tree limbs. When my legs became trapped and I almost lost my shoes, I retreated to the clearing. I repeated the effort in a different spot with the same results, getting more desperate with each beat of my heart and snag of a tree limb.

I tried to control my rising panic and convince myself to find a comfortable place to sleep until sunrise, but the clearing seemed smaller than when I'd first entered it. Suddenly, I realized that *it was* closing in on me!

Did that tree just move? Something grabbed my hair! I spun around, and a twig from a nearby branch scratched my face. *Was that there before?*

I paced around the dim, shadowy glade, trying not to lose control of my imagination. The runaway thoughts feeding my fears were ridiculous. I scolded myself; I was not a child to be frightened by scary, campfire-side stories, but the clearing did seem tighter. My mind turned to dead hoboes and rotting corpses. There was a rustling in the leaves behind me and something grabbed my coat. The tentative hold I held on my nerves broke—my heart raced—my adrenaline dumped—my eyes rolled back like a horse that smelled a mountain lion, and I bolted!

Within a heartbeat, I was barreling in an all out sprint through the woods to wherever my feet would take me. "Aaaahhh..." I hollered as a hundred hard gnarly fingers grasped at me and roots and branches slithered across my path trying to trip me. I stumbled as I ran, tearing my coat and pants, along with tufts of hair from my head in my flight.

Abruptly...I was slammed to a halt and almost bowled over at the waist. Then...relief flooded through me, the field I had entered from stretched out before me. I'd made it!

I quickly clambered over the barbed-wire fence I'd ran into and stumbled fifteen more feet out into the field, putting some distance between myself and the haunted forest behind me. Only then was I able to rein in my panic.

Safe at last, I leant over, my hands on my knees, trying to catch my breath. When my heart rate slowed and my panic subsided, I realized how lucky I was not to have hurt myself in my frantic flight. And...how stupid the whole thing was. I was embarrassed and glad no one else was around to see my little meltdown. I reached up and felt the scratch across my face, and found a two-foot-long twig tangled in my hair. I couldn't help but laugh at my foolhardiness.

Foolhardy or not, I still refused to turn my back on those trees and paralleled the fence-line from fifteen feet out in the field, keeping my distance from the dark foreboding thicket. I knew full well I was trippin', but as I plodded my way over the furrowed rows of the field, I swore I could still feel wickedness watching me from the dark recesses of the underbrush.

It was three-quarters of a mile to the next service road that sliced its way south through that patch of woodland. Even though I knew I was being childish, my anxiety still hung around my neck like a hangman's noose. I traveled down the center of the gravel track, keeping the trees on either side as far away as possible.

This road didn't take me all the way to the highway as I'd hoped it would. It stretched due south for a mile before butting up to another service road running east and west. I heard the jake-brake of a big-rig in the distance. The highway couldn't be far, but going forward meant tackling another half-mile-wide dark and tangled forest, and honestly, I just wasn't ready for that yet.

I turned west, figuring to walk down the gravel path for the rest of the night. I'd deal with the trees in the light of day when I could see what I was doing. Plus, I was still a little shook up from earlier and hadn't completely shaken the eerie feeling of being watched.

The section-road paralleled the highway. The moon was out but the wind had picked up and was blowing wispy clouds across the sky, blocking its glow. With the wind the temperature dropped. My breath was coming out in frosty streams, whisked away as fast as it came out of my mouth. I wrapped my coat tighter around me and kicked a rock down the gravel lane. I was miserable, but I was going to make it. Another bout of shivers quaked through my body. *Shit, if it would just warm up!* I silently pleaded with the night.

After a mile or so of walking west, I saw another service road coming in from the north to butt up to the one I was on. On my right there was a pasture, however where the road came in was a stand of trees. The corpse was only made of a handful of chinaberry trees and some over-grown mesquite bushes, but they effectively blocked my view of the incoming road.

Following my standard procedure—keeping the brake between myself and anything that might be hiding around that corner—I crept up, staying low in the tall grass of the bar ditch.

I was twenty feet from it when I saw a green, four door, Ford Torino sitting in the middle of the road right behind the tree line.

As I got closer I could hear the engine idling. I crossed over the fence and stalked up to the wooded area between me and the car. When I looked through the brush that had grown up around the chinaberry trunks, I could see the exhaust coming from the Torino's tailpipes in a steady stream. It was not a county cruiser—there were no law enforcement insignias on the Ford, but nonetheless, I knew that the occupants of the vehicle had been stationed there looking for my companions and me.

The windows were fogged up, obviously running their heater. I couldn't see who was inside, but I was jealous of them in their warm comfortable car. An owl called out from somewhere nearby and I realized I hadn't heard any animals for hours. The old hooter sounded cold, too.

I examined my options. The smartest move would be to backtrack thirty yards or so and cross the road before coming into view of the sentry. From there I could travel south through the last stretch of brush until I reached the highway. The only problem was that thicket had looked every bit as foreboding as the one I'd just been stuck in. I knew it wouldn't take much to push me over the edge again and I'd been very lucky not to hurt myself the last time.

My second alternative was to creep up the north road behind the car, far enough not to be seen by the people inside of it, get around them and keep on my westerly path.

Or...I could sit down out of sight, rest my feet, and wait for them to leave. I assumed they wouldn't be parked there for long. And, when they drove off I would know which direction they went.

My exhaustion, and my new found fear of the forest, won the debate. I decided to wait them out. It was cold and gusty, but the trees made a natural windbreak. I hunkered down in the underbrush, keeping it, the trees, and the fence, between me and the men in the car. My coat was insulated, I pulled it tightly around me and laid my head against a stump. I snuggled into a ball trying to get comfortable and retain as much body heat as possible until they pulled away. Sleeping was a bad idea, I knew, but my eyelids were heavy and I didn't think it would hurt to close them for a moment.

....there was an irritating, chattering sound in my ears. A loud clacking. *What the hell is that noise?* I wondered. I opened my eyes. My brain was numb and groggy. I'd dozed off...there were clouds of white frost billowing from my nose and mouth when I exhaled. The sound, I realized, was my teeth clicking together while my body quaked from a bout of shivers that resembled a grand mal seizure.

An icy mist had blown in. Snow was accumulating in the scrub grass. I had no idea how long I'd been asleep, but the mercury had plummeted, and the wind had picked up. Frost was in my eyelashes. I was freezing! I felt my nose with numb fingers and there was no sensation. Snot had frozen into the peach-fuzz growing across my top lip. This was horrible. I should never have stopped moving!

Before getting up to stomp some feeling back into my feet. I crawled under the barbed-wire and through the underbrush to make sure the car was gone.

I heard it before I saw it. The Torino was still sitting there; still quietly idling. The windows were still fogged up, and the assholes inside were still warm and toasty. I scooted back on my side of the wire and cursed, I was still in the same predicament I'd been in before I went to sleep. Except now, I was stiff, hypothermic, and aching all over. The nap only served to let my adrenalin subside and my scrapes, bruises, and sore muscles have time to start sending distress calls to the pain receptors in my brain.

When my legs were functioning again I crossed the fence and stood in the trees eyeing the nice warm car. *Those bastards don't deserve to catch me,* I swore to myself. But honestly, in the shape I was in I wasn't sure I could afford not to get caught. Between the change in the atmosphere, the way my core body temperature had dropped, and the fact the windows of the sedan were now completely fogged up, I knew I'd been asleep for at least an hour. I was miserable; dangerously so. Whatever the folks in the car were doing, one thing was for sure, they were comfortable and not in fear of losing an ear to frostbite.

The frigid mist dampened visibility to no more than a few dozen yards. The sentinels most likely couldn't see out of their windows any better than I could see in. I squatted on my haunches, watching, and planning my next move. I was sure I could slip around them and be on my way. All I had to do, was to do it.

But, I couldn't move; I wasn't sure that I wanted to. Once I left this car behind there would be no telling when I'd have another opportunity to get out of the cold. I feared literally freezing to death if I didn't warm up soon.

Finally getting hold of my determination, I stepped out and crouched behind the back bumper of the car. If I would only get out on the road and commit to moving on, I would be alright. I felt my face again with my bandaged hand—I could not feel my touch. Another bout of shivers threatened to shake the marrow from my bones.

My body betrayed me, and in a blink I was standing next to the driver's side window. I hesitated. I told myself there would be other chances to escape. Before I could change my mind, I knocked on the window.

CHAPTER 4

DODGE HOUSE

The men in the car didn't respond. *You're freaking kidding me*, I swore to myself. I knocked harder. This time I could sense movement inside. Momentarily, the window rolled down and I found myself staring at a thirty-something, clean-cut, brown-headed man in plain, but warm clothing; obviously just waking up. Sitting next to him in the passenger seat was a slightly older man wearing a camouflage-colored hunter's jacket, his matching hat pulled snugly down over his bald head. He was waking up also, and clearly surprised to see me standing outside of the car looking in the window. The warm blast of air coming out of the open portal made me want to climb in through it, right over the top of them.

"Hey-y-y," I said, fighting to keep my teeth from chattering, "are y-you g-guys from H-H-Helena?"

"Yes, we are," the driver answered. "Are you?"

"Y-Yes, and I'm f-f-freezing. Can you let me in?"

"Are you alone?" He was looking around as if he was expecting an ambush.

"Y-Yes, I am."

The passenger stretched across the top of the front seat and pulled the door locks for the rear driver's side door. I opened it, climbed in and pulled it shut behind me without a moments hesitation. Officially giving up.

The warmth of the car wrapped itself around me like a mother's embrace. My hands went straight to the heater vent.

"Stick you mitts up here where I can cuff you," the bald one ordered me. "Which one are you, anyway?"

"Maxwell," I said, leaning forward to stick my forearms across the top of the front seat. I held my wrists together so G.I. Joe could cuff me. He frowned at my bandaged arm then he clicked them on right over the top of it. I winced, but he didn't seem to care.

The driver was staring at me through the rearview mirror. "Where are the other two?"

"I have n-no idea," I replied truthfully, before sinking back in my seat. Even though the car was warm I was still shaking from exposure as my body thawed out. On the ride back to the juvy prison I knew I was going to regret turning myself in, but right then, peering out the window at the snow-flurries blowing by, I was just glad to be out of that freezing November wind.

The men informed the institution over their radio that they had "caught me" and were on their way in. The institution allowed they were getting a cell ready in the Dodge House. Thirty-five minutes later the two state employees drove me through a back gate and walked me straight to the lock-up unit.

Once inside the squat, white stone, one-story structure I was handed off to a couple of other officers who strongly resembled Gomer Pyle and Sergeant Carter, uniforms and all. One was tall, and a little goofy looking; the other short and angry. Although, there is where the comedy ended. Before they led me down the faded gray and black tiled hallway to put me in one of the twelve cells that lined it, they took me in the office and asked me again where my cohorts were. For which, I summarily told them to, *fuck themselves*.

In frustration, the Sergeant Carter look alike took his uniform cap off and pushed his stubby fingers through the spikes of his graying Marine hair cut. "Put him in the box?" he sneered, and then grabbed my wrists and clicked the cuffs a few notches tighter, since ol' Mr. Gungho in the car hadn't bothered to double-lock them. "Leave the jewelry on this asshole for a while."

I glared at the man but held my tongue. *Now—comes the regrets*, I told myself.

The tall Gomer Pyle looking cop ushered me down the hall to the end cell. "Sergeant Phillips is just in trouble for losing your friends, he was the shift supervisor when y'all left. He's not usually such a hard-ass." He leaned forward and whispered, "I'll take these off after he leaves," waving his hand to indicate the manacles.

Compassion; go figure. Although, I was glad for it and I nodded my gratitude.

The cell they called "The Box" was the same as the others except there was padding on the walls, the window was blocked off, and a staff member had to flush the toilet from outside the room——just in case one of us Devil's spawn tried to flood the cell by stopping-up the commode and continually hitting our own crapper button. I'm not sure if the toilet issue was the cause, but for some reason this room stank like three-day-old human shit.

I paced my cell, flexing my fingers, feeling pugnacious as hell, but exhaustion soon over-took me. Ten minutes later I was curled up on the blue-and-white-striped, piss-stained cotton mattress, which was thrown across a metal cot bolted down in the middle of the floor.

There was no pillow, and it wasn't comfortable with my wrists painfully pinched and my hands growing numb, but as soon as I laid down I was asleep. I sank into a nightmare of blood, butcher knives, and smelly hoboes with decaying teeth chasing me with claw hammers through a forest of skeletal trees.

The dream started off real enough, except when the men closed in they turned into ghouls, and when I stabbed them they only laughed. They changed from living men into decomposing corpses, and their faces stretched into elongated skulls with bits of hair and flesh hanging from them.

Fighting was futile, I couldn't hold my knife because my hands seemed to be made of rubber. I did my best, but the more I stabbed and slashed at them the bigger their ghoulish grins became. When the knife stuck in the skinny one's ribs he cackled with glee at my confusion and fear.

Somehow...I was on the ground, they were holding me down, and dozens of hands, tree limbs, and roots were clawing at me, tearing me apart. The rotting smell was overwhelming. "Come join us in Hell boy. It's where you belong. But first, let's have them eyes!"

The hammers in their hands morphed into long, wicked looking talons that extended from their finger bones. I was held by thorny roots wrapped painfully around my wrists. My heart beat like the pistons in a stock car engine, and panic set in as the claws dug into my eye sockets. Someone, me, was screaming in my head. One of my eyes came out and my equilibrium tilted. My vision split in two directions at once. I could not make sense of it, and my stomach lurched. The other hands were tearing at my rib cage. I was more terrified than I ever was in reality. Completely helpless and frozen in fear. All I could do was scream.... "Aaaaaaagh!!"

I must have yelled out loud, because it woke me up. Sweat was pouring down my forehead. I knew it for what it was, it wasn't the first time I'd had that nightmare. The wicked forest and killer tree-roots, however, were new.

I heard knocking and looked up to see the tall guard staring in the little plexi-glass window that was in the middle of the door. "Are you alright?"

I held my hands out. "Yeah, but my wrists hurt and I can't feel my hands."

"Oh...I forgot. Come on I'll take them bracelets off." He leant down and pulled the chow slot open.

It took a couple of minutes for him to get the cuff off that was cinched down over the bandaged arm. But soon I was free of them, he was gone, and I crawled back into my bunk.

I didn't go back to sleep, there were still echoes of my dream rippling through my mind. I laid there rubbing feeling back into my fingers, remembering El Paso and that day I walked in on the two homeless men robbing my friends, Rick and Bud's trailer. I knew I shouldn't have any compassion for the men, they were bad men and looking forward to hurting me before I got the upper hand, but they still haunted my dreams. When I got spooked like I did in the woods, it was always them I felt were in the shadows watching me.

I had hoped when I left El Paso, Texas, and moved back to Guymon, Oklahoma, that I would be freed from guilt. I wasn't, and it was not something I could get off my chest by confessing in some friendly sympathetic ear. So, I just battled it out with their ghosts in my nightmares.

Still avoiding sleep, I laid on my back staring at the water stains on the ceiling and thinking about my life and what brought me to this place in it.

Moving back to Guymon had been nostalgic for me. Ever since my step-father kicked me out I'd known I would eventually return to the little panhandle town. I was born there; my aunt and uncle, and grandparents lived there. I'd spent my third-grade year there when my grams stole me away from Texas and the abusive step-father I had at the time. Which was, hands down, the best ten months of my young life, and allowed me the chance to stock-up on a few treasured childhood memories.

As a little boy, I remember the joy and excitement I felt when the annual Pioneer Day Parade came to town. A couple thousand people lined-up along Main to wave at the cowboys and girls riding down the middle of that red-brick street; followed by a wagon train, a few floats, and a string of early model automobiles. It was awesome to ride in my grandad's Model-T and smile at the spectators standing in front of the shops. Considering the torment my life in El Paso was in those years, times like those in Guymon were Heaven to me.

Guymon wasn't much different when I moved back. There were a few more housing editions, and a couple more apartment complexes, but it was still your average mid-western small town. Main Street was paved with red-brick and was lined for three blocks with storefronts.

The sidewalks passing in front of their plate-glass windows shaded by forest-green awnings that extended to the street.

South Main still passed in front of the multi-story, Victorian style courthouse, then crossed the railroad tracks, went by the Arrowhead Drive-thru, and across Highway 54 before running off into south side, dirt road oblivion.

North of the business district the four-lane main street was still lined with nice manor-style homes shadowed by huge oaks in almost every yard, whose leafy branches would reach out to meet in the middle, cooling the hot road. From there Main continued past the Sonic, Walmart, and Otascos store before eventually merging into Highway 67 on its way to Boise City.

As far as the teenage kids in town were concerned, Main Street only consisted of a mile long loop from one fast food drive-thru to the other. There were parking lots scattered between the two, each claimed real-estate. The hoods, dopers, and rejects held down the lot south of the tracks, next to the crossing; the rednecks congregated in the feed stores parking lot adjacent to them; the jocks and snobs had the car lot across from the convenience store, off 7th Street. Nerds stayed in their vehicles or hung out at one of the drive-ins. The cruisers would turn into the Arrowhead from the southbound lanes and exit onto the northbound; hollering, starting fights, or looking for hookups as they passed each lot. At the Sonic, on the north end, they would circle through and do it all again like a scene out of American Graffiti.

Guymon wasn't as fast paced, nor as intense as El Paso was, but it had its charms. I'd taken my friend Rick's advice and disappeared into the heartland of rural America. Where I immediately stuck out from kids my age, like a half-grown mountain lion in a box full of kittens. I certainly wasn't the child that bounced on my grandfather's knee and who was content to play gin rummy with his grandmother anymore. I was a worker, a drinker, a fighter, and most importantly... a survivor.

It took a couple of weeks for me to land a job at a transmission shop, and within two more weeks, I'd met a girl and moved out of my grandparents' home and in with her. The next thing I knew the police were looking for me, my grandmother had reported me as missing. Which landed me, smack dab, on law enforcement's radar. The Law didn't know anything about my past, and I managed to slip the noose, but they knew who I was and kept an eye on me from then on.

I was a good worker and made friends fast. I went through a few jobs before ending up on a service rig for an oil company. Naturally, I lied about my age, so my friends were all older than me. Roughnecks partied, cursed, and fought hard. With what limited life experience I had, I partied, cursed, and fought with the best of them.

Tina Jarvis, was my first love, and my Achilles heel. Street savvy as I was, love was new to me. She was a short, blonde-haired, blue-eyed, little hottie a couple of years older than me. She was, also, completely unfaithful. And I was totally willing to fight anyone and everyone to discourage them from giving into her lascivious charms. Which didn't do much good, but did hone up my boxing game. There were a few other girls in town I'd had a short interest in before Tina and I became serious. Rhonda Redmond a pretty, brown-haired down to earth tomboy came close to circumventing my relationship with Tina before it began. So did Tina's younger sister Trisha, but it took me going to jail to truly break the hold that Tina had on my heart.

I laid on my metal cot in the Dodge House thinking about the letter I'd received from my friend, David Snowdy's wife, informing me that David had had to run several guys out of my apartment who Tina had been "whoring around" with. (Lisa's words.)

David was a good friend. He was in his early twenties, short, stocky, with curly brown shoulder-length hair—and tough as a pit-bull. His wife, Lisa, I counted a friend, too; a slight-built, pretty blonde. David was always clowning around, pulling his wife's shirt up and flashing her boobs at me just to see me turn red. We were close. He and Lisa were on the run from some misdemeanor warrant out of Minnesota.

Right after I called my mother and found her crying because Charlie, my step-dad, had slapped her I went over to the little one-bedroom trailer they rented a couple blocks from the courthouse. "I'm going to kill him!" I raved at David. "That sonofabitch picked on me nine ways to Sunday, and now he's taking it out on my mom!"

"El Paso is an eight or nine hour drive. How you gonna get there?" he asked, squinting at me through a thin haze of marijuana smoke.

"I don't know. I have enough money for either gas, or tires. Not both. I'm going to have to steal one or the other." I waved off the joint he was trying to hand me.

"There is no guarantees that crap-ass car of yours will even make a trip like that. Although, I understand how you feel. I'll help you steal some tires, it will be safer than you trying to wha-hoo gas all the way there and back."

Later that night I parked my car beside the Country Mart convenience store, which sat across a side-street from the jock's parking lot on Main. David and I hoped we wouldn't be noticed when we crossed the street and jogged up the alley carrying my long jack and four-way lug-wrench to the back fence of the car-lot. We'd spotted some wheels earlier in the day that would fit my Galaxy. The car they were on was parked against the car-lot's office building, which stood between the vehicles on display and the customer parking area where all the kids hung out.

"Was anyone paying attention to us?" I asked when David caught up to me at the property-fence. It was a warm summer evening, and Main Street and the "lots" were full. And though the sky was dark, the Strip and car-lot were well lit.

"I don't think so. Screw them jocks if they did." He gave me a cocky smile.

I shrugged and handed him the jack before turning to the fence. Back here, the fence that bordered the car-lot extended out eight feet from the corner of the office building before making a ninety degree turn to parallel the alley. When I climbed over the six-foot tall chain-link barrier, I came down in the bed of a blue Chevy pickup sitting on the other side. There were streamers tied to its antenna, and "For Sale" written across the windshield in white paint.

David handed me the jack and wrench. "Wait a minute." He leant over and picked up a couple of cinder-blocks laying next to the building, "Take these. We'll need them to stick under the hubs when we pull the tires off." I took them and he handed me two more before he climbed over himself.

The wheels we were after were on a late model, LTD, backed-up to the building next to the truck I was in. Its windshield "For Sale" sign also faced the car-lot. There were five or six more vehicles backed up to the wall in the same way, shielding us from the people cruising Main and the snobs chatting it up on their lot. The rest of the automobiles were lined up in three rows that stretched to the end of the block. They faced Main Street to showcase them to passers-by.

We wasted no time jacking up the LTD, and soon had the rear passenger-side tire off and its bare axle sitting on a concrete block. I'd already started breaking the lugs loose on the front tire when David noticed a police car cruising down Main Street.

"Jimmy," he said getting my attention. He was crouched, staring over the hood. "This cop just hit his right turn signal." He suddenly dropped below the nose of the car and looked at me. "Shit, he's turning in. We gotta go!"

David sprang up and jumped into the bed of the Chevy on his way over the fence. There was no time to worry about our tools, nor for me to go over the fence behind him. The city cruiser seeing David making a break for it, sped onto the lot and skidded to a stop in front of the LTD. I had just enough time to roll under the Chevy, before the policeman jumped out and ran between the truck and LTD hollering at David as he disappeared down the alley.

The pickup I was under sat a foot and a half off the ground. I feared being exposed if the officer leaned down. While he was still focused on my buddy running off on the other side of the fence, I hooked my feet around the transmission end of the drive-shaft and my arms around the rear-axle, then I pulled myself up as tightly to the truck's undercarriage as I could.

I heard the policeman curse—he was far too over weight to scale the fence and run David down. His blue pant legs, with a yellow strip running down the seams, and his shiny black shoes paced back and forth two feet from me. It was unnerving, to say the least. The cop was obviously assessing the situation. When he leaned over the bed of the truck to inspect the LTD tire that I'd already thrown in it ready to be tossed over the fence, his feet came so close I could see my reflection in the glossy toes of his shoes. *I'm going to jail, there is no two ways about it,* I told myself. Sweat was making the palms of my hands slippery.

From there the law man turned and looked at the jack, which was still holding up the car. When the officer bent over to pick up the lug-wrench laying on the ground, I tensed and tried to blend into the dirty, greasy underbelly of the pickup. Though I had quit breathing, the acute acrid scent of the oily grit from the truck's previous mileage was strong in the back of my nostrils.

When the man straightened back up without noticing me hanging from the drive-shaft like a giant sloth from a tree branch, I closed my eyes, then slowly breathed out a lung full of tension I hadn't realized had seized me.

The policeman's feet shuffled back and forth a few more seconds before he got back in his car and drove off—presumably to report the attempted theft and search for David.

After he was gone I remained glued to the drive-shaft a few more seconds before working up the nerve to lower myself to the ground. My muscles were in knots. The officer would be back soon or send another squad car to follow up on the scene. It was time to get out of there while I had the chance.

After rolling into the open, I jumped up scanning for signs of the law-dog or any other potential problems. Not seeing any, I walked to the row of vehicles facing Main. The street was full of people in cars waving and hollering at each other, however I didn't have time to waste trying to be covert. I stepped out emerging between a black van with a porthole-style window high on its rear quarter-panel and a tan Thunderbird that had, "Fully loaded $2,000" painted across its windshield.

My sudden appearance didn't seem to draw any undue attention, even though I'd emerged directly under the brightest streetlamp on the block. At least, not until I went to cut across the Jock Lot. I realized there was grease all over me about the time one of the snobs who frequented that parking lot stepped in my path. "Hey. Were you back there messing with those cars?" Apparently, the officer had stopped around there asking questions.

The kid's comment was drawing attention. I glared at the junior sleuth, "I don't know what you are talking about, but you'd best get out of my way." I kept walking toward him. He and his buddies moved aside, but kept throwing questions at me.

I left them grumbling in their lot as I stepped off the curb and walked to my car parked on the side of the small store.

When I reached in my pocket for my keys I discovered it was full of lug nuts. They went into the glove box before I started the Galaxy.

What I didn't know, was that several of the wanna-be Hardy Boys from the lot I'd just pushed my way through were flagging down an officer driving past on Main. By the time I started my car and was backing out, the cop was sliding to a stop behind me trying to block me in.

I took in the situation quickly. Angry...I hit my gas-pedal, revving my engine and throwing my junky Ford Galaxy backward. The squad car pulled up a few feet not wanting me to ram him, but then he stopped, apparently deciding to sacrifice his city car. I stopped also. Hitting him would only make the situation worse. Slamming my palms against the steering wheel I cursed. I was caught.

Five months, and several court hearings later—and here I was laying on a piss-stained mattress in Helena Home for Misfits with no idea which direction my life would take from there.

The next day a ferret-faced guard in his forties peered in the small window of my cell. "You'll have plenty of company back here, real soon," he sneered. "The hounds have tracked your friends into a patch of woods about ten miles southwest of here."

After he walked off I scooted up to the door listening to the radio chatter coming across ferret-man's walkie-talkie. The dogs, from what I overheard, were definitely onto something, or someone; however, the cops weren't able to penetrate the brush to confirm what, or who. The brake, they claimed, was so dense the animals couldn't even get through. There was no way for me to know for sure, though my guess, given the direction the posse was reporting from, as well as the description of the forest they were stuck in, was that the hounds were actually tracking me into that spooky tangled thicket from the night before. I smiled. The jack-ass guard could be snotty all he wanted— Niegro and Tracy had beaten them.

I laid back down, flexing the fingers of my aching hand. I never should have given up. The day had warmed a few degrees with the sun, even though the early morning did spit out a couple hours of freezing sleet. Still, if that was my scent the dogs were following—they were way behind. I could be halfway home myself by now!

As the days dragged by and the weeks passed the angrier and more miserable I became. Thanksgiving came and went, with no more than a slice of turkey loaf and a spoonful of watered down gravy. The way it looked I would be in there for Christmas, too. My hand hurt like it was on fire but my complaints fell on deaf ears, and finally, it quit hurting. It was obvious my friends had made it, and I most likely would have, also, had I toughed it out. After all I had been through, facing the fact I'd quit the game five yards from the goal line was a hard load to carry. It is possible I would have lost a toe, finger, or an ear to frostbite, but... "No guts no glory," my granddaddy used to say. I finally decided: what is done is done, but I swore never to quit again.

I passed the time counting the bricks in the walls. At seven hundred and eighty-eight I got bored and started counting the layers of paint that had been painted over them. The Dodge House must have been around for awhile, the paint was a quarter-inch thick and had changed colors many times. At least thirty layers. I got a few letters—which I read over and over—Tina apparently had lost our apartment and was living with some dude. For Christmas, my grandmother sent me a box of Louis L'amour books that I devoured. I should have been born in a different century I decided. I pictured myself a young Tell Sacket, although I never did figure out that two-handed punch that L'amour always has his heroes using in his cowboy fights. I was more of a one–two, hook, combination kid myself. I laid in my rack, twiddled my thumbs and replayed my life, reliving all of my mistakes over and over again. Still, the reasons I made so many, remained elusive.

One day a turn-key opened my door. "Alright Maxwell, you're getting out. Roll up your bedding and throw it in the bin at the end of the hall." What do you know...it was Gomer Pyle, the nice cop that took my cuffs off when I came in.

Just like that I was on my way back to Impala.

CHAPTER 5

IMPALA

When I stepped out of the Dodge House I had to squint. Winter was in full effect. The grass, trees, and bushes were covered with snow. After the relative gloom of my cell the bright, unbroken blanket of white across the grounds hurt my eyes. The air was cold, but the sun was warm on my face, and the sky baby-blue. We were deep into the season, and after the initial shock to my eyes, it was beautiful. For sure it was better than the blustery and frigid gray-wash that covered the landscape when I first arrived there. Still, spring was just around the corner and summer, my favorite time of year, not far behind. One thing for certain, it wasn't going to be any fun being locked down when it warmed up. I needed to find a way home by then.

The Dodge House was tucked back behind the chapel in the northwest corner of the compound. The guard escorting me to Impala guided us along a series of sidewalks between two-story housing units filled with kids. We walked past the auditorium and the long sprawled out education building, which those of us in receiving would not attend until we moved out of the orientation phase of our incarceration. Then, it would become mandatory.

We approached Impala from the west and walked around to the

front steps. Mr. Green was waiting on me when I came through the barred front door of his unit. He pulled his tan slacks up high on his waist and peered over the top of his glasses at me. "Bob warned you when you got here there weren't nowhere to go other side that there fence, didn't he?" The aging house-parent chuckled to himself as if I was daft for even trying, then turned down his hearing aid before circling back around behind his desk. I didn't bother pointing out that three of us had run off, *and I* was the only dumbass who didn't make it. Something I intended to rectify—soon.

Although I'd been in the Dodge House just over a month, when I looked around the dormitory I saw very few familiar faces. The kids who were still there were ones I hadn't hung with anyway. Nathan was gone. Timmy—the nose picker—told me Nate finished his intake assessment and the powers that be moved him to Mustang. A whole world away as far as I was concerned.

Several of the Lawton blacks we'd fought with were still there, and now that I was alone they didn't bother hiding their disdain for me. No big surprise. I didn't bother hiding mine for them either. It was just a matter of time before we were at it again. What did throw me...was Kilo. He was now running with them, and would hardly even look at me.

When I spotted our dark-skinned friend and started walking toward him—he turned his back on me and mumbled something about "...damn crackers" to his new buddies, which I guess they found amusing since they all got a laugh out of it.

What the fuck...? The smile I wore at seeing him fell off my face and turned to a scowl. Confused, and a bit hurt, I shoved my hands in my pockets, turned away and stalked off cursing him under my breath.

I put the bedding I was given and the few letters, Christmas cards, and books I'd accumulated while in lock-up in my cubicle. Mr. Green had assigned me a bed between two new guys.

The boy in the bunk to my left was a small-framed cocky fifteen-year-old from Tulsa. "Name's Billy Beasly. I'm a burglar. I heard you run off from here. Purdy cool, man." He brushed the hand he'd just shook mine with back through his boy-cut straight brown hair.

"Been a lot cooler if I'd of made it."

"At least y'all made them fat-ass guards get off they fat-asses." He spoke with a slow southern drawl which made him seem like a naive country boy, though his eyes betrayed the hardships he'd seen. Easily recognizable from one tortured soul to another.

The new guy on my right was Wayne Womble. "I'm from Broken Bow. I'm in for cattle rustlin'," he said with a grin.

"More like the judge put you away for being full of shit," I shot back with my own mud-eatin' smirk. Right off I could tell I would like him.

Wayne was weeks away from turning seventeen, but seemed like he was going on thirty, at least that was the airs he gave off. He wasn't much taller than Billy who was about five-six, but he was stockier built. Wayne had frizzy brown hair hanging to his shoulders, and a single eyebrow a Neanderthal man would have been proud of. It sat like a long caterpillar over wise-looking hazel eyes. It was an odd combination, but appeared to work for him.

They seemed alright, but other than the standard introductions I didn't spend much time thinking about them. I was still sulking about Kilo giving me the cold shoulder.

As I predicted it didn't take long for trouble to find me. At dinner that night, Leroy, the mouth and self appointed leader of the Lawton crew cut in front of me while we were waiting for our evening dose of mashed potatoes and Salisbury steak.

Leroy wasn't real tall, but he was wide for a teenager. His black curly hair was cut close to his head. He had a thick nose, small ears, and a scar that ran through his right eyebrow. I was pretty sure he shaved the spot to make it look more intimidating; which it did.

"Hey man, try that shit with someone else," I said to the back of Leroy's head. "You ain't cuttin' in front of me."

Leroy turned to face me with a sneer. "What'd you say peckerwood?"

I could see a couple of his friends, watching and waiting, ready to jump in at any moment. This was a set-up from the start and considering I didn't have anyone I could count on to back me up anymore, I decided my best defense would be a strong offense.

While there was still a few feet between Leroy and his help, I unconsciously wrapped my hand around the aluminum fist load attached to the brace still bandaged to my arm, and—*BAM!*, I nailed the line-cutter with a short, chopping left. I hit him before it occurred to me that my hand was far from healed. Still yet, it knocked him halfway across the nearest table. The boys sitting there threw themselves backward as their food and trays went flying.

Leroy caught himself before he rolled onto the floor, and grabbed me as I came barreling after him. We spun and rolled off of one table and onto another. From the corner of my eye I saw the guys who were sitting there snatch their trays and step out of the way just before we crashed through their space fighting our way across the room.

Since the brace kept me from grappling Leroy with my left hand, I held him with my right and used my braced fist like a hammer, clubbing him to the floor. I was surprised his friends hadn't jumped in—I'd seen them moving toward me even as I'd lit into him.

Somewhere, people were yelling. Racial slurs were hurled back and forth across the room.

Leroy and I broke apart. We both panted for air and snarled at the other. I watched a flattened scoop of potatoes and a chunk of Salisbury steak peel itself slowly off one of Leroy's blue chambray shirt-sleeves, before falling to plop on the floor like something out of a Tom and Jerry cartoon. I had gravy in my hair, as well. Leroy complained to his buddies that I'd sucker-punched him.

"Whatever," I said. "Where I come from when you cut in front of someone, you'd best *be ready* to fight."

There was blood running from his nose and a red film across his teeth where I'd smashed his lips against them. I hadn't escaped the battle bruise-free either. There was a goose egg growing under my right eye and a deep scratch stretched from my left ear to my chin. I, however, was still floating from foot-to-foot, waiting for round two.

Leroy's friends were lined up in a half circle several feet from us, held at bay by none other than my two new bunk mates and Timmy the nose picker! Billy was standing to my right cursing the other boys, threatening them with an ink pen in one hand and a sharpened pencil in the other. Wayne was beside him. He had broken a broom handle and was holding the jagged end out like it was a two-handed broad sword. Timmy the nose picker was protecting my left flank, timidly brandishing the rest of the broken broom. He didn't look very intimidating, but I was impressed that he was standing with us at all.

Besides, Billy and Wayne made up for Timmy's lack of aggressiveness—they were hunched over and daring Leroy and his friends to try anything. Whether my new-found friends were scared to shed real blood or not I couldn't tell you, but they didn't show it if they were.

About that time Mr. Green stepped through the crowd. "Break it up! Break it up, *RIGHT NOW!* I have already called security, and if all of you don't want to spend a couple of weeks in the Dodge House you will go to your bunks."

Someone looking out the window confirmed that the cavalry was running up the sidewalk, so we broke up and headed back to our cubicles.

When a couple of Leroy's "homies" moved out of the way...there was Kilo...standing where I hadn't been able to see him, but standing against me, nonetheless. He looked ashamed, or maybe it was just my imagination. Still, I walked off thinking my grandfather was right; *black people would never like white people, so there was no point in trying to be friends with them.*

It didn't take long for the "Goon Squad," as we called them, to come rushing into the housing unit. There were six or seven regulars on that crew—and though one was the older, out of shape, Sergeant Carter looking cop who had clamped my cuffs down so tightly when I was brought in from my escape, the rest seemed young and fit, at least relative to the rest of the staff around there. They were also assholes, known to have sent more than one kid to the hospital.

"Sit on your bunks! Sit on your bunks...*NOW!*" each of the gungho storm troopers hollered as they came through the door. Only to find, the fight already ended and all of us already tucked quietly away in our cubicles.

"Mr. Green, what's going on here? You said they were fighting." The man speaking was thirty-something with a narrow-shaped face and a short army-style crew-cut. By his demeanor, it was obvious he was the one in charge.

"These two boys here." Green pointed at us. "Maxwell and Brown. Brown stepped in front of Maxwell in the chow line and Maxwell hit him. They stopped when I told them to."

"It doesn't sound too serious," the super trooper in charge commented.

I was sitting on my bunk listening to them talk, and holding my hand—it had begun to throb again.

"Bill, you and Joe take Brown," Mr. Crew-Cut directed. "I'll send Maxwell with Sarge and Chett. We'll give em' a couple days in the Dodge house to cool down."

It struck me funny that Phillips, who I'd dubbed with the Sergeant Carter moniker was actually a Sergeant. *Huh,* I thought. *I must have been too aggravated to snap to that before.* I was smiling and shaking my head as they cuffed and led me back to the hole less than a day after getting out of it.

The facility nurse met us at the lock-up unit to look over our abrasions and make sure we had no serious injuries. She was pretty and had long brown hair. When she leaned close to check out my hand, I could smell the fresh scent of her shampoo.

"Oh my! That's definitely re-broken," she exclaimed when she pulled the bandages back. "What did you do...hit him with your already screwed up hand?" The way she said it made me feel like a complete marble-head. Looking sheepish, I just nodded.

True to Crew-Cut's word—Leroy and I only stayed in "The Hole", for two days. Once we agreed the fight had only been a spur of the moment thing and we were over it, they took us back to Impala.

Whether Leroy was really "over it" when he said it, or not, after I got back from the Enid hospital with a three-pound plaster cast wrapped around my fist and halfway up my forearm like a cement boxing glove; he at least pretended to be.

From then on, he and his cronies handled me and my new friends Billy and Wayne with a lot more respect. Leroy told me he'd never been hit by a white boy like I'd hit him. I guess that was meant to be a compliment. My reputation as a fighter was born.

Kilo tried to talk to me after that, but it was my turn to shine *him* on. He had hurt my feelings. My grandfather's words echoed in my mind.

Because of the fighting and my escape attempt, the people in control of my life made me stay in orientation an extra month. Several kids moved on through the system. Leroy, Kilo, and many others faded off into different buildings, while I lingered behind. On the bright side, I got to know and grow quite fond of my new compadres.

Wayne, as it turned out, was not a cattle rustler after all. No shocker there. What he did do, was steal an enclosed trailer and give it to his cattle rancher uncle as a birthday present. Just once he wanted to make his family proud. The only problem was he'd lied about how he obtained it, neglecting to tell his uncle it was stolen. The first time his father's brother pulled it into town, he got hemmed up by the local police. Wayne had to turn himself in to get his uncle out of trouble.

Wayne, Billy, and me were in the bathroom smoking a cigarette Billy had swiped from Mr. Green when he told us the story. "That was a pretty righteous thing to do," I said through an exhaled cloud of smoke.

Wayne squinted his eyes as he tried to French inhale his drag. He ended up coughing through his words. "Yeah...cough...cough...you would think my folks would have appreciated that, too...cough...but they were just mad, and wouldn't even come and get me out of jail."

"Purty damned shitty, if'n yer ask'n me," Billy commented before tossing the expired snipe in the toilet and flushing it.

Billy...was what he said he was; a burglar. He had dozens of stories about breaking into places. He would crawl through the air-ducts, break through walls, or go in through the floor. Once, he told us, he even hid in a washing machine box in the stockroom of K-mart store until it closed. The list went on. He had racked up quite a rap-sheet before getting sent to Hotel Hell with us.

Timmy the nose picker—who none of us would have ran with until he stood with us against Leroy and his gang, was just a scared kid. He'd been abused by more than one stepfather. From what he told us, it didn't sound like his mother cared much for him either. Timmy acted out by running away from home and vandalism. The first time his "parents" were required to spit up some cash because he had kicked all the walls out of a vacant house, they had him shipped off to Helena. Two weeks after the fight he got moved to Thunderbird, another first floor unit just down the sidewalk, west of Mustang. Geek though Timmy may have been, we had still grown attached to the kid and worried that he no longer had our protective friendship covering him.

When my month was finally up, I was also informed it was time to move on. They assigned me to Mustang, to a bunk right next to Nathan.

Mustang, and Cadillac its upstairs unit, were in a long rectangular building like Impala and LTD, except it sat flush on its foundation and didn't have the extra half story above ground. It had a concrete, railed-in porch, instead of Impala's wide cascading steps and colonnaded entrance.

When I walked into the unit Nathan was sitting on my bunk with a shit-eating grin on his face. "Cost me a pack of smokes, but I got them to put you next to me. I'm in the cubicle over." He pointed across the top of the dresser/desk/partition that separated our beds. "I missed our late night rap sessions."

Looking around I could see the place wasn't set up much differently from Impala, although the building seemed quite a bit longer. The main difference here, was most of the cubicles were two-man spaces, set-up with bunk-beds. Those cubicles had a six-foot tall wooden closet on each end of the partition, with an equally tall ply-board wall across the back of the dresser from one locker to the other. It effectively walled off each set of beds from its neighbor. However, mine and Nathan's cubicles were still the coveted single-cots. We had lockers too, but they stood back to back and we could see over our partition.

It was good to be with Nate again. As we sat passing a Marlboro he had scored from somewhere, back and forth, he filled me in on how the coach discovered us missing so quickly. Also, relating his fears for us when the alarms went off. I, in turn, caught him up on my adventures after leaving him and Kilo in the gym. I ended my tale with the fight, and told him about our new friends, Billy and Wayne.

When I told him how Timmy had stood with us, Nathan leant back and slapped his leg in astonishment. "I'll be damned. Never thought that kid had it in him."

I finished by telling him about how weird Kilo acted toward me. And, my disappointment in him.

"Yeah he don't like me anymore either. He was mad, or hurt we didn't offer to let him come with us," Nathan said as we walked the length of the dorm on our way to the foosball table. "Plus, you guys hadn't been gone two days when those black birds from Lawton jumped him in the bathroom. Mr. Green was reading a book, had his hearing aid turned down and didn't hear a thing. Not many people did. Kilo never hollered once—just grunted when they were kickin' him. He got worked over pretty good, lost a couple teeth. For sidin' with us whiteboys wuz what they were sayin'. He started runnin' with them afterwards. Go figure."

We stopped walking and started setting up the game. "Why didn't you help him?"

"First of all, there were like five of them." He lined up a shot with his foosball men. "Second; my dad would kick the shit out of me if I ever jumped in to help a black boy."

WHAM! He sank the ball right between my men.

I was caught off guard, by more than his game. "I don't get it man, he was our friend and he helped us. And, he helped Tracy in that juvy place in Oklahoma City. No wonder he hates us."

"Look Jimmy, you hate him now, too, don't you? It didn't take much for him to turn against you, you were not the one who didn't help him—I was. He was always Tracy's friend, not ours. If they would have gotten you down he'd of been right there with them kickin' on you. It's just the way the world is. Black and white...Oil and water. Hell, you see ninety percent of them think they are better than everyone else."

I made a slap-shot Nathan easily blocked.

"Hey Jordan," Nathan hollered at a skinny black kid who was getting a drink from the water fountain. "Tell Jimmy, Black people ain't never gonna like white people, are they?"

"Hell no! White people always fuckin' over black people," he stated matter-of-factly. "And the ones that ain't still thinks they better'n us."

"Yeah? What-the-fuck-ever," I said.

Jordan smiled a big 'don't shoot the messenger' smile that showed all his white teeth, and held his hands up like he was being arrested. "Well...Nathan asked. That jus be the way it is, don't 'spect it to change anytime soon." He walked off chuckling.

Jordan was trying to be funny, but it left me thinking about the duality of his words. I spun my wrist, and—*BAM!* I finally got one in the goal. I looked at Nathan, "All that may be true. And, maybe Kilo is a shit-ball for riding against me, but I still would have helped him, and you should have too."

It's funny the way life works, I thought. *How from the same trunk of the humanity tree one act, attitude, or misunderstanding of racism (or just plain negligence) can branch us off in opposing directions—feeding the limbs with ethnic divisiveness, anger, and suspicion until we grow to hate one another.* I really hadn't had that many negative dealings with black folks. I was raised in El Paso, Texas, which is predominately populated with whites and Mexicans. The whites and American Mexicans all gritting on the Juarez Mexicans who come over the border and steal American jobs for pennies on the dollar. We had black kids in my schools and I fought a few when I wrestled and boxed, but I never had any reason to feel enmity towards them as a whole. However now, by no conscious effort of my own, I could feel mistrust for blacks taking root in my soul. And though confused as to exactly why, I sensed imaginary battle lines being drawn, pushing Kilo and I further and further apart.

A couple of weeks later a pair of facility henchmen came and got me, they leg-shackled my feet and cuffed my right hand to my belt leaving my casted hand free. There was no getting a cuff over that hunk of plaster. They then took me out through the front guard shack and into town. Destination: A local doctors office. It was time to cut my cast off.

We drove down the same long straight boulevard the Guymon deputies had driven me in on. This time though, I was tucked away in the back of a white state SUV. The street didn't look much different than when I'd rode up it from the other direction, except now I stayed alert and paid much closer attention to everything around me instead of just the institution at the end of the road. I hoped to discover some lapse in security I could exploit later.

The van stank. One of the guards—who both looked like they'd been cut from the same cloth as Elmer Fudd in a Bugs Bunny cartoon; round pudgy faces, thin hair, and goofy hats—was puffing on a stogie as big around as my thumb. It was stifling. Luckily the clinic was only a half-mile up the street and I didn't have to endure it very long before we were there.

When we pulled in, I reached for the door before the officer in the passenger seat—the Stogie Smoker—could get out to open it. To my surprise the sliding door rolled back for me. It was not locked! *That's interesting*, I thought.

The clinic was a small, brown brick building with a "No Smoking" sign right on the front door. As it was a nice day, as February goes, the smoking Elmer decided to wait outside to finish his cigar. The waiting room was empty. The non-smoking Elmer didn't really seem to be watching me that closely, and when the doctor pulled me into the exam room he opted to sit in the lobby and read a magazine.

"Come in here and let's have a look at you." The gray-haired doctor directed me to hop up on a cushioned table covered in white sterile paper. The place looked and smelled like every other doctor's office I'd ever been in. Big glass jar filled with Q-Tips and a ubiquitous, eye, ear, nose, and throat scope hanging on the wall. The doc, who looked like an older version of Alan Alda, in *MASH*, wore a traditional white lab-coat and peered over the top of his spectacles as he examined the cast on my hand. Soon enough he was buzzing through the plaster with a little round-bladed saw. I watched, wondering how he could tell where the thick cast stopped and the skin of my arm began. Apparently he'd been a doctor long enough to know what he was doing, because when he cracked it open there was nary a blemish on the pasty white skin of my shrunken forearm. It stunk like my junior high gym locker, however, and the doc and I both wrinkled our noses at the same time.

After examining the bones of my hand, the doctor wrote down a couple notes and made some unsatisfactory sounds. "Hmmm...Umm. Hmm." Cigar smoking Elmer had came in from outside and was now reading a Popular Mechanics magazine—while his compatriot was scanning a Vanity Fair. "Could one of you come in here?" the doctor asked through the open door.

They both came.

The doc was old and frail—as typical as they come, but he spoke with authority to my two jailers. "The hand is healed," he said pushing his glasses up on his nose, "but the bones feel like they've mended wrong. I'm scheduling him for an x-ray and a visit to my colleague in Enid. Is there a problem with that?"

One of my two Elmer escorts appeared completely lost. *'Who me? Are you asking me a question?'* I could read his thoughts by the slack look on his face. The other guard, however, had been around awhile and apparently was the one in charge. He stepped up: "Whatever is necessary. Send your findings and recommendation to the facility nurse and she will make the arrangements with the director."

The doctor gave me a cherry sucker before I left. *What am I, seven?* I thought. Nonetheless, I took it with a big grin on my face.

They took me back to the van with out even putting any cuffs on me. I licked my sucker and mulled over what the breach in security meant. It wasn't like I could go anywhere with leg shackles on. Handcuffed, or not, I was in a small, literally tiny, town out in the middle of nowhere. Still, the longer I was with these guys the more they seemed to loosen up. *I wonder who will be driving me to Enid when I go? I might still make it home by summer after all.* That thought had me smiling all the way back to the reformatory.

The property I had brought with me from Guymon was laying on my bed when I got back to Mustang. It had finally been released to me because I was no longer in orientation. They sure hadn't been in any hurry to give it to me. I had forgotten all about it. My eyes scanned through the items scattered across my cot. Soap, shampoo, cologne, body powder, a Reach toothbrush, two pairs of tube socks, four boxer shorts, and there in the midst of it all a big tube of Crest toothpaste. I hesitated to reach down and grab it—suddenly paranoid—afraid it was a set-up. I could almost feel unseen eyes watching me. As if "the man" had discovered its secret in the months it was in their possession, and were only waiting to confirm that I did too.

After glancing around through hooded eyes, I snatched all the toiletries up at once and put them in my drawer. It would be easier to examine the rolled-up end of my Crest tube, without being observed, in the confines of the dresser. Finally shaking my paranoia when I could verify the end had not been tampered with.

"Nathan, come here," I whispered with a blissful look on my face.

Nate was laying on his bunk reading one of the Louis L'amour westerns my grandmother had sent me. He looked over the counter top between us. "What's up?"

"Do you want to get high?" I asked him.

"Do I! Is a penguin's pussy cold? But how?"

"Let's go brush our teeth, and I'll show you," I said holding up my toothbrush and toothpaste.

On our way to the bathroom I explained to my buddy that I had been out on bond when I was waiting to come to Helena. And, that I self-surrendered the morning of. Which gave me an opportunity to prepare a little care package. I slapped him on the shoulder with my tube of Crest, for emphasis.

"Me and my girlfriend, Tina, took my little weed bowl; sifted and cleaned what I had down to almost fine powder. Then rolled it up in a baggie and wrapped it in rubberbands. The Crest has a folded and crimped end. I just worked it open, pulled out three or four spoonfuls of toothpaste, stuck the package in, rolled it back up and—presto— there you go..."

I'd been standing at the sink, fishing the stash out as I finished telling Nathan the story. I watched his reflection in the mirror stare at the little package in my hand as I rinsed it off.

"Wow that was pretty smart. I wish I'd of thought of that. I'd 'a brought a bunch of Purple Microdot. My dad was selling acid before I got in trouble. Of course, he'd of beat my ass if'n he caught me in his stash."

"Well it ain't much, just a few joints really. And it sure ain't no Purple Microdot. But, it'll beat a blank."

A tall slim kid we sometimes kicked around with, walked into the bathroom. He was clean-cut, wore glasses, and kept his blond hair short and neat. The boy was kind of a loner—and most of the other kids were glad to leave him alone. He'd shot his step-dad in the face with a shotgun while the drunken man was beating his mom with a pair of channel-lock pliers. We liked him though, and the kid liked us back.

"Hi Shifter, do you want to get high with us?" I asked him.

"Huh?" His eyes looked big through the lenses of his glasses and he grinned when I held up my little baggie. "Is a pig's pussy pork?"

Nate and I looked at each other, and yelled, "Jinx!" at the same time.

As it turned out, I'd sifted the weed so fine that it was hard to smoke, and it had been in the toothpaste so long that it had turned Menthol! But by the time we got two of those weird tasting hooters puffed up we were all cackling like kindergartners.

Over the next few days I fell into institutional life, getting my classes lined out and talking to my case managers and counselors, etc. Occasionally, I would see Timmy and Kilo at the school building.

Timmy would run up to me like I was his best buddy. It was a little embarrassing, but I did my best not to let it show. He'd earned a place with us and I couldn't deny him the opportunity to let the other kids, who were watching and lived on his unit, know that he had friends. Although, I did have to slap his hand away from his face a couple of times to break him of picking his nose.

Kilo I saw, too. My angst toward him had softened a few degrees since I had learned the reasons for his betrayal. But it still felt like betrayal from where I was sitting. He probably thought the same things about me. We would make eye contact once in awhile, and in a buried part of my mind I sensed the little kids in us who were once color-blind reaching out to one another wanting to play in the sandbox together. Although, the older, hardened, more jaded parts of us would only nod, or raise our chins ever so slightly, before turning and walking in opposite directions; taking a few more steps along the path of enmity and distrust for one another.

A week and a half later the Elmer Fudd twins came to take me for my x-ray in Enid.

CHAPTER 6

ENID

As it turned out Elmer the Smoker's name was actually Will. The non-smoking Elmer's name was Cal. Short for Calvin, who I discovered dipped Copenhagen. He'd spit a brown stream of nastiness into a McDonalds cup every minute or two. Calvin was fifty-one, divorced, lived alone on four acres and had a pet pig named Penelope. Will was forty-nine, had a wife who was apparently as big as Cal's pig and had a disposition that would make a badger run for his hole. Will spent a lot of time away from home in the local pub, for which he was currently nursing a hang over. All this I gathered from the two men's monotonous non-stop conversation with one another in the front seat of the same white state suburban with the Department of Juvenile Affairs emblem on its doors as they were driving when they took me to my appointment in Helena. I was sitting in the back.

I had hoped since my escorts did not bother cuffing my wrists at the clinic—due to my hand injury—they would forego that little formality this time. No such luck. My legs and my wrists, were quite securely shackled.

That, however, didn't necessarily derail my plans. I'd already assumed I would be at least in leg restraints and was prepared for it. In my mouth, bent in the shape of my bottom gum-line, was a flat hairpin

I could use to slip their locks.

Picking cuffs came easy to me, I had literally been doing it since I was nine. My grandfather gave me a pair of real, police-issue, handcuffs for Christmas the year I lived with him and my grandmother. I'm sure the subliminal message was: *If you don't straighten up and be a good boy, one day you will be wearing a set just like them.* Inevitably, I lost the keys to the manacles and, by trial and error, became quite adept at picking them with any number of items I could find laying around the house. My favorite tool was a flat hairpin. So the fact I was handcuffed and leg-shackled was just an inconvenience which would cost me more time, but was far from a game changer.

The one thing this dynamic-duo did forgo was double-locking my restraints. I'd already accidentally clicked my right cuff down where it was now biting uncomfortably into my wrist. Asking my escorts to loosen it would only prompt them to engage the secondary lock to keep it from happening again. Given that, I endured the numb feeling growing in my hand while I listened to Calvin telling Will how Penelope his pig had won second place in the Pork Pageant at some county fair the week before.

While the two guards droned on, I stared out the window at the scrub-brush covered cattle pastures we were driving past. It was nice out, looking like it might be an early spring, if not a bit windy. For that matter; it was a bit windy in the van too, I snickered at my inside joke. When I coughed a laugh that blew a booger out of my nose, Cal, the Copenhagen dipping Elmer, eyed me through the rearview mirror.

"You alright back there, Maxwell? You got a little something on your face."

"Yeah," I said, wiping my cuffed hands across the bottom of my nose. "Just sneezed."

"Well, God bless you then." He spit in his cup as we passed the Enid city limits sign. "We'll stop at McDonalds after your appointment. Get you a burger and fries. Won't we, Will?"

"Yup. I'm hungry enough to eat my own boot." Will grinned at me like he thought I would recognize how he'd just come up with that witty and intellectual metaphor all on his own. And then he blew out a big smelly cloud of cigar smoke over the top of the seat.

"Well, that sounds great to me"——I coughed—"I'm hungry enough to eat the bottom out of your wife's bloomers." I wanted him to know I could be witty, too.

Will frowned for a couple of seconds then smiled for the first time—probably ever. He was missing his right eyetooth. "Ha. Cal, we'd better get this boy something to eat quick, he must be starving to death. We both know that them bloomers would choke a horse!"

They both laughed out loud at that. I had to admit, that was pretty funny. Score one for Will.

"Yeah...I gathered. I heard you talking earlier," I said sheepishly.

Cal and Will were still chuckling to themselves as we pulled into the parking lot of the Enid hospital. There were three big buildings to the complex. We by-passed the emergency turn-in and hospital proper, pulling into a space in front of the east annexed building.

When we got out I took in a big breath of fresh air. The grass, trees, and bushes had begun to green. Mother Nature was waking up. The parking lot was partially filled. However, we seemed to be the only people moving about. It was ten minutes to eleven according to Will's watch. To my left, sparrows were chirping to each other in the trees, while the leaves rustled in the morning breeze. I wondered why the sky always appeared to be a brighter blue and the clouds a softer white on the outside of the fences? I swear it even smelled fresher.

The silly romanticized thought almost got me giggling again, because as we walked—I should say, *they walked*, I shuffled; rattling chains with every step toward the glass double-doors of the hospital wing my appointment was apparently in—"fresh" was not actually what I smelled. Asphalt, tire rubber, and car exhaust was more like it. Revising my initial assessment, I realized what I really smelt was potential and opportunity. Which could mean freedom, and freedom...freedom, smelled "fresh".

There was no way for me to know if I would have an opportunity to escape while on this medical run or not. It wasn't imperative that I did. Although, it would be my best chance for the foreseeable future. And going from Enid had its obvious benefits. For one, the whole town wasn't working for "the man", and two, I didn't have to trek through twenty miles of nowhere to get to a danged road. So, I stayed alert and ready. I had my lock-pick; these Elmer Fudd bookends weren't especially "on guard"; and I'd been through Enid, Oklahoma, enough to know where I was in relation to which way I needed to go. If that "opportunity", which I smelled wafting through the air like the aroma of a gas station mechanic's bay, did present itself, I would be ready.

Cal held the door for me and Will to walk through. We must have come in a side entrance, because we had to make our way down a long sterile hall to reach the main desk.

"I hate hospitals," Will grumbled.

Cal looked a little green around the gills. "I second that. I spent six months in Mercy Regional, in Oklahoma City when I had that combine accident back in '72. Haven't been able to abide them since. It's the smell, ugh."

At the desk a round faced black woman with rosy cheeks greeted us. I stood back while Cal—who seemed to be in charge—stepped up to the desk to inform "Betsy", her name tag said, that we were there for my appointment.

Will stepped around the wall and discovered the waiting lounge. When he walked into it to find a place to sit, I told Calvin I was going to the bathroom to take a leak. It was a few feet back up the hall. He nodded, and resumed his conversation with Betsy.

My pulse suddenly sped up, pumping *potential and opportunity* through my veins. *Could it be this easy?* Will was already sitting down digging through a stack of magazines laying on the low table in front of him. I would have thought after my first escape attempt, my escorts would be on high-alert while they had me out and about. However, these two had never mentioned my failed bid for freedom. And, they were not the officers who brought me into the hospital when I first rebroke my hand. They didn't seem to know I was a flight risk. Or, more likely, they just didn't care and were confident, chained the way I was, I couldn't go anywhere anyway. *With a little luck I may have a chance.* I mentally crossed my fingers as I half-stepped in my chains to the bathroom.

Once inside I spit the hairpin into my hand and quickly shuffled into the last stall. *Eeew gross!* Someone had left a ten-inch turd draped across the bottom of the porcelain bowl like a beached battle ship. Dirty toilet paper decorated it like a tattered white flag. I moved to the next stall wondering how a person could forget to flush something like that.

The commode beside it was clean and I sat down. My mind mentally ticking off the moments, wondering how long I could expect those two old goat-herders to leave me unattended. I unfolded the hairpin and straightened it, flat side out. Since they were not double-locked I could close the cuff all the way and slide the thin metal pin between the teeth in the locking channel of the manacles. That depressed the unsecured teeth in the cuff housing allowing the teeth on the hinge-side to slide freely on the thin metal strip of the hairpin— and wham bam, thank you ma'am! It's open. It's a little more difficult when it is double-locked but you would be surprised what a bored third-grader with a pair of keyless handcuffs, and a lot of unsuspecting victims, can figure out.

I started with the hand already growing numb. My wrist was swollen from the constant pressure it had been under, and it hurt worse when I squeezed the restraint even tighter to get the hairpin past its last locking-teeth, but it was an instant relief when I got the pick in place and was able to jimmy the cuff open.

Not only did the blood rush back into my hand relieving the pain and pressure around my wrist, but when the locking mechanism gave and the hoop swung open my brain dumped a flood of adrenalin. It rushed through my veins with each quickening beat of my heart. I was now in the 'do or die' zone of the operation. At that moment, if either Elmer got suspicious and came to check on me, I'd be literally caught on the crapper; halfway home, but still quite helpless.

With the right cuff off, and no swelling in my left wrist, the left cuff came open easy enough. The leg shackles were not double-locked either—I checked on the ride over. Working with kids must make the staff at Helena lax, that and the fact many of them were just farmers who needed an extra job to supplement an unpredictable agricultural market. To my benefit, only a dozen of them had any real law enforcement experience.

My chains off and laying on the floor next to the toilet, I ran to the door. I'd thought about tossing the hardware into the sunken ship, shitter bowl, just for laughs. My two Elmers, however, hadn't done me any harm and were already going to catch enough flak for losing me.

All in all, I hadn't been in the bathroom more than a few minutes. Although, honestly, more than enough time for any diligent guard to come looking. I feared since they hadn't, that one of them must be watching. *What if they are staring right at the door when I look out?* I stiffened my resolve. If that was the case, I'd just have to break and run for it, and hope for the best.

With that contingency plan firmly in place, I leant forward and ever so slightly pulled the door open enough to see the reception desk.

Cal was still standing there. He wasn't looking in my direction but had turned so he could easily see me when I came out.

I'd been mentally making fun of these two guys up till now, but the reality was there were two of them, they were grown men, and suddenly, fifty didn't seem so old. I was scared. One misstep, one slip, and they would be on me. And, though a lot of the guards who worked at the reformatory were local townies, and for the most part decent people, those who had been brought in from other places and had worked in law enforcement previously could be down right mean. I'd only avoided having the shit kicked out of me up to then because of my broken hand. No one wanted to get blamed for breaking some kids bones again. There had been a stink a couple of years earlier over staff hospitalizing some kid. There were stories still going around of what they would do to the segregated kids who lived in LTD when they got out of line. So me taking this escape lightly, or under estimating my jailers, was what I was not going to do.

Standing there with my thumb up my ass was what I was not going to do, either. I would never have a better chance than right then. After taking a deep breath...I jerked the bathroom door open and ran.

I broke cover like a deer hit in the ass with buck shot, scrambling fast as my feet would carry me toward the glass doors at the end of the hallway, not even sparing a glance at Calvin. He yelled. Within five steps Will, also, was yelling for me to "STOP!" Then they were coming.

There was only twenty more feet to the door, and my freedom, when a fortyish-year-old man in a business suit walked through them. He could clearly see I was being chased by Will and Cal. They were hollering for me to stop, and for someone, anyone, to help them detain me.

The man was as tall as I was, and thicker, mostly through the waist. He saw what was happening and planted himself like a goal tender right in front of the door. I was sure I could fight my way past the guy but I didn't have time to grapple with him. Elmer and Elmer were coming up fast.

Barreling straight at the man, I watched him set all his weight on his front leg preparing for the impact. At the last second I dropped and slid right into the stiffened limb. The guy yelped and tumbled to the ground over my head, right in the path of the two guards running after me.

I sprang to my feet, glancing back in time to see Cal and Will stumbling over the man and crashing to the floor. It would have been comical if it weren't my freedom at stake. I hit the doors. They flew open, and I ran.

After bursting out of the south-facing double-glass doors I turned west. There were a couple of people in the parking lot now, but they were too far away to pose a threat. They had no reason to try and stop me anyway. At that moment, no one was behind me, all they could see was some crazy teenager dressed in jeans and a heavy sweat shirt, running like Freddy Cruger was after him. Which, in and of itself, did draw attention but didn't seem like a cause for public alarm.

At the end of the building I turned north, sprinting across another parking lot and shooting for a side street. My ears told me my pursuers were back on my trail before I cleared the open space. I ran west along a one-way avenue before turning north again. Then west. Then north. Trying to zig-zag my way away from the hospital.

The problem was the streets were lain in a grid, and Cal and Will would have the Enid police involved very soon. They would search for me in square blocks, and all the zig-zagging in the world wouldn't do me any good. What I needed was distance. My lungs, however, were already beginning to burn. I was running out of gas.

My pursuers were behind me. How far behind was a mystery. At a place where two buildings abutted each other with only a small, chest deep, space between them; I slipped into the gap. The walls of both structures were old brick; and back here, chipped and marred. The gap was filled with detritus that had piled up through the years. I squeezed sideways along the narrow slot, climbing over the trash until I made it around a corner. It was just as tight there, and pressed just as closely to another red-brick building on the other side.

Out of sight, I stopped for a few moments to catch my breath and listen. At first the only sound was the heavy pounding of my heart. Then...silence. Sweat was rolling in big drops between my shoulder blades.

I was young and healthy and recovered quickly. I had to keep moving. Although I'd lost Cal and Will, I was still in the area the search would be concentrated the heaviest on.

Where I was, the hidden gap was even tighter than where I came in. And, had even more discarded garbage; along with bricks and boards that had rusty nails hanging out of them. The way was blocked.

So I backtracked around the corner. The dirty walls were so close to my face I could smell the crusty paint. I shuffled, kicking empty pop cans, grocery sacks, and other trash out of my way as I did.

I didn't like emerging from the same hidy-hole I'd disappeared into. Especially with no idea where Cal and Will were. They may not even know I came this far north, but if they did they would have had time to catch up by now.

With the sweat creeping down the back of my neck, now dripping into the crack of my ass, and more beading across my brow...I took the last couple of feet in one shuffling step and popped out of the narrow slot onto the sidewalk.

No one was on the street except a guy up the block removing a trash bag from the receptacle in front of his business. And he was not looking in my direction. *Whew!* I wiped the moisture from my face, turned and took off walking at a brisk pace.

The section of town I was in was a mish-mash of businesses and residential buildings. The streets were narrow and the structures packed tightly together. I walked—half jogging—west. Two blocks later I came to a four-lane boulevard which I had to cross. It was open and exposed, but at that point all I could do was act like I belonged there and make for the other side.

Four steps into the crossing, I heard the roar of an engine. *Shit.* Coming over the railroad tracks fifty yards down the wide road was the very state Suburban I had been dreading to see. It was too far away to tell who was driving, or even if both men were inside. I ran. The engine howled like hounds on a fox hunt.

This time I sprinted catty-corner across the street and dove over a four-foot-tall chain-link fence stretched between two buildings. I cut through the back avoiding discarded car parts, a rusty pile of metal, and a stack of miscellaneous bald tires before making it across the alley.

The SUV had to continue to the end of the block in order to follow. The engine was straining. It was the only sound in my ears. I sprinted through yards and hurdled fences trying to get beyond the next street before being cut off. The screaming of their engine told me the van was paralleling me to the north. As I listened, it braked to make the turn back towards me. *Dammit!* I was not going to get across the road without him spotting me again, and I couldn't keep running full-bore much longer.

I stopped on the west side of a large white house with a big open porch and a couple of evergreen trees growing next to it. I searched for a place to hide. The bushes were too small and the tree branches were well up off of the ground. There was no access under the porch. The SUV was now coming south. I was cut off. Trapped. In moments, he would see me exposed against the wall of the house, like the last man in a dodge ball game.

Suddenly I noticed how the trees filled out the higher they went. With no time to waste I sprang for the nearest one, pulling myself up into its lowest branches. The engine approached. I climbed faster. Soon I was above the roof-line. The limbs were not as concealing on the east side of the tree. To make matters worse, there was a man in coveralls working on the flat roof of a business just across the alley. He was looking right at me!

The SUV had slowed, and was now creeping along the street in front of the house, trying to figure out where I went. Right then a cop car came blazing across the railroad tracks to join the hunt. The man on the roof could see the law-enforcement vehicles were searching for me and started waving his arms trying to get their attention.

No! I wanted to scream at him.

There was no going back down. If I dropped behind the house where the roofer couldn't see me I would be exposed to the road. I hugged the tree, my hands sticky with tree-sap, and ignored the ants crawling on my sweaty skin. The guy was now jumping up and down hollering at the cars he could see going by.

"Shut up, you fat freak," I hissed across the open gulf between us.

He looked over at me. Then at a cop car passing by on the main boulevard. "Hey...hey! He's over here!" he yelled, waving his arms again.

"Fuck you asshole," I hollered, wishing I had a rock to throw.

The busy-body could see he wasn't getting anywhere trying to get the chase vehicles' attention. I saw him mentally switch gears...then head for his ladder.

The SUV was right in front of the yard my tree was in, slowly driving north this time. I was stuck for a moment, but soon as he went by I dropped to the ground. Crossing the street behind the truck while it was still in sight was risky, but I didn't see any choice.

I ran for it. Traveling ever west.

Whether he saw me or not, I couldn't tell, there was too much noise and too many vehicles tearing around now for me to distinguish one revving engine from another. Although I did see the van's left turn signal blink before I lost sight of it. He was turning in the direction I was running. I sprinted for the end of the block before he could get back around, just in case he did see me.

The city block I was on had no cover. The buildings along its sides were all linked in one long, stone facade. The only obstructions on the whole block were a few four-foot tall, two-foot wide mulberry bushes, which had been planted individually every ten feet between the sidewalk and two-lane street I was running up. There was, literally, nowhere to hide.

Twenty yards from the end of this exposed stretch of street, I spotted the front bumper of Cal and Will's state vehicle coming around the corner of a tenement across the way. They were driving slow, traveling south down the very avenue I was trying to reach.

Just before they came into view I ducked behind one of the round bushes, the only cover there was. It was crazy, next to the shadow in the cow pasture, this was the lamest hiding spot ever. However, it was either this or run out right in front of them and hope for the best.

The SUV turned the corner onto the street I was on. My mind screamed, *RUN FOOL RUN!* I benched the panic-stricken thought and, instead, hugged the bush. I had to move with the truck. As it turned the corner...I turned with it. When it got on the straight away...I crept further around, keeping the bush between us. I just prayed no one came from the other direction catching me between them.

The state employees rolled slowly down the street, looking for potential hiding places. They obviously believed they had seen someone run across the road behind them when they passed earlier. I'd worked my way to the west side of the bush before they reached the end of the block and turned south again.

That was insanely lucky, I thought. I couldn't believe it worked. As pleased as I was about it there was no time to celebrate. I hurried to the end of a long stucco building where I found a thick row of bushes growing against its west wall and crawled behind them.

The shrubbery extended to a tall and wide fir tree standing in a corner created by the building and an adjacent rock wall. The tree's branches reached all the way to the ground, and were flush with green needles facing the avenue. I sat where the wall abutted the building. Here, low in the corner, nothing grew. When I was a kid this would have been the perfect fort. I could see out but no one could see in. This was where I would wait the search out.

I geared down and relaxed peering through the branches at the cop cars driving up and down the road in front of me, confident for the first time that I was going to make it. I felt a tinge of guilt over burning Cal and Will, I didn't necessarily want to cause them any trouble, they were funny guys, but it's a dog eat dog world and there was no way I was going to be chained-up in the yard until I aged-out of that place.

Several hours later, when I was sure the manhunt had moved on, I crawled out of my hiding place. On sore, stiff legs, I hobbled across the road to the nearest gravel alleyway, my head on a swivel, searching for signs of pursuit. There were none. Cal and Will would've had to get back to Helena and the local police had bigger game to hunt. Although I had no doubts that every squad car in town would be on the look-out for me, I was confident they were no longer actively beating the streets.

I'd crossed into a residential neighborhood. The alley I found myself in was just a rutted one-lane service-way splitting the block between people's backyards. It was a common thoroughfare for trash trucks and meter readers. The service-roads were dirty and often smelled like refuse since they were lined from one end to the other with trash cans and dumpsters. There was very little common traffic on them, and a man, or boy on the run, could travel across town virtually unseen. The sun had moved into the western part of the sky by then. I followed it wanting to make it out of town before dark.

Working my way to the edge of the small city went without incident.

The tricky part, however, would be getting down the highway and out of town without being noticed by the cops.

An even bigger danger, to me, was that not everyone who worked at Helena lived there, some commuted from Enid and could be coming or going at any time. And, since there were only two routes between the two, getting out on the road would be a gamble.

The way Calvin and Will brought me that morning was considered the "backway". It entered into Enid from the north and was the least preferred by commuters because the roads were smaller and less maintained. However, it would take me right to the reformatory's front door step, and was not an option.

Highway 412, the only way left for me that traveled west out of Enid, was the main route. There was a turn-off ten miles out, which brought a person into Helena from the south. The same highway the Guymon deputies drove me in on from the opposite direction. It was by far the most traveled and more hazardous for me. From behind a pile of broken cinder-blocks that had been discarded in a grassy ditch, I watched its east and westbound lanes. From there, four-twelve was the only highway to Woodward, Oklahoma. The next step in my journey before heading down the panhandle to Guymon. There was no other feasible choice...not if I wanted to go home. Anyone looking for me was bound to know that. After the Helena turn off I would probably be safe, but the ten miles between Enid and there would be fraught with danger.

Stealing a car or hitchhiking were my only options, and it was too early in the evening to be skulking around in peoples' driveways. With the sun starting to make its downward descent toward the western horizon, I took a breath and boldly stepped out onto the side of the road walking with my thumb out.

Fifty cars and trucks must have went by while I shambled west along the highway. I spun around with my thumb in the air whenever a vehicle approached, my nerves sizzling like bacon on a hot-plate with each one that drove past; knowing the next one could be a cop or detention center employee. My luck would only hold for so long. I prayed for a ride soon.

The sun was sinking fast and a breeze had picked up. It had my long hair whipping around my face. Another car approached—it slowed down but when the driver got close enough to get a good look at me he sped back up.

I shot him the finger. "Fucking prick," I cursed. The longer I was out there, the more nervous and aggravated I was getting. I considered getting off the road and walking the ten miles past the turn off before I tried hitchhiking. It was an option—but not one I liked very much.

Putting a road sign between myself and the approaching traffic so they would not see me until I could see them, was my next move. If a cop, or someone else looking for me came along, I hoped to be able to determine their intent by the way they hit their brakes. Giving me time to run into the field I was walking beside.

No sooner than I put that plan in play, a car braked coming to a stop thirty yards down the shoulder of the road. It was a two-door, maroon Monte Carlo.

My first instinct was to run. It wasn't a cop but I didn't know what the employees from Helena drove. When it started backing up I was torn, but I was out there to get a ride. Shoving the fear of getting caught into a little imaginary box in my gut, I ran to meet the car.

When I reached it, no one jumped out, which I took as a good sign. The passenger door opened to let me in. There were four men inside, ranging in age from twenty-something to fifty-plus. "Awww man...we thought you was a girl," a young guy in the back passenger seat said when he got a good look at me.

I pulled the bucket seat forward and pushed my way in the back between him and another man before they had a chance to change their minds. "Well I'm not, but thanks for the ride anyway." I was relieved to be off the road. *I might just make it yet*, I thought.

The driver peered at me through the rearview mirror and pulled back onto the blacktop. "Well it will be a short one, we're turning off at the gas plant in about ten miles. But a little help is better than none, right? Where are you headed anyway?"

"You bet. I'm good with whatever gets me closer to Woodward."

Looking at the men, I could see this was some kind of car-pool. The younger man sitting to my right offered me a cigarette, that I gladly took. Then I rode along listening to the men jape at one another; reminding me of my oil field days. Quicker than I would have thought ten miles could pass, the older guy driving informed me they were coming to their turn.

As my luck would have it, their turn-off to the gas plant was the same junction that branched off to Helena. Only, they would turn south instead of north. I would be getting out right under the "Helena - 12 miles" sign!

I kept my concerns to myself. Nonetheless, as we pulled to a stop I was scanning the roads in all four directions for headlights. Once beyond this intersection I would probably be in the clear, but until then, I would be as vulnerable as a jumbo hot-link in a women's prison.

"It wasn't much of a ride, and there ain't nothin' out here," the driver pointed out. "You gonna be alright?"

"I'll be fine. And, I'm grateful for what I got."

With that I jumped out and waved at them as they turned left, and sped off. The sun had set and it was almost full dark. Looking west, I could see an elevation the highway climbed over about a hundred yards further down. I decided I would not feel safe until I was over that hill and set off running for it.

As it turned out, I didn't see a car going either direction until I was already a mile past the crest of that little knoll. Apparently there wasn't a lot of traveling between Enid and Woodward that night. When a car or truck did come by, they just blew past. A couple of them took the time to honk their irritation at me for surprising them. A phantom materializing from the dark, on the side of the road, in the middle of nowhere. For the most part, though, it was a lonely sojourn stumbling along a quiet moonless night. At least the temperature remained mild, I was more than thankful for that.

The later it got the darker it became, but still I trudged on walking the westbound shoulder of the road. I glanced to my right and saw the dense inky forest I'd been in before. It sat hulking blacker than the sky above it. I wondered how close I'd come to making it to this highway the last time. I remembered getting tangled in those spooky woods, and how freaked out I got.

As soon as I thought about it I knew I shouldn't have. The darkness stretching off to my right instantly took on a sinister feel. My foot-falls echoed in my ears as I quickened my pace.

I jerked to a stop. Feeling foolish for scaring myself again, I leaned over picked up a rock and hurled it into the trees. "Ain't no such thing as ghosts! You don't scare me..." I shouted.

Suddenly something flew at me out of the darkness.

I fell backward, landing on my ass in the road. *What the hell!*

Thump. Thump. Thump. A huge owl beat its wings as it gained altitude over my head.

My heart was pounding.... *Dammit, I'm not going through this again!* I was more angry than scared this time, cursing and kicking the dirt.

Just then a set of headlights came around a curve in the road I'd rounded a hundred yards back. I stuck my thumb out.

The driver saw me and immediately braked. It was a pale-colored Impala. I prayed it wasn't a cop but with the weirdness going on in the woods again I didn't even care. The car stopped right beside me. No state emblems, that was good but....

The passenger side door swung open and the interior light came on. Leaning across from the driver's seat was a middle-aged balding man dressed in a blue and white striped short sleeve button-up shirt and slacks. "Hey son, what are you doing way out here? Do you need a ride?"

"Do I." I wanted to hug the guy.

The man had the passenger seat full of folders and brochures. He grabbed them and threw them in the back. "Climb in. I can get you as far as Woodward at least."

Ted, he said his name was, got me to Woodward without any problems, and dropped me off at its only truck stop. Forty-five minutes later I found a ride with a trucker named George, who would be passing right through Guymon.

Dawn was turning the night sky the color of a three-day-old bruise by the time we passed the "Guymon city limits" sign.

I'd made it home.

CHAPTER 7

GUYMON

The rig pulled over before turning off of Highway 3, to head north up fifty-four on its way into Kansas. I thanked the driver and stepped down from the big truck, slapping the door to let him know I was clear before he pulled off. I stood still listening to the diesel engine purr and watched smoke shoot from its stacks as it turned onto the wider four-lane black-top, leaving the brightening sky with the distinct aroma of rubber and exhaust.

I breathed in deep through my nose, sure enough, it smelled like freedom to me. So happy to be home I was tempted to fall on my face and kiss the oil-stained asphalt. However, I settled for throwing a stupid smile on my mug and skipped across the highway like an eight-year-old playing hop-scotch to the neighborhood streets on the other side.

The highway junction left me a ten-block walk to Tina's mom's house, where I assumed she would go after losing our apartment. Guymon city blocks were not all that long and they went quickly.

Even though David's wife, Lisa, had written that Tina had been cheating on me, I was still excited and my heart was pounding when I caught sight of her mom's place. Strutting out of the alley I thought about Tina. I wasn't trippin', too much. At our age, things like infidelity were bound to happen under circumstances such as these. Hell, I'd slept with two of her sisters during short breaks in our relationship. One of which, claimed I fathered her child. Though, personally, I wasn't so convinced. What mattered was, that I was back, which meant whatever else was going on was over.

Tina's mom's house was a cream-colored, two-bedroom, square box with tan trim sitting on a two-foot-high raised foundation. No trees, bushes, nor grass around it, at least nothing that was green. When my girlfriend wasn't living with me, she usually stayed here with her mom and four sisters: Darleen, nineteen; Trisha, who was my age; and her two youngest siblings, a set of thirteen-year-old twins. Suzy and Sara. Tina had been mad at Darleen and Trisha for sleeping with me, but she had gotten over it, so I didn't have any reason to think Tina wouldn't be there when I jogged up the three steps leading to their stoop and knocked on the front door.

A pretty blonde haired girl answered, cracking the jamb a few inches to peek out. She was wiping sleep from her emerald-green eyes. Her hair was mussed.

"Jimmy!" she gasped, suddenly recognizing me. She stepped out on the porch bare-footed, in a pair of panties and a long black t-shirt with a Jack Daniels logo on it, and hugged me. "What are you doing here? Tina said you'd be locked up for another six to eight months."

"I escaped. Is Tina inside?"

"No. But your daughter is. Come in here before someone sees you."

We stepped into the house. I couldn't help but admire the way her long tanned legs ran up from her ankles to the half-moons of her heart-shaped ass, only partially concealed by the hem of her shirt. When she bent down to pick up a sleeping baby her thin panties stretched and clung to her curves giving me a glimpse of what I once walked away from. Trisha's bed was made on the couch, the crib right next to it. Everyone else was still asleep.

"Trish—don't wake her up," I pleaded.

But she was already walking back with her. "Misty Dawn, your daddy is here."

Trisha held out a beautiful brown-haired five month old baby. I took her and held her as she cooed at me sleepily. Misty Dawn, was the only member of the Jarvis family who wasn't blonde-headed, and either green- or blue-eyed. She was brown over brown, like me. Which I would have taken as a pretty good sign that I was in fact her father, except...Trisha's regular on and off boyfriend, Larry, also had brown hair and brown eyes. And, since Trish left the "father line" blank on Misty's birth certificate, and had told us both depending on what suited her at the time, that we were Misty's father—in my mind at least, Misty's paternity was in question.

Although, that baby took to me like she'd known me forever, which she had. And I couldn't deny the fact, that she *could* be mine. And even if she wasn't, I loved her like she was—as much as a buck-wild sixteen-year-old kid was capable of, anyway. The whole debate was a standing point of umbrage between her and her older sister, Tina...my girlfriend.

Misty Dawn opened her eyes a moment, looking at me real big. Then gave her binky a couple of sucks before snuggling her head into my chest and closing them again.

"She's beautiful, Trisha." I rocked Misty in my arms and cooed at her. "How are you and Larry getting along these days?"

"We're not. Why do you ask?"

"Because you're wanting me to play Daddy again." Her whole little game frustrated me. It wasn't fair to Misty, me, or lame-ass Larry for that matter. Though I really didn't care about his feelings one way or the other.

"I only told him that because he was my boyfriend. And besides, your grandmother didn't think I was a fit parent and threatened to take her away from me. Look at her. You know she's yours." She stepped closer to me so she could smile down at the baby in my arms.

Misty, did bring a warmth to my heart I had never felt before, but, I did not "know" she was mine, and truthfully, doubted it. What Trish didn't realize, it was for that reason, only, my grandmother had backed off the custody suit.

Trisha leaned against me when I transferred the sleeping infant back into her arms. I could smell a hint of the body wash she used and felt her purposely brush her breast against my arm. Suddenly, the warmth in my heart spread to other parts of my body. "So where's Tina?" I asked, trying to change the subject that was, quickly, coming up.

"She's got a new boyfriend she lives with. Some guy who moved to town a couple of months ago."

My eyes were drawn back to her half-naked bottom as she leaned over to place Misty in her cradle.

"Well, fuck him. He'll just have to move around—"

Trish stepped over and kissed me before I could finish what I was saying.

I pulled back. "Damn it, we're not starting this again. Where does this, 'new boyfriend', live?"

"Forget him. And forget Tina, she doesn't deserve you." She smiled, brushing her fingertips over the crotch of my jeans. "I can tell you want to…"

There was no denying the growing desire in my pants. I'd been gone over four months—between that, her touch, and the way her t-shirt barely covered her ass…not to mention the I-wanna-fuck-you-pheromones coming off of her, I was about to give in. The moment, however, was interrupted by one of the twins walking into the living room. She was wearing flannel pajamas and rubbing sleep out of her baby-blues.

"Hi Jimmy. When did you get out?"

"Yesterday."

"I'm glad. I don't like Tina's new boyfriend." She walked into the kitchen, plopping one foot in front of the other across the linoleum floor like a sleepwalker. "Are you hungry? I have to make Mom breakfast before she goes to work."

"Sure Sara, that would be great. I'm actually starving."

Trisha leant in and squeezed me through my jeans. "We'll pick this up after Mom leaves."

This time I didn't argue. I just sat down, hoping that my full-blown erection wasn't as noticeable through my blue jeans as it felt.

I leaned back realizing how tired I was. I'd fallen asleep for about an hour in the truck's comfortable passenger seat, between Woodward and Guymon. That was all the sleep I'd had in the past twenty-four hours, and in that time, traveled many hard won miles. Close to dozing, I fought it off. Soon the sounds of bacon frying and the smell of toast had my stomach rumbling.

Misty Dawn woke up and Trisha put a bottle on for her. Overriding my protests, Trisha was just laying Misty back in my arms wanting me to feed her, when Trish's mom came out of her bedroom. Her full-length flower-print nightgown, fluttering around her feet.

"Hi Jimmy. When did you get out?"

"Yesterday."

"I didn't think you were supposed to come home for another six months."

"Well..."

"...he escaped, Mom," Trisha finished for me with a sly smile. "He had to come see his daughter."

I groaned, inside.

"Well that's good, but you can tell your grandmother, she's not getting this baby."

It was easy to see where the girls all got their looks from. She was a thin, shapely blonde with bright-blue eyes. However, she was well past her prime. She drank and smoked too much, which left deep lines in her face and around her lips when she drew on one of her Virginia Slims. It showed the hard haggard life of a woman who'd spent half her existence on a bar-stool and the other half on her back. Though, there was no doubt that at one time she'd been truly beautiful.

"You don't have to worry. I have already called her off. She only wants any child of mine to be taken care of."

"She could give us some money. That would help."

"Mom—" Trish started....

"Y'all would have to straighten the whole, blank birth certificate and telling Larry he was the daddy, also, issues out for that. And...if you did convince her, there would be no way to stop her from trying to gain custody."

Sara brought me in a plate. I kissed Misty on her pink pudgy cheek and handed her back to Trisha who was now mean mugging her mom.

"Well...she's obviously, yours. She looks just like you, and doesn't even like Larry. Cries everytime he touches her."

I didn't know about the crying part, but in my opinion Misty looked as much like Larry as she did me. Though I kept that thought to myself.

Momma J sashayed by me to grab some toast. "I haven't got time to eat. I'm running late and I have to be at the plant in twenty minutes. Trisha, when I'm gone you can move Misty's crib into my room and you and Jimmy can have it. I'm sure he's tired if he's been running all night."

She leant over and gave me a peck on the cheek. "I'm glad you are home, but remember, when they figure out where you've gone this is one of the first places the Guymon cops will be watching for you."

I knew that, and nodded. "Thanks Mom. I won't be here that long." She smiled her appreciation of my understanding her meaning and went about the business of preparing for work.

Trisha graced me with the honor of burping Misty. She was just throwing up on me about the time Trisha's mom was heading out the door. Trish pulled the messy towel off of my shoulder and carried the baby crib into her mom's room. Sara took over Trisha's spot on the couch, and was soon back asleep. I got up and carried a cranky baby into the bedroom.

Trisha's mom's room was a typical single woman's sanctuary. Her dresser and vanity-table were a cluster of makeups, oils, and creams. The curtains and bedding were all flowers and feminine prints, and the closet and chairs were covered in discarded ladies clothing; dresses, bras, pantyhose, and tops—clean or dirty was hard to tell.

"Do you want to change her?" Trish asked.

"Absolutely not," I said, handing her "our" baby.

Trisha laughed at the look on my face. "Ain't so tough after all, are you?" She kissed me on the side of my mouth and brushed her almost bare hip against my leg before laying Misty on her mother's bed. Then very proficiently began the process of changing Misty Dawn's diaper.

Standing to one side, I watched Trisha's svelte and sexy form bending and turning while she went at the task. I was trying to avoid the look and smell of the mess Misty had somehow created in her pants. "You're going to have to learn how to do this one of these days, Jimmy," Trish said finishing up and laying Misty back in her cradle. She cooed over her, and gave her back her binky. I took my sweat shirt off and laid on the bed watching the pretty blonde gently rock the cradle until Misty's eyes began to droop. It dawned on me how Trisha was actually a pretty good mother. I was impressed.

I knew what Trish was doing. She was on the outs at the time with Larry, and I was the perfect mechanism to make him jealous, which is how our relationship started in the first place. It worked for me—especially since Tina was off screwing someone else. Because Tina was insanely jealous of Trish, too. So the two of us had an unspoken arrangement. One which allowed us to take advantage of that situation by fucking each others brains out whenever we had the chance. At least, that's how I looked at it. Though, Trisha had tried more than once to convince me she would dump Larry for good, if I would only commit to her. Something that sounded good in the throws of passion, but I didn't really believe and even if I did I was still in love with Tina. Regardless, of what Tina may or may not have done I felt guilty and put an end to our little trysts.

Soon Misty was fast asleep, blowing little air bubbles around the sides of her pacifier. When Trish was satisfied Misty wasn't going to wake right back up, Trisha stood, giving me a lascivious grin before walking over and locking the door. She turned the stereo on with the volume down low, and stretched so the hem of her shirt rode-up showing off her pale-green bikini-cut panties and flat stomach. Then she hooked her thumbs in their waist band and playfully tugged them down, showing me the top of her clean shaven cooter.

There was no denying the effect she was having. Trisha smiled and turned her back to me. She glanced over her shoulder with a twinkle in her mischievous eyes. Then, with her legs pressed together, slid her bottoms all the way down, bending only at her waist.

The way her legs pressed her sex together made me move one of my hands to the straining buldge in my pants. It was obvious she was turned on too, her muffin was fat, pink, and moist. Her hips were toned. And her legs were velvety-smooth. She stepped out of her panties then turned around. She was toying with me and liked the reaction she was getting. Trisha twirled her lacy underwear around her finger and lifted the bottom of her shirt so I could see her perfect V from the front. There was no doubt, she was phenomenal.

Morning was in full swing. The sunlight was soft and diffused coming through the curtains. Trisha came around to my side of the bed and pulled my tennis shoes off before sliding her warm, soft body on top of mine.

Trish kissed me, and I slid my hands over the mounds of her ass to cup her naked bottom. Joan Jett was on the stereo softly singing *Crimson and Clover*. Even caught up in the moment as I was right then, I liked Trisha too much to take her under false illusions.

"You know Trisha, I am still going to find Tina, don't you?

She sat up straddling my hips. I could feel how wet she was through my jeans. With one motion she grabbed the bottom of her shirt and pulled it over her head. She took my breath away. Flat belly and breasts the size and shape of Florida peaches. "Just shut up. By the time I'm through with you, you won't even remember her name."

I reached up and cupped her breast in my rough hands, capturing her nipples between my thumbs and forefingers. She threw her head back and moaned before leaning into me. Then we locked onto one another and lost ourselves in the fiery flames of young lust.

I was like a starving street urchin, who had been put in front of an all he could eat buffet. I did forget about Tina, for a time, and immersed myself in Trish. A half hour later we lay in each others arms covered in a sheen of sweat. I was too tired to get up and take a shower. With Trisha's head on my chest and her drawing little hearts in the perspiration that puddled across my stomach, I fell asleep.

"Jimmy! Wake-up! Wake-uuuup..." Trisha was shaking me. She was standing beside the bed, fully dressed in skin-tight, holey blue-jeans and a faded, pink t-shirt with a teddy bear smoking a joint silk-screened across it. She sounded stressed.

"Whaa...what time is it? What's wrong?"

"It's two o'clock. But listen, the cops just drove by—twice!" Her words came out in an urgent whisper, as if just mentioning the police out-loud would bring them back.

What she was saying only took a moment to break through my sleep clouded mind. In a flash I was up throwing my pants on.

Trisha was watching the street through the thin material of the curtains. And by the time I was tying my shoes, announced that they were back; pulling to a stop along the curb across the drive. Considering there was only a vacant lot where a house should be over there, it was obvious where their interest was directed.

My heart was thumping like a jack-hammer, I did not want to be caught. I wondered if they were coming in, and if they had the back covered. I ran out of the bedroom with Trish right behind me. My mind was scrambling, almost in a panic, for an escape route.

In the living room Suzy and Sara were standing behind the coffee table looking around their older sister Darleen, who was standing between the table and couch. Darleen was pretty also, she was the oldest and most stable of the girls. I assumed, from having to fill the mother role for so many years while their actual mother ran wild. She was watching the cops through the big bay window that faced the street. She had Misty Dawn in her arms and was bouncing her gently to the soothing sounds of her coo-cooing in her ear.

Darleen looked at me as I came in. "Hey Sleeping Beauty. Don't panic, they'd have to have a search warrant or something to get in here and I'm not letting them without one."

"Thanks." I stood behind the twins, where I could see without being seen, and peered over their heads out the window. All I was able to make out was the car. "What are they doing?"

I went into the kitchen, with Trish nervously following right behind me, and peeked around the curtain hanging on the backdoor to see if there were any more black-and-whites covering the alley. I didn't see any, but that didn't mean they weren't there. I felt trapped.

Darleen hesitated, studying them before answering me. "They are not doing anything, just sitting there. To hell with this. Here Suzy, hold Misty."

"What are you going to do?" I was barely holding my panic in check.

"I'm going to find out what they want."

After handing the baby to Suzy, Darleen walked boldly to the front door and walked out. She made sure she pulled the door closed before trotting down the steps. She walked as if she didn't have a care across the street and stood by the passenger window until the officer rolled it down.

The twins moved onto the couch to get a better view. I took up a position where they had been, watching from the shadows. Trisha was gripping my arm tightly, hiding behind me as if she was the one they were after.

Darleen wasn't an animated talker, it was hard to get a read on what was being said. She waved a couple of times, like she was pointing across town and shook her head often. Finally, Darleen nodded and turned back to the house.

Whatever she told them must have satisfied the policemen, because they pulled off while she was still walking up the sidewalk.

"They are definitely looking for you, Jimmy," she confirmed when she stepped inside, "but, they don't know for sure if you will even be coming to Guymon. Tina sent letters to you from here, so they were just having a look."

She took Misty back from Suzy—stepping back into the mommy role. I noticed it was a habit she displayed with all the girls, except for maybe Tina. "I told them we thought you were still locked-up. And, that Tina has a new boyfriend who lives across town at the Grady Hotel, or somewhere near there. And, that Tina now lives with him. I assured them we hadn't seen you and would call them if we did. I don't think they will be back right away. But...you never know."

"Yeah, you're right. I'd better get out while the gettin' is good. Did you say this new boyfriend lives at the Grady?"

"Yeah, but you can't go there. That's where I just sent the cops."

"Yeah Jimmy, stay here, we'll hide you. Won't we, Darleen?" Trisha was holding my hand and looking at me with water in her green eyes.

Uh oh...I thought. I couldn't afford to get caught up in an emotional triangle right now. Besides, if I was apprehended there, after Darleen said I wasn't, it could cause them or their mom problems. "No. I need to go."

Trisha didn't like it but after explaining my reasons, she grudgingly admitted that she understood.

Sara brought me a bologna sandwich that I could barely get my teeth around. She'd made it for me while I was asleep, and had it waiting in the icebox. Her and Suzy were like little sisters to me. I quickly smashed it, then thanked them all, giving the young girls and Darleen a hug. Trisha jumped on me and kissed me so hard that her sisters had to pull her off. I knelt down and brushed my fingers through Misty's soft brown hair. *If only you* were *mine*, I thought. I smiled at her, nonetheless feeling a warmth I've only felt with the kids I've had since then. I kissed Trisha one more time, admiring how she filled out her jeans before heading out the back door.

Once outside I felt exposed. I considered changing my mind and taking Trish up on her offer to hide me out. But the reality was; I knew that their mom, as cool as she was, would not appreciate me over-staying my welcome. Not with the police already watching her house.

With no real choice, I jogged down the back steps and into the alley. It was three in the afternoon and the sun was high in the sky. I stayed close to the fences and trash cans, trying to keep my exposure to a minimum. Still, I felt vulnerable as a duck target in a carney's sharpshooting booth. I was headed to Arley Larson's house—he lived four blocks northeast of Tina.

When I got there I breathed a sigh of relief. I hadn't seen any sign of the police. Arley's mother let me in, "Hi Jimmy. I thought you were in some juvy hall or something."

"I was. I'm out now."

Arley's mom was the spitting image of Mrs. Cunningham on *Happy Days*. Regardless of how she appeared, she was cool as a fan. I probably could have told her the truth. His dad however, was not. And, was sitting right inside on the living room couch where he always sat, watching the TV and griping about the government, Iran, and the price of gasoline. He was drinking from a brown bottle of Budweiser sandwiched between his palms when I stepped in.

Arley's dad had lost eight of his fingers between the elevators and a well-head in an oil field accident five years before. All he had left were his thumbs—and a big settlement that would take care of them for the rest of his life. However, he was not a happy man. At least, he didn't seem to like me very much. He reminded me a lot of my step-dad, Charlie. Only with out fingers.

Mr. Larson scrunched his face at the sight of me. Although before he could say anything, Mrs. Larson waved her hand toward the back of the house, "Arley is down in his room."

I took that as my cue, and headed across the living room and through the kitchen. Arley lived in an add-on, three steps down from where their backdoor used to be. He had it fixed up with three-foot-tall Pioneer speakers in each corner, and a dozen black-light posters of one acid-trip-inspired, other-worldly scene after another adorning his walls.

When Arley saw me he jumped up so fast I thought he had sat on a bumble bee. "Hey man! When did you get out?" He was a tall, skinny seventeen-year-old. He wore his brown hair, short but shaggy, and already had a pretty good little mustache growing, which I'd always been envious of.

Arley slipped out and swiped us a couple beers from his dad's stash. His pops kept cases of liquid gold in an extra refrigerator in the garage. We sat and drank them, smoking on a pack of Marlboro 100's that Darleen had given me, while I caught him up on my life since he'd last seen me.

"That was pretty cool of Darleen to cover for you like that. I've always wanted to hit that."

I kept my own little tryst with her to myself. Because ever since the one time when we found ourselves alone, drunk, and lonely at her house, we'd always acted like it never happened. The only one who seemed to remember it was Tina. Why we thought it was only right to tell her, I'll never know. "Yeah, she handled it pretty good. So what do you know about this clown Tina is screwing?"

"Not much. His name is PR, stands for Puerto Rico. He's half Mexican and half white. Twenty-something-years-old and thinks he's all that. Although, I have a feeling he's about to find out, he ain't." Arley peered at me over the top of his beer bottle and laughed before taking a drink. He knew PR would not be the first grown man I'd beat-down over my misguided love for Tina. "He lives in one of those rent by the week shacks next to the Grady Hotel, not in it. But, Darleen is right, you can't go over there. Not right now anyway. The cops will be sniffing around wherever they believe Tina is. But...Tina and PR are supposed to be at a party tonight at The Pit. Catch him out there."

"That's a good idea," I said swirling the last couple of inches of liquid around in my bottle. "Are you going?"

Arley had stolen us a couple more beers, and as dry as I had been the last few months was already feeling the first one. A couple more and I would be in a peak fighting mood.

"Can't. Mom and Dad are going out and I have to watch my little sister."

"Well, before they go, borrow your mom's car and take me to David and Lisa's. I don't want to try walking out in the open."

After promising his mom, five times, to drop me off and come right back, Arley was able to secure the car long enough to drive me to David's—with one slight detour by the Grady Hotel. However, we spotted a cop car sitting in a parking lot a half block from it, and changed course before we got there.

"Damn! They are going above and beyond. I may have to leave town if I want to stay out." I huffed, and slapped the car door my arm was hanging out.

"Guymon is definitely too small to hide in for very long," he agreed. I could see he was nervous, also, because he kept taking one hand off the wheel and rubbing his little mustache.

In no time we were pulling up in front of David's trailer. I thanked Arley, got out and watched him pull off. As I went to knock on David's front door, it opened, and a smiling—half drunk—curly haired dude hollered: "Jimmy! God damn Lisa and me have missed you!" He grabbed me in a bear hug and squeezed. David wasn't tall, but he was wide...and strong.

"Ugh...let me go you freakin' ape," I gasped. He let go and just grinned at me. "I half expected you to be at work. What are you doing home?"

"Oh yeah...thought you'd get out of the joint and come knock off a slice of Lisa pie while I was away, did you? I don't need to be gone— I'll watch!" He gave me a bug-eyed look and hooted. "Lisa. Show Jimmy your boobs. He ain't seen any in a few months." He laughed so hard he snorted beer out of his nose, which he did a lot. I could tell he'd had more than a couple of bottles already.

"No dork. Sorry Lisa I don't want to see your boobs either.... Seriously, why are you home, and drunk, on a Friday afternoon?"

"Well..."

"...he's between jobs right now," Lisa finished for him, bringing us both a beer from the fridge.

"Yeah, well, remember when you got canned from that service rig for beatin' up that derrick hand? I call your derrick hand, and raise you one tool-pusher. I knocked the slick mouth prick out on my last well-site. It kinda killed my references." He chuckled, "Just going to have to go back to working service rigs, I guess."

"Well you look sad," I said, even though he really didn't. "I know the perfect thing to cheer you up. We're going to a party tonight, out at The Pit."

CHAPTER 8

THE PIT

Lisa made dinner while I caught them up on life in the reform school. Since David was with me for the great tire heist that got me thrown in the can in the first place, and never got caught, he was down for helping me anyway he could. Especially considering he'd been half-ass on the run himself at the time.

It was already dark by the time we pulled into The Pit. With the sun down, the temperature had dropped a few degrees and the evening air had a little nip to it. The name the younger party goers around town had tagged this patch of party paradise with was a bit misleading. It wasn't really a pit. It was just a place on the outskirts of town where a fifteen-foot dirt cliff fell off beside the road. You could drive through a cattle-guard and circle around and down to the hollowed-out cut in the land, which ended at the face of the drop-off. Big logs had been pulled into a circle creating a large fire pit.

There was a dozen or more cars and pickups parked haphazardly at the mouth of the arroyo. David and I pulled in next to a black Ford F-150 and piled out of his jeep already about half lit. Twenty or thirty people mulled around or clustered in small groups, some already stumbling. The logs seemed to be reserved for the couples. There were several hugged-up, sitting on the make-shift benches that encircled the fire.

Everyone, either had a bottle or can they'd brought themselves, or a plastic cup of beer from the keg sitting in a trough of ice just outside the log ring.

The crackling flames of the bonfire sent bits of red glowing embers spiraling up into the dark night sky like flaming fire-flies dancing their way across the heavens.

It was quickly apparent I didn't know very many people there. Most of the crowd were made up from the Jock, Socials, and Redneck lots. I counted four Hoods besides David and me who I could possibly depend on in a pinch. But honestly, I didn't really care, if the snobs wanted to get in my way—sorry for them. I had a Buck knife in my back pocket that I didn't think any five of them wanted to tangle with...if it came to that.

My intention was to play it cool. As far as I knew, Tina didn't even know I was in town. I planned to walkup smooth as you please, move her out of the way, and say: "Excuse me, I think you have been boning my girl." Then bust Mr. Don, PR, Juan in his mouth, and go from there. Although, as it happened, when I spotted the two love birds all curled up on the log—his grubby hands pawing all over Tina's bosom, his tongue moving around inside her mouth like he was mapping her teeth—I bellowed like some enraged wild beast, and threw my beer bottle into the fire pit; sending shards of glass exploding in every direction from its impact with a flaming tree stump.

So much for subtlety. Everyone was now looking at me, including PR and Tina. PR was about my size. A hundred and eighty pounds, give or take. He had mid-length frizzy brown hair, and sported a hairy mustache reminding me of Gabe on *Welcome Back Kotter*.

Tina gasped. "Jimmy! What are you doing here!?" She jumped away from PR like he'd shocked her with a cattle prod.

"So this is Jimmy? He don't look like so mu—"

I was moving at "He don't...." Two steps and I was airborne, football spearing him before he could finish his sentence. PR's feet went up in the air as I pile-drived him over the top of the log and into the dirt. It knocked the wind out of him, and I took full advantage of the opportunity, pounding him in the face with a barrage of flying fists.

"No Jimmy. Stop!" Tina yelled.

Others were hollering as well.

"Break-up the fight," someone said. "That kid just attacked PR for nothing!" said another. "He's fucking up the party. Stop them!"

There was grumbling all around.

I felt someone grab me—then let go when David clothes-lined him. However, that incited more people to jump in. Hands were swinging and pulling at me from different directions. Suddenly PR hit me in the side of the head with a rock. Between being yanked on and blind-sided, I was soon overwhelmed and PR crawled away from me.

There were others yelling and fighting, but there seemed to be a crowd looming over me. Blood was running into my eyes. I freaked and grabbed for my blade—

Snick!

The sound of the knife opening, gave me some space, and I came up in a cloud of dirt, hair, and flashing steel.

"Aaaaah...He cut me!" one of the jocks yelled.

I stood my ground, growling deep in my throat. The guy had only sustained a flesh wound. In my mind this had turned from one thing into something else—I was now in survival mode. Everyone backed up, except one cowboy, who was holding an empty beer bottle by the neck and crouched like he was ready to go to war.

David let go of his second victim, and stood to my side. Along with two other guys that frequented the Hood lots. More than enough to catch my back. Shine and Blake, I thought their names were. I couldn't see PR anywhere. After wiping the blood out of my eye, I turned all my focus on the cowboy.

"No Jimmy. Stop this." Tina stepped in between me and the drunk redneck. "I'm sorry. I'll go with you, just put the knife away."

I looked over at her—although she had screwed me over in the past and I had forgiven her—it seemed like I was seeing her for what she truly was for the first time. "What? Did your new boyfriend run off and leave you? You know what Tina—I'm done Trisha is a better lay anyway."

I can't lie, even though I was drunk, mad, and had a knife in my hand, the way her face changed right then into a demonic mask of hatred...scared me a little bit. She tried to launch herself at me, but the redneck and a couple of bystanders restrained her.

"Let's go David. I'm finished here."

David handed me his torn up shirt to wipe the blood off of my face, then the four of us headed to our vehicles. Blake and Shine jumped in their Bronco, and David and me in his jeep. We were laughing when we shook hands and parted ways.

When we got back to David's trailer, I went straight for the shower to wash the blood and grime off. Lisa gave me some of David's clothes to wear and washed mine. Then she sat down and cleaned my wound with peroxide and a dash of alcohol. I winced, and gave her a mean look. She laughed and told me not to be a pussy. Then, she butterfly stitched the split over my eye with some bandages they had in the medicine cabinet. I randomly thought that Lisa smelled like flowers and lemon fresh cleaner. All while David and I relived the whole fight for her, start to finish.

Between drags of a Marlboro I'd borrowed from Lisa—where mine had went I had no idea—I declared: "I flattened that bitch-ass PR."

David took a swallow of beer and laughed. "Too bad you got your ass handed to you."

"Bullshit, I was smokin' that fool."

"Oh? Do I need to remind you who was leaking blood all over my favorite shirt?"

"He hit me with that rock trying to get away from the ass-kicking he was getting," I complained defensively. I started to flick my cigarette at him, but it was only half finished, so I took another drag instead. I could tell he was in his big brother, mentor mode. He did that when he was drinking from time to time.

"There ain't no doubt you were tougher than him, but in the end he hurt you worse. Running away or not. Just like you won and shut all them loud mouths punks down when you lost your shit and accidentally cut that jock."

"Whatever, David. You're drunk, and full of shit. No matter how it turned out, Mr. Tough guy ran off and left Tina to fend for herself. And to me, that was worth a little blood." My cigarette was short by then, so I flicked it right into his chest.

He laughed and picked up the burning snipe from where it eventually landed on the arm of his chair; took the last drag and said: "Right on all three counts. And that is why I love you like you were my own little brother."

Lisa was coming from the kitchen and glanced out the window. "Oh shit. The cops just pulled up!"

"What?" David and I said at the same time, then both of us peeked around the living room curtains.

There were only two officers that we could see. They were already out of their car. One was middle-aged and heavy-set, a little thin on top. The other was shorter and slimmer, with a crew-cut. I couldn't see him as well; he walked to the side of the trailer out of view.

"Go out the back door Jimmy," David whispered.

I turned and ran down the hallway, the soft, brown carpet muffling my footfalls. I realized that my shoes were still in the bathroom after my shower. There was no time to grab them now. At the rear door I looked around the curtains. The flat-top cop was at the corner of the trailer.

When I heard the knock at the front door I gave up the idea of sneaking out the back and began trying to find a place to hide. It was a mere matter of moments before I realized there was nowhere to go. The bathroom was small and Lisa had the cabinet under the sink crammed full of cosmetics, hair sprays, curlers, and dryers; things that would make a lot of noise were I to climb in on top of.

That only left their bedroom. It was small also, containing only a dresser and a bed too low to get under. David and Lisa's voices could be heard answering the door in the front of the trailer. With no choice, I climbed into their one and only closet.

On the bright side, it was crammed with clothes and miscellaneous clutter. All of the hanger space was full and some of Lisa's dresses almost hung to the floor.

The sliding doors opened from either side, so I picked the corner with the most concealment and pushed my way to the back wall; moving shoes, boots, and bags in front of my feet. With my body as well hidden as possible, I arranged the longest hanging clothes in front of my legs. Still there were places where my pants seemed exposed. I hoped they would appear to be another pair of jeans hanging in the back. At that point there was nothing to be done about it.

Sweating and listening, trying to control my breathing, I could hear what sounded like arguing, then the officers were in the trailer!

I knew that David would not want to let them in his place, but I also knew he wasn't in a position to make trouble. If he pissed them off, they may discover his warrant out of Minnesota. However they did it, they were in, and their voices were getting louder. I could hear David telling them that he was pretty sure they needed a search warrant to be in his home. The officer was explaining that a search warrant didn't apply, because they had a credible tip that I was there. Sounded like bullshit to me, but I was in no position to say so.

David said, "Look, Jimmy is my friend, he was here earlier but he left. Besides that, he's just a dumb kid your partner doesn't need to have his gun out. You are scaring my wife."

"The tip also said he assaulted someone earlier tonight; we're just being careful. Holster your gun John. Mr. Snowdy is right, the boy is only fifteen or sixteen. Just stay ready." The same speaker continued, "What's down here?"

There was no way to see what was going on, but the officers sounded so close that if the wall hadn't been there, I believed I could have reached out and touched one.

"The bathroom and our bedroom," Lisa chimed in, "and I don't want you guys back there eyeballing my girl stuff!" She was doing her best to keep them from searching any further, but at that point I knew it was hopeless. I began planning what to do when they caught me.

My heart was pounding so hard, the cops probably could've heard it if they'd stopped to listen.

The bathroom cabinet opened...then closed. Moments passed, I tensed, they were now literally on the other side of the closet door.

Swooosh...one side of the slider opened. A flashlight beam bounced around highlighting the shoes, boxes, and a suitcase that sat inside.

It was the moment of truth. I held my breath as they slid both of the panels to the other end of the door tracks.

In seconds a flashlight beam found my exposed patch of pant leg. The officer stepped back—then suddenly one jerked the clothes apart while the other threw down on me with his revolver. I couldn't see past the barrel of the gun for the light shining in my eyes.

"Freeze—or I will shoot you!" the policeman holding the gun yelled.

"We've got you, so come out of there and don't give us any trouble," said the one shining the light.

The bore of the pistol looked as large as a quarter, and the cops standing behind it smelled of Brute and Old Spice. I felt a sense of deja vu, like I'd been there before and this was becoming a pattern in my life.

David was standing behind them, "Damn Jimmy, I thought you had left."

The cops pulled me out of the closet and cuffed me behind my back, then herded us into the living room.

The policemen put Lisa and David on the couch. "We could charge you with harboring a fugitive," Flat-top threatened, "though I doubt it would be worth our time in the case of an escaped juvenile."

"They didn't know I had escaped. I never told them."

"Well you were damn sure hiding in their closet," the balding one countered. "Anyway...where are your shoes?"

"In the bathroom."

The flat-top cop directed me to sit in a chair, then glanced at Lisa. "Mrs. Snowdy, would you get his shoes for him, please?"

Now that they had me and the situation under their control, the county cops relaxed, being polite, even smiling...at Lisa anyway. It crossed my mind that they probably did need a search warrant, and didn't want to make any more waves. But in the end, it made no difference, I was still cuffed and stuffed.

Lisa came out of the water closet carrying my black and white Converses and sat them on the floor in front of me. "Here you go Jimmy. I'm sorry." She looked like she was about to cry.

I felt bad for her. "Thanks Lees."

Before sitting in the chair, I slid my hands down over my butt and to the floor. I put one shoe on then the other. Once I had them tied I stood up with my hands in front of me, hoping the officers wouldn't re-cuff me behind my back.

The lead policeman indicated for me to follow him, then turned and walked out the front door. I followed close behind, with flat-top, bringing up the rear.

There was no rail on David's small, red-iron porch, and only single-wide steps leading down from it. The bigger, older officer was already descending them as I was passing over the trailer's threshold.

When I stepped onto the porch cool air blew across my skin and I could see the moon had finally came out and was shining its soft reflective glow down upon the small town drama unfolding below it. When my foot touched down on the porch. I jerked away from the officer trailing behind me, and with a sudden burst of speed, sprang from the iron-grate patio—exactly how I had planned it in the closet. This was even better than I'd hoped for, because I hadn't expected to have my hands in front of me.

The guy behind grasped for my sleeve, catching nothing but air. He yelled for me to "Stop!" but I was already three steps into the gravel driveway by then.

From the corner of my eye I saw the big cop was quick to respond. He was reaching for the door of the squad car one second, then was pursuing me the next.

I lost sight of them as I burned around the corner of the trailer kicking up gravel and dust. Although, the sound of their boots pounding the ground behind assured me they were only steps away.

There was another trailer behind David's, then it was an open field from there to the next cross street.

One set of footfalls stopped. I assumed that meant that officer was going for the car. However I could not look back, the man behind me was keeping pace, literally breathing down my neck. But, one dropping off was enough to encourage me to run even faster. I saw myself sprinting across the open ground, leaping over the sparse scrub brush and veering around obstacles like a twelve-point buck running from a pack of hungry wolves. I leant my head back and ran holding my cuffed wrists close to my chest. Still the man stayed behind me. I wondered how long he could keep up his pace. I wondered if he smoked. I found myself praying over and over that he did. I told myself that I was young and strong, and he would surely tire before me.

A hundred yards across the field I felt a slight hitch in my side as my lungs struggled to keep oxygen in my blood stream. Though I dared not show it for fear of encouraging him.

We hit the street and ran down a branching avenue. At the next block I turned. *Please smoke, please smoke*, I kept repeating in my head. *How much longer can this guy keep it up?*

I was starting to get desperate, the stitch in my side turned to a low aching burn as we rounded a corner and headed down another side street. Still I ran all-out, refusing to show any signs of the debilitation that was creeping through my muscles.

Finally, I heard a disruption in the rhythm of pounding footfalls behind me. My hopes soared. *Thank you, Lord!* Knowing the man only needed a little more reason to give up, I gave it everything I had left ignoring the pain. Somewhere I found a boost of speed and sped up. It had the desired effect. Within moments of my acceleration the officer gave up and came to a huffing, bouncing stop. I was across the street turning down an alley between two big stone warehouses when I had my first chance to glance back.

I was surprised to see it had been the bigger, older officer who had pulled off that amazing effort. He was just getting his gun out and gasping for me to "stop". He was in the middle of the road holding his side with one hand and a shaking revolver with the other. I lost sight of him when I disappeared up the service-lane.

To truly be in the clear I needed to get away from the buildings, across the railroad tracks, and duck into one of the neighborhoods before the officer made it up the alley. The problem was I was running out of gas fast. I told myself I could make it if I just keep going.

At the end of the alley separating the two warehouses, and past an over-flowing dumpster that smelled like rotting meat, the gravel access-road I was on veered sharply to the east paralleling the tracks. Abruptly all my hope and remaining strength ran out of me, and I stumbled to a stop.

Ahead and to the west was a half acre square of overgrown waist-high grass. On the other side of the field, between the tracks and service-road, was an eight-foot-tall chain-link fence. It ran a hundred yards east before ending at a railroad crossing. To my left it circled around the half-acre grassy patch and met a corner post where another eight foot fence branched off and connected to the far side of the warehouse I had just ran past. There was no way to get over that fence wearing cuffs, and no way I had the wind to run another hundred yards to get around it. I was effectively corralled. The sound of sirens were closing in. The cavalry would soon be in the chase as well.

With no choice, I looked for a place to hide. There was nothing except a few trash dumpsters to the right along the access alley. And a few ply-boards leant against the back of one of the buildings down the same way. Far too obvious. Which left hiding in the tall weeds. These thoughts flashed through my mind in a glance.

The cop would be coming any second.

Out of time and praying for a miracle I ran into the grass. It reached my hips. There were places throughout the overgrown field where a rusted car frame lay, or a pile of brick and rock debris. Several places had broken boards, and discarded sheets of plywood pressing the grass down. I realized I needed to watch my step when I saw how many jagged nails were sticking up through them. All that, still nowhere to hide. Right then I heard Captain America shuffling down the alley I had just stepped out of. I took the only option left to me, and dropped to the ground where I was, curling into a fetal position a few feet from a stack of concrete and masonry detritus.

The weedy, wheat-grass swayed two feet above me. It was thick, but not thick enough to be hiding from the cops in. From where I laid I could still see through it to the end of the alley. It appeared the path I had made running into it was still slightly separated from my passing.

Suddenly the big officer appeared. He was back-lit from the street lamps at the front of the buildings. I froze, and held my breath. He stopped in the same spot I had, pistol still in hand, and scanned the horizon the way I had—taking in the same obstacles.

He looked in the dumpster, then walked into the weeds toward me. Spotting something he wanted to investigate, he veered south stepping between me and the building. I could hear him shuffling through the tall grass as he made his way slowly, avoiding the nail-driven hazards, around to the corner of the fence. I dared only lean my head a few inches and strain with my eyes, but I could see his silhouette. He had his back to me staring through the fence into the distant neighborhood on the other side of the tracks. Finally, holstering his gun he turned away.

Flat-top showed up, pulling their squad car to the end of the alley. *Just my luck!* I thought. The most direct route for Captain America to exit the field and reach his partner was right over the top of me!

Too afraid to move a muscle and look, I lost sight of him. But I heard him plain enough as he moved around behind me. He stumbled and cursed as he slowly made his way back to the alley by the same path he had followed in. Spots started flashing in my eyes and I realized I'd been holding my breath. I let it out quietly as my heart fluttered in my chest. I couldn't believe it, he'd walked around me.

No sooner had I began savoring my good fortune than I heard another squad car pull up. I couldn't see the new arrivals, but their murmuring voices reached my ears through the grass. My two original pursuers climbed into their police cruiser and pulled off. A dog gave a sharp bark. *What the hell is going on now?* The second car came into view. It was rolling slowly east along the service-road. Then I saw, through the slight break in the grass, another officer leading a canine on a leash.

My heart seemed to stop, lurch, and speed up all at the same time. There was no way I could beat a police dog! Right then a grasshopper chose to leap from the weeds and land on my face. It stuck to my cheek with little horny feet, and tickled my eyelashes with its antenna. Its huge looking head staring at me eye to eye was unnerving, but I remained as still as the rusted car frame laying a few feet from me.

The officer had his dog sniff the dumpster, then pulled him away to follow the car that was creeping around the buildings. The German shepherd paused in the middle of the gravel lane and craned its neck in my direction. *He smells me*, I thought. The grasshopper had walked across my face and was crouched between the bridge of my nose and my brow. I wanted to sneeze...but tensed every muscle instead, and told myself to be lifeless as a cinder block.

My heart wouldn't cooperate. It thudded away in my chest, and the blood rushing through my veins sounded like Niagara Falls to my inner ears. The shepherd's ears flicked as if he could hear my beating heart also, then his handler gave his leash a tug and the dog turned away to follow the squad car and sniff at the buildings along the way.

The irritating insect finally hopped off of my face. I remained stiff, taking only shallow breaths for ten minutes after no longer hearing the second car. Even when I relaxed and was able to breath normally, I stayed put, waiting for more searchers to come. Envisioning someone staking out the area, watching for me to show myself.

While I laid there I wondered what my family were doing. My grandparents, aunt and uncle there in Guymon. My mom and brothers in El Paso. Suddenly, I suffered a rare moment of home sickness. It dawned on me that if I wasn't such a delinquent I could be home right then instead of hiding in a dump, running from the police, and jumping at every sound.

An hour and a half passed and I was getting a chill in my bones before I worked up the nerve to emerge from the grass. Even then, I did it carefully, raising only my eyes above the top of the weeds. From that vantage point I studied the alley, the buildings, and the neighborhood across the tracks for signs of law enforcement. It was dark and quiet.

Even though I was confident the cops had given up the search for me in this area—hopefully altogether, since I had a ways to go before I could get off the streets—I was still nervous and had to force myself to stand up. When I did, it felt as if I was lit up like a Vegas casino announcing my exact whereabouts to the authorities. Who were surely just waiting in the in the shadows to pounce.

Patience paid off. There was no one. No cars lurking around the corner of a building, or men hiding in the dumpster waiting for me to show myself. Still, I did not stick around. I'd restored my batteries while laying in the grass, so I took off running toward the end of the fence and circled around it, crossing the railroad tracks to vanish into the nearest neighborhood alley.

I found a discarded rag and wrapped it around my cuffs. After traveling a couple blocks, hiding from the few headlights that I saw, I eventually had to decide whether to go for Trisha's house, which was closer but was probably literally staked out at the moment, or back to Arley's. Considering how angry Tina was at me I opted for the longer and *safer* choice.

CHAPTER 9

GETTING EVEN

The street the Larson's lived on was dimly lit by a scattering of porch bulbs and corner-lamps. I moved across grassy yards, holding to the darkest shadows thrown across the neighborhood by the trees and shrubs along the way.

It was midnight by the time I reached my friend's house. The only glimmer of life I saw appeared to be an over-the-oven light on in the kitchen. I approached warily, slipping down the driveway past the side door, and crept up to Arley's window.

I tapped on it. No response. I tapped harder. The kitchen door opened.

"Who's out there?" a woman's voice called out.

"It's me, Jimmy, Mrs. Larson. I need Arley and didn't want to wake anyone else."

"Well come in here before someone sees you skulking around like a burglar and calls the law. Arley told me you were on the run from that place." She stepped back in, waving me to follow. "Be quiet. You don't want to wake-up Frank, that's for sure." As I entered she stood aside fidgeting with her nightgown.

"It's a little late to worry about someone calling the cops," I confided, holding up my wrists. "I need Arley's help getting these off. You wouldn't happen to have a hairpin would you?"

She opened a kitchen drawer and quietly dug around before handing me exactly what I needed. "I don't even want to know how you got in this predicament, but you'd better stay indoors the rest of the night. Arley can sneak you out of here in the morning."

"Thanks Mrs. L. I'm wore out anyway."

After my conversation with Arley's mom I went down to his room and woke him up.

"Jimmy? What are you doing here?" he asked, rubbing the sleep out of his eyes.

I flipped a lamp on and showed him my cuffed wrists, then told him what had happened since he dropped me off at David's. "Your mom is the coolest, by the way. But I guess you already know that. She told me you filled her in on my escape status." I held the bobby-pin up, "She gave me this."

"Yeah, she is cool. Thinks of you as a surrogate son. You remind her of Henry. I was a little kid when he died, he was your age now. Dad on the other hand...thinks you are nothing but trouble." He looked sideways at my cuffed hands and grinned.

"Guess he has me there," I admitted, and we both laughed.

Arley sat up and watched me bend the tip of the hairpin into a tiny little L. Even though the officers had not stopped me from moving my manacled hands in front of me back at David's, they had, however, double-locked them. Leaving me no choice but to actually pick the locks.

With my wrists so closely bound, getting the bent end of the pin into the keyhole was proving to be awkward. I talked Arley through it. Handcuffs are truthfully one of the simplest and most unsophisticated locking mechanisms ever designed. You can see that by examining a key to a pair. However, they are finely machined—you need the right tool for the job.

I directed my buddy to stick the bent end of the pin into the keyhole. Then work the flat spine of the tool between the round post in the keyhole's center, and the hole's outer edge. "You're going to have to try sliding the piece inside the lock in both directions. I can't remember which way unlocks the safety catch."

Arley seemed to get what I was saying without too much criticism.

His brows were drawn together in concentration, as if he was trying to crack a bank vault. "How will I know when I've got it?"

"The pin on the bottom the cops push in to doublelock them, will pop back out. You'll see."

I was able to guide him through the process, and soon the secondary lock disengaged. I was glad for his help, it would have been much more frustrating on my own.

Once he had the hang of it, I had him slide the makeshift key the other direction, disengaging the lock's teeth. Within minutes the first cuff was off. I took over from there and quickly had the other one off, also.

"Wow! I can't believe we just did that." Arley was grinning, now wide awake.

We sat around shooting the shit for another hour before calling it a night. It had been a long day for me, and I was asleep within seconds of my head hitting the pillow.

The next morning Arley's mom came down to tell us her and Frank would be leaving soon. She said there were biscuits and bacon already cooked, warming in the oven for us, and a pan of gravy on the stove. They would be gone a couple hours, giving me plenty of time to slip out.

I thanked her and covered my head back up.

A half-hour later Arley rousted me saying his parents had left. While we had breakfast, my friend inquired about my plans for the future.

"Don't know, yet. I'm gonna stay away from Tina that's for sure. You should have seen how mad she was when I threw Trish in her face."

"Hell, she's probably the one who sent the cops to David's." He tossed me a pack of his dad's Pall Malls. "Keep 'em."

"Naw. She wouldn't go that far. There were a lot of people out there, a couple who got hurt. It could have been any one of them." I talked while packing the cigarettes against my palm.

"Girls are weird...but you know her better than I do. Anyway, where does that leave you?" He took the cigarette I offered him and lit it.

"I don't know," I confided.

"By the way, Rhonda Redmond got married."

"What?! To who?"

"Some twenty-six or seven year old dude. Don't know him myself. And, I don't think things are going so well between them. She was asking for your address when she was telling me about it. Said she wanted to write you. I didn't have it, though."

"She's still fourteen for two or three more months, how is that even legal?" The news of her getting with someone while I was gone like that hurt my feelings a little bit. "She must have really wanted out of her house to do that," I huffed.

"I don't know if it's legal or not, but I guess her mom signed for her."

"Wow. And her mother didn't want her hanging out with me because she said I was bad influence. Whatever, even as down and mature as Rhonda may be, there's still something wrong with a mother fucker almost thirty chasin' after a girl her age." I finally lit the cigarette I was holding. "Anyway asking her for any kind of help is out, and I can't involve my family. I'll probably have to go back to El Paso."

The phone rang. Arley answered and mouthed that it was Brenda, Tina's best friend—most of the time. Supposedly they were on the outs at the moment. But you never know with Girls.

"No...I don't know where Jimmy is at..." he was saying into the receiver and rolling his eyes at me. "Why are you looking for him?"

He listened for a little while, then continued: "I'll tell him if I see him, but honestly, he knows my dad would be quick to call the cops on him. I doubt he'd come around here." Arley held his thumb up and grinned at me. "Okay Brenda...I promise. Bye."

After hanging up, he said, "I think that girl wants you to hit it."

"Why do you say that?" I pulled a deep drag on the Pall Mall I was smoking and looked at him through the haze that hung between us.

"She said she heard you had a falling out with Tina, and 'since that bitch fucked you over', her words, she and Aunt Jackie wanted to help you out."

"What about that makes you think she wants to throw the puss on me?"

"Dunno, just the way she made me promise to tell you that she wasn't talking to Tina right now, and how bad she wanted to get you the message." He lit a cigarette and blew a smoke ring—poking his finger through it. "I'd do her in a heartbeat. She may not be all-that in the face, but she's got a banging body. Besides, it would give you somewhere to hide for a few days."

He was right about that, and at the moment somewhere to lay low was what I needed until I figured out my next move. "Where did she say she was...Aunt Jackie's?"

"Yeah, but Jackie don't live where she did before you went to juvy. She moved across town somewhere." He snubbed his cigarette out in the left-over gravy on his plate.

I snubbed mine in an ashtray, and washed my dishes in the sink while I thought about it. I was sure Brenda was on the up and up. She was good people. And...this wouldn't be the first time she'd had a falling out with Tina.

Arley was right, Brenda was homely as hell, her face was just too narrow to be considered "pretty". She did, however, have attractive long, straight, sandy-blonde hair, and at five-five and curvy had a truly smokin' hot body. She was a couple years older than Tina. The fact that she would never come in first, or even a close second, next to her, was something my girlfriend seemed to have a way of flaunting. It was done subtly, but Brenda was smart enough to see it even though she pretended not too. I felt sorry for Brenda and I think she felt a little sorry for me, as well. She hated that Tina cheated on me and I was too love-struck to see it, or so she said. One time even ratting Tina out, swearing me to secrecy about how I learned the truth. I didn't tell Arley, but Brenda had let me know many times, in many ways, that she had a secret crush on me. There would no doubt be expectations attached to the offer her and Jackie extended. Though I liked Brenda I was not attracted to her, so I would have to be willing to play the game going into it. I guess she thought now I might be mad enough at

121 | P a g e

Tina to take her up on it. Which at the moment, didn't seem like such a bad idea. Really, it was a win—win—win. A place to hole up until I left town, get laid again, and chap Tina's ass on my way out. I just had to accept being a scumbag ahead of time.

Aunt Jackie was tall, slim, dark-headed, and already a little haggard as she aged into her forties, but she was cool also. Jackie lived in a duplex behind a small house Tina and I had before moving to our last apartment. We called her Aunt Jackie because her niece lived with her for awhile, I guess the name just caught on. She fit the role. Aunt Jackie was your classic middle aged single alcoholic bar-fly. Hooked on strong liquor and bad men. Well...all men it seemed.

Jackie took to us for some reason. Maybe she saw herself in Brenda and Tina. Jackie and their mothers were definitely all cut from the same cloth. I have no idea why she liked me, but she did. I could trust her.

I called them back and they drove to Arley's and picked me up. That's how I found myself hung-over and waking up next to Brenda the following morning.

We'd started drinking when they picked me up around ten a.m. Cruising the dirt roads all day and stopping at different party places on the outskirts of town, getting quite drunk as we went. The more we drank the tighter Brenda clung to me. At one point she confided in me that she'd always wished I'd give her my attention. I knew from the people that we saw in our travels that Tina would soon hear that Brenda was getting it.

As dusk fell on the small town we hit the bars. Well, "hit the bars" is a little misleading, there were only two watering holes in Guymon that I could get into without an ID, the fake one I brought from El Paso, was long gone. However, the two bars we could get into...we drank dry. In the second one Jackie decided it wasn't fair that Brenda had her "a beau", and wanted to find some company for the evening also. Within the hour she'd snagged a beefy forty-something year old truck-driver with buck teeth and a receding hairline. And after a few spins around the dance floor, we were headed back to her house.

Like Arley said, Aunt Jackie had moved while I'd been gone. She now lived on the southwest edge of town, in a one-bedroom adobe house. The rest of the night passed in a blur. I remember looking down at Brenda as I was sliding into her. Jackie's bedroom had two beds in it. Jackie's buck-toothed trucker was grunting and pumping away between her legs in the other one. I guess we all grasp for love and companionship wherever we can find it. Even if its only a cardboard cutout of it.

I woke up the next morning earlier than anyone else, like I said—hungover. Before opening my eyes the night's memories came flooding into my foggy mind. I groaned when I saw the homely, naked girl sleeping beside me with a happy contented smile on her face.

Jackie's man was snoring—with her curled up right next to him like she'd known him forever. No doubt holding onto the illusion that she was not alone in this world, as long as her sated, subconcious mind would allow it.

I was embarrassed, and ashamed that I had used Brenda the way I had. What made it even worse was knowing how she felt about me. She wanted me enough to provide herself for my twisted revenge only to be discarded like a used condom when I was done. All for a one-night fantasy, which she held to knowing that I would walk away and not look back. It couldn't end any other way. We both knew I was not into her, and I, at least, had been motivated by spite. At the cost of her friendship with Tina. I shook it off, it didn't really matter, Tina wasn't much of a friend to begin with; to either of us.

What did matter, was the fact that I was no longer drunk, and my anger at Tina had dissipated with my erection. Now—I was left with the overwhelming need to get away from Brenda. Which made my guilt that much more poignant. I was officially a piece of shit. Not that I was some saint who'd never used a girl to get laid before, but not one I liked as a friend as much as Brenda.

I gently pulled my arm from under Brenda's pillow, untangled my legs from the sheet and slipped out of bed. I couldn't handle her waking up right then, trying to kiss and cuddle me. Guiltily, I exited the scene.

The curtains in the living room were thin enough to see through. It was still early but the sun was up. I laid down on the couch under a side window and smoked a cigarette.

Considering we'd partied for hours in this room before gravitating to the back, the house still looked fairly neat. Beer bottles and full ashtrays crowding the coffee table were the only remaining evidence of the roaring drunk we pulled off, that and my hangover. I laid there thinking about what I was going to do.

There wasn't anything for me in Guymon and now the cops were on my trail. There was no way I could hide in my hometown, not and expect to stay free of the net. It was time to get out. I would leave from Jackie's house and head straight for Highway 54. From there I would hitchhike my way south back to El Paso. Her place was only a few blocks from the interstate. Once I was away—out of state—the authorities most likely wouldn't even bother with me. Hopefully, the police down there weren't looking for me for anything.

With that plan firmly in place I snubbed my snipe out in the overflowing ashtray, and got comfortable on the couch. It was not a heavy sofa, more of a wicker frame with cushions and a bed-sized afghan draped over it hanging to the floor. Though it was comfortable enough.

I was dozing thinking about seeing my little brothers and checking on my mom, wondering if any of my friends would still be in El Paso, and where I was going to stay. Regardless, I'd at least get the chance to deal with my step-dad, once and for all. My thoughts were five hundred miles away when someone started banging on the door. BOOM...BOOM...BOOM.... *What the hell*—

"Police! Open up!" Boom Boom Boom they banged again.
Oh shit!

I jumped up looking around for somewhere to hide. Jackie could be heard moving around in the bedroom.

There were two doors, the front faced east and the kitchen door to the south. Both were in view of where I was crouched beside the couch. I considered going out a window. The one the sofa was under looked out toward the north. As I reached for it a shadow passed by on the other side of the curtain. I pulled my hand back like I'd touched a hot stove.

There was nowhere to hide in the house. My mind scrambled, desperately searching for an answer—anything.

Boom! Boom! Boom! "Police. Open up. We have a warrant." The men on the other side of the door were persistent, and apparently prepared.

Jackie must have found her nightgown. "Hold on...I'm getting my clothes on," she muttered half to herself, and half to the cops who couldn't hear her anyway.

The couch I squatted beside was light weight. I pulled the afghan back that hung down to the floor. There was a five-inch-wide wooden rail across the front, but behind it was empty space. It was unexpected and I hoped the cops would miss it, too. With no time to waste and no other options, I laid down and lifted the edge of the wicker couch and slid under, hiding behind the rail.

Jackie was coming out of the bedroom. She saw me and ran over to straighten the afghan and make sure it hung evenly across the front. She then turned toward the kitchen door where the cops were still banging.

"Just hold on! I'm coming!" Now she was yelling, making herself heard.

Under the couch I was sweating ball-bearings. I was tucked inside the wicker frame as best as I could be. A last milli-second check. Everything was pulled in. Even on the wall side, in case someone looked behind it.

Jackie was back at the door fumbling with the lock. "What do you want for Christ's sake?" she cursed as she opened the door.

"Step back Miss Chapman," one of the officers stated flatly. "We have reason to believe James Maxwell is here and have a warrant to search your house for him."

"What, Jimmy? He's not here. We saw him at Sunset Lake last night. Said he was leaving town—drove off with a dark-haired girl in a black van."

"Well, that is not what the tip we received this morning claims. It assures us that he can be found at this address with Brenda Miller." He held up a warrant. "This was signed by Judge Ogden this morning. So, please, step aside."

They pushed themselves into the kitchen, forcing Jackie to give way. I could hear several men enter.

The first one yelled: "Maxwell. We know you are in here, come out with your hands up!" Then he stormed through the kitchen with his revolver up and clenched firmly between his fists. Several other cops ran in right behind him.

There was a two inch gap between the comforter that was draped over the couch and the floor. From the shadowy recesses of my hiding spot I could see snatches of the kitchen and living room. I counted four sets of feet. Two of the officers were now repeating the first one's words as they spread out through the house.

I held my breath as they filed through the living room. They could see at a glance there was nowhere to hide in here, or in the kitchen. Though one cop did open the cabinets under the sink, just to be thorough.

"He must be in the back," one whispered to the others. They all moved down the short hall, guns drawn.

"Jimmy Maxwell, we are coming back. Keep your hands where we can see them, or we will shoot you." *The same voice. He must be the lead dick on this* I absently thought.

"Brenda and a friend of mine are the only ones in there." Jackie tried to head them off as they were rushing through her bedroom door.

There was some scuffling—and I heard Brenda give a frightful little shout. The cops were yelling at the truck driver until one of the more intellectual members of their brain trust jumped in, "Hold on. Jack, Phil, that's not him! Maxwell is a teenager."

They were griping and apologizing as they released Jackie's trucker and cleared the rooms and closets back there. Then they all came back into the living room with Brenda trailing close behind, a bewildered look on her face. I'm sure she too was wondering where I was.

"I told you he wasn't here before you ever came barging in my home. This shouldn't be legal," Jackie complained to the lead detective.

"Well we felt we had reliable information that he was here. Considering the relationship our source had with James we accepted it at face value."

"Well your inform—"

Brenda jumped in cutting Jackie off. "Tina! Tina called you guys and sent you over here? That bitch!"

"I'm not at liberty to say where our information came from, ma'am." The detective turned to Jackie, "We're sorry Miss Chapman."

I couldn't believe it when they all filed out the same door they'd come in. As soon as the door shut behind them, the tension ran from my body like water through a hose and my head fell back to the floor. I breathed a relieved sigh.

I lifted the couch and was trying to get out from under it. Brenda was surprised and jumped up and down with a huge smile on her face. Jackie was laughing nervously, she obviously couldn't believe we made it through that either. The buck-toothed trucker was just cursing.

I don't know if we made noise, or if the detective was listening at a window, but suddenly there was pounding on the door again. It happened fast. The police pushed their way back in before Jackie could even slow them down.

Luckily I hadn't had time to rise from the floor and shot back under the couch like a roach running from the light. The cops caught Jackie reaching for the door and Brenda standing in the living room, stunned and confused. There was no time for anyone to adjust the comforter on the couch.

"I *know* he's in here!" the short balding detective who'd been running the show shouted.

The blanket was still draped over the sofa but it was uneven and bunched in places. From where I laid in the shadowy recess of my hiding place, I could clearly see him and four other men re-enter the house.

My heart was fluttering and sweat pooled across my forehead. The fact that I could see them much better this time raised my anxiety even higher than when I couldn't. I stayed frozen—afraid to move a hair in fear that it might make a noise.

Jackie shouted angrily: "What are you talking about? You've already looked! What do you think...he's in the oven?"

One of the brighter cops in the bunch opened the oven...just to make sure.

"I thought I heard something when I was leaving," the detective was saying to her when his team came out of the bedroom shaking their heads.

"You must have heard my boyfriend talking or something. I told you, Jimmy is not here." The woman stomped a fluffy-slippered foot and wore a genuinely irate expression on her face. "You are not going to keep barging into my house like this. It can't be legal."

When the man apologized again, my hopes began to rise. Then I saw him glance in my direction. His thoughts were written on his face clearly as the words on this page. He hated being wrong, and he hated giving up even more. He was grasping for anywhere I could be hiding when his gaze fell on the couch. With the blanket skewed, super cop could see that it was made of wicker. "Just let me look behind the couch Miss Chapman, and we will be out of your hair."

Oh no!

I quickly did a mental inventory of my positioning. Everything except my big toe seemed to be back in place. The toe was hung-up under the back-rail of the frame. To move it would make noise. With my nerves strung tighter than a zip-line I gambled that my toe was far enough back to not be seen when he looked down the wall.

There was no time to second guess the decision, the dogged law enforcement officer was there in three steps.

Tensing, I held my breath. A bead of sweat ran from my temple into my ear.

He walked to the end of the divan and glanced down between it and the wall under the window. He was so close I could smell the polished leather of his shoes. As much as I wanted to pull my foot in just to be sure, I was unable, my muscles were locked in place. After seconds that seemed like eons the man stepped away, and I breathed a silent sigh of relief. I'd made it. I couldn't believe it!

Then...with a rush of movement the detective and another officer stepped back to my wicker hiding place. Quick as I could blink they grabbed the end of the couch and stood it up exposing me. I was busted, again.

While the cops converged on me to roughly re-cuff and take me into custody, the detective turned on Jackie: "You're going to jail, Miss Chapman, for harboring a fugitive!" His face was flush with indignant anger at having been lied to.

Jackie looked desperately at me. The fiery front she'd put on over their intrusion now turning to panic. "I didn't even know he was there. How did you get in here Jimmy?"

"I'm sorry Jackie. You guys were all asleep, so I climbed through the window and crashed on the couch. When I heard the cops pounding on the door I hid before you came out."

The story was seamless. And the cops knew my history well enough to know that whether what I said was true or not, I would stick to it. Charges against Jackie would be pointless.

The detective turned a couple shades redder, but let it go. He glared at me: "Where are officer Peffer's handcuffs? Are they here?"

"I lost them in an alley."

"God damn this kid!" the man yelled at the room. "Bring his ass outta there," he ordered the uniformed cops before turning and storming out the door.

As we pulled away I glanced through the rear window of the squad car. Brenda stood, sad-faced, peeking out the kitchen door. I was sad too, and had a feeling it was going to be a long time before I would see any of my friends again.

CHAPTER 10

LTD

It didn't take the authorities long after my apprehension to get me back to Helena, and when they did I learned why the LTD unit had such a bad reputation. I was taken straight to it—do not pass Go, do not collect $200. A pair of officers, who looked like back-woods dirt-farmers, but were deceptively strong, bounced me off each step of the back stairwell on my way up. It appeared I'd finally pissed them off; however, the staff who worked that corner of the compound were said to be particularly sadistic anyhow. Of course, those of us in LTD were supposedly the worst of the worst kids in the state, and even the ones who weren't necessarily psychotic to begin with, upped their game to compete with the kids who were. Moreover, the hateful attitudes projected by the staff assigned to their special unit caused a great deal of animosity. You mix that with a bunch of "special needs" kids and you are bound to have problems.

Nursing a sore shoulder, I was led through the heavy steel door at the top of the stairs. Even though LTD was right above the orientation unit where I had begun this bid, its only similarity with it was the metal grating covering the windows. Up here there were cell doors lining the walls rather than cubicles. Convenient: no need to drag kids all the way to the Dodge House, and from what I'd been told these cells were intended as a more long-term solution.

Several juveniles stared from the small, square windows in their doors; black, white, and Spanish faces peering from their gloomy worlds like morose color-coded flash-cards. The few kids I saw wore various looks of despondency, despair, nonchalance, and pugnaciousness. None were smiling. One black kid looking at me from the dim shadows of his room was sucking his thumb. It must have been a life long habit because his front teeth had pushed out into a 'V' from the constant pressure, giving his face a distinct ferret shape. I saw a total empty void in his wet, brown eyes. More than anything, his mysterious trauma made me pause and question what I had just been dragged into.

From the locked doors I surmised the "dayroom" was more for looks than anything, as it was obvious solitary confinement was the norm on this unit. I had a distinct feeling, that solitary confinement could be the least of my problems.

I'd heard stories, everyone had, about the deplorable conditions of the LTD unit, and worse, how there was a particularly ruthless night shift crew who would beat up on its kids, and sometimes leave them hog-tied, or straight-jacketed for days at a time. There had even been trouble for the institution years before when an over enthusiastic staff member had taken his abuse too far. Broken bones are hard to cover up. From that incident a garden of horrific rumors had taken root and grown into a forest of frightening tales of torture and abuse.

Even though, it was obvious LTD seemed to be an entity unto itself where the rules which applied on the other side of the door didn't hold as much water on the side I was on now. And even though there may be a glimmer of truth to some of the myths, I knew that legally the cops were bound by certain restraints and couldn't possibly get away with treating underage minors the way the stories described. Therefore, I wasn't buying into the hype—and I was completely caught unprepared for the reality coming my way.

The place livened up after I was put in my cell and the officers left. I could hear kids in other cells yelling, trying to warn me that the cops would be back; that very few "newbies" made it in without meeting the "welcoming committee". I heard advice, such as: "Don't let the cops cuff you"..."Take the fight to them if you wanna stand a chance" ...some were just yelling to be yelling. Clueless, I had no idea what they were talking about.

When my special set of red-neck transport officers tossed me in my room two hours earlier; they'd told me then they weren't done with me. Kids in other cells had been hollering trying to get me to come to the door so they could see who I was and give me the heads up. Lonely and defeated, I just didn't feel like talking.

I laid on my cot staring at the cracks in the chipped, gray ceiling. Wallowing in my own ignorance. *Why the hell didn't I leave Guymon when I had the chance? Why did I go to Guymon in the first place? Could Misty Dawn really be mine? Why couldn't I stay out of trouble? Why did it take so long for me to see through Tina?* A dozen other self-deprecating thoughts ran through my mind. *Fuck, I was stupid sometimes!*

Laying on my back idly picking paint chips from the wall, I remained in that position tormenting myself until I heard a familiar voice.

"Maxwell? Jimmy Maxwell, is that you down there? Bro, it's Tracy B."

I got up and went to the door. "What the hell are *you* doing here?"

"Man, they got me. Sorry we couldn't wait on you...did you get away? Are they just now bringing you in on it?"

"No dude, I got caught. Couldn't get a ride. They're bringing me back on my second escape. Got away this time." I squatted down and pressed my ear closer to the crack of the door. "What happened to you, did Niegro make it home?"

From the sound of it, he had laid down and was talking under his door, apparently getting comfortable before he told the story. "When you didn't come through the window right away we thought the coach might have seen you. We took off. Once we got over the fence we went into town and I stole a pickup. I drove back by the auto shop gate hoping to see you, but when the alarm went off I didn't dare stick around. It was obvious they knew we were gone. We called Niegro's sister from Enid and she met us in Oklahoma City." He told me the whole story, then asked, "What about you?"

"Wow. I saw a truck nosing around the perimeter road. I thought it was the man. After that I ran straight across the nearest pastu—"

"Uh, oh. Here they comeeee!" someone hollered.

Boots were pounding up the stairwell and keys were rattling in the steel door from the stairs.

I heard them come through it.

When I stood up and looked out the little square window in my door, five men were already gathered on the other side of it. I recognized them for the little hit squad we'd heard about on the yard, but rarely saw. I'd had dealings with a couple of them before. One was with the guards who ran in on us downstairs when Leroy and I had gotten into it; the other was the prick in the passenger seat of the Ford Torino who brought me in from my first escape attempt. All of them were cut from the same Okie redneck wanna-be-a-cop cloth, and they were all looking at me like I was the one who just stole their teenage daughter's virginity.

A mid-thirties, hatchet-faced lieutenant stepped up to the door and unlocked it. "K. Carver" was stenciled over his right breast pocket. "Turn around and face the wall while we cuff you."

"Don't do it! Fight'em don't let'em cuff you!" a kid yelled from another cell.

"Yeah fuck them dick-heads!" Tracy B.'s voice echoed across the empty dayroom.

"We can do it the easy way or the hard way. It's up to you," K. Carver said.

Behind him an over-weight farm-boy-looking man with a buzz-cut glared at me over his shoulder. The other three stood tense, shifting on their feet also. It was plain they were expecting some action. However, the obvious threat they represented was not why I complied; the reason I complied was because I didn't have any reason not to. At least, other than the continued warnings called out by my peers down the run, which I assumed were just trying to get me to fight with the cops for their own entertainment. After all, up till then, I really hadn't had a big problem with the people who worked there.

I stuck my hands out—wrists in.

The lieutenant motioned for me to face the wall. "Behind your back."

"Don't dooo iiiit—"

"Shut up down there or you'll be next!" The overweight farm-boy/man snarled off to his left at a cell beyond my view. He had the sleeves of his dark-gray uniform rolled-up showing off his beefy biceps.

"Get a list of 'em Walter, we'll deal with them later," the cop from the Ford Torino said to the farm-boy cop.

Other kids were banging on their doors, but apparently the threat carried some weight, because there was no more encouragement voiced my way.

As far as I was concerned it didn't matter how they cuffed me. I turned around and put my hands behind my back.

The lieutenant quickly shackled me, then stepped in close leaning his forearm across my shoulders and the back of my neck, forcing my face and chest against the gray utilitarian wall. It smelled like stale urine with my nose pressed against decades of grime, and paint layers. "Will and Calvin are our friends. You made fools of them and Will broke his wrist chasing you in Enid." He ground his elbow deeper into my shoulder blade. "You got them in trouble. That, was a mistake."

At that moment I realized what the other kids were warning me about and pushed against the forearm in my back. That was what they were waiting for, the other four had filed in while the lieutenant was delivering the threat and immediately grabbed me. Suddenly aware of their intentions I coiled my body and shoved away from the wall kicking and squirming for all I was worth. However, I had already given them the upper-hand, and as hard as I struggled they still soon had me face-down in the floor bending my legs and stretching my manacled arms as they bound everything up tightly behind me. The Ford Torino officer squeezed the cuffs down painfully on my wrists, while a skinny one I hadn't seen before pulled the cinch-strap between my leather-cuffed feet and chained hands as tight as he could. The others punched and kicked me in my sides and thighs. Farm-boy, Walter I guess his name was, got a kick into my short ribs that took my breath. If I hadn't been so full of spit and fury right then I would have probably passed out.

It was a hard night. I remained in that position until the day-shift came on in the morning and released me so I could eat and use the bathroom.

I spent the day nursing my ribs and other injures. I talked to Tracy a bit and learned that I was not necessarily being singled out, but they did seem to go harder on kids who had done something against a staff member.

I'd learned a valuable lesson from the night before. When the hatchet crew (as I came to think of them) came back that evening, I backed up against my bunk and faced them as they ran in on me. Young and strong I gave them the best I had, but of course they overwhelmed me and eventually got me restrained.

I'd worn them down a little and they were tired. "I'm getting sick of this kid," Walter said, he and the others only kicking me a few times before leaving this round.

More importantly, I had accomplished staying tense enough while they were tightening the straps which bound my feet to my hands that I gained enough slack to work at the buckles and latches holding the cinch secure. Once there was room to get my fingers working I was able to loosen the bindings. By morning one of my leather leg-cuffs was all the way off and my hands were in front of me. The other leg restraint was held tightly with a small pad-lock. Still, I slept like a baby that night.

My third night back I laid panting; face pressed against the black and white checkered-patterned tiles that covered my floor. I had just went through the latest round with the "Tactical Response Team"— that was what they were called, though "Goon Squad" was more accurate. I'd put up a pretty good fight, regardless I was still beat-up and restrained. They said I was going to rue the day I'd caused Will and

Cal so much trouble; hell, I could have told them I already did. The coppery taste of blood was in my mouth; I rubbed my tongue over the raggedy edges of a busted lip. *Fucking bastards!* I laid there cursing their mothers under my breath while I worked on getting my shackles off (which were looser than I'd ever had them), and thinking of how I could overcome their numbers and take advantage of the small room the next time we met.

The knowledge I'd gained from the previous nights and the slack in my restraints allowed me to attack the belts, buckles, and locks that had me bound. It wasn't long and I was sitting with my hands in front of me working the leather leg shackles off over my heels. The perspiration from my efforts making the leather supple enough to stretch the raw-hide the extra little bit that I needed—and boom!, there I was, free of everything except the steel cuffs on my wrists. Without a wire or hairpin I would just have to be stuck with them.

I gathered up the restraints I'd shed and stuffed them under the door so everyone could see what I'd done. Then I howled like a wolf and yelled for them to come try it again! I was mad, and I was hyped, and this time I was equipped with a plan.

When the other kids looked out of their windows and saw my leg-cuffs and restraint-belts laying in front of my cell, they erupted, hollering and howling right along with me.

The guard didn't know what to think, he ran up to my cell door and stared in through the small window. What do you know it was the older, flat-top cop from the Dodge House, the Sergeant Carter guy, Phillips was his name. He was so angry at the sight of the restraints in the day room that his whole head was red. I held up my cuffed fists, then extended my middle fingers giving him the universal sign of what I thought of him. Then I stuck a piece of wet toilet paper over my window so he couldn't see in.

"Maxwell. Take that down. Or else!"

"Nobody's home. Go away, you barnyard pig fucker."

"You are going to regret this," he growled through the door, "Kyle and them have been taking it easy up to now. And I'll be comin' with them next time. You just wait!"

"Yeah? Go finger-pop yourself. Tell them to bring it on. And be sure to let 'em know I think all of you are a bunch of backwoods child abusing pussies, too!"

I wanted them mad, and I wanted them careless, and if Mr. Sergeant Phillips on the other side of the door was any indication, I was definitely accomplishing my goal. I could almost hear the steam coming out of his ears. I pictured the cartoon of Foghorn Leghorn's head turning into a red, boiling hot steam-whistle blowing its top, before he stormed off; presumably, to call "Kyle" and his cronies to come back and teach the smartass kid in cell 203 some respect.

It would take about thirty minutes for the goon-squad to get suited and booted and get back up there. My heart was pounding. Glancing in the scratched metal mirror on the wall above my small sink, I saw my reflection staring back at me. Seeing myself wild-eyed, face flush with excitement, it occurred to me that there were two sides to me. The side looking out from behind my eyes was scared shitless, and didn't know why in hell the crazy son-of-a-buck staring back from the chrome looking-glass was stirring the pot and daring the goons to beat our ass. Because, without a doubt, that was what was about to happen. But my reflection just grinned back and howled once more. *Story of my life*, the sane side of me thought.

The moment gone. Time ticking. I went to work, preparing myself and my little eight by twelve foot cell for the coming storm.

First I squeezed half of my shampoo out of the bottle and rubbed it all over my body. I rolled up my pants legs and spread more over my shins, calves, and feet. My t-shirt was already torn from the earlier beating I had taken so I ripped it the rest of the way off and smeared soap over my arms, shoulders, and chest. Even sliming my cuffs. Next, I filled the rest of the bottle with water and shook it up; squirting another half of it in the floor, concentrating on the first few feet right in front of my door.

By then I could hear heavy boots stomping up the stairs. I refilled my bottle of soapy water and retreated to the cot stretched across the back of my cell.

"Maxwell. Take the paper out of your window and face the wall!" It was Carver, and he sounded pissed.

When I didn't reply he went on to inform me that I was really going to regret this. Then I heard him quietly mumbling some instructions to his crew.

I couldn't see them, but I could feel the angry tension emanating like heat waves as they bunched up outside my door. However, I could also sense a hint of uncertainty. They had been fighting me for days, but this was different, I had changed the game. I knew my reprieve wouldn't last long, though. I was scared, but also bouncing on my bed from foot to foot with excitement.

I looked up at my light, it was a square metal box with a couple 75 Watt bulbs in it. The ceiling was too high for me to reach even from on top of my bed. It had a cover over it, though someone in the past had somehow broken out half of the thick protective lens that covered it. The hot, bare bulbs glowed bright, partly exposed.

Keys in the door.

"Get ready," Carver told his squad.

"Here they coooome...Jimmy!" Tracy yelled, from what seemed like another state away.

Suddenly, the door was jerked open and a line of men, one behind the other, flooded in. They looked frightening rushing at me like that. I squeezed the bottle with both hands and shot a stream of water right into the light fixture—with a pop! and a flash, the lights went out.

They were just getting a glimpse of me bouncing around on my bed when the first three hit the shampoo puddle on the floor. As they went down, I squirted the three behind them with what I had left in my soap bottle aiming for their eyes. They were tripping over their buddies in the floor when I dived off the bed on top of them. I spotted Walter trying to catch his balance and brought my cuffed wrists down on the fat man's head.

The fight was on.

When the guys in the other cells realized that I was taking it to the goon-squad, they erupted, yelling and kicking their doors in support.

As I slipped and slid around with the officers, I was actually surprised that my plan was working so well. What made it even better was that they were so mad they were hitting each other as much as they were hitting me. I had sufficiently ambushed them. I was also pretty damn sure that I was never going to get another opportunity to pull something like this off again, not with them anyway. So I gave it all I had while I could.

There was enough soap and water covering my arms, chest, and waist that it was hard for the men to get me pinned. I managed to hammer Walter all the way to the floor and split his eye with my cuffed wrists before someone finally got a hold of the chain between my manacled hands. After that, it was just a matter of stretching me out and holding me down.

Walter came up off the ground with his face fire engine red and stomped me in the ribs. He looked me straight in the eyes, before viciously aiming a large black boot right at my head. I am not sure what happened after that—the world went dark.

I woke up later with a sharp pain in my ribs, my nose clotted with blood, and one side of my face swollen and bruised.

I moaned loudly. "Damn, my side hurts!" Immediately I regretted using the air it took to talk, as sharp pains shot through my rib cage. "Oh man, it hurts," this time talking quietly to myself.

"Maxwell. Jimmy Maxwell. Is that you?"

"Yeah," I groaned. It was Tracy. "I can't really talk right now, my ribs hurt and my jaw is swollen."

"Alright buddy, I am just glad to know you are alright. We all have been hollering at you for an hour."

A black guy whose cell was across on the other wall from me, agreed. "Yeah man, you had us worried. My name is Bobo, from Okmulgee. I could see some of it from my window. You is one crazy wood. You have inspired us all. They will never have an easy time with me after some of the tricks I just learned from you, that's for sure."

"Well I don't feel like much of an inspiration." Just breathing sent pain through my chest. "How come they didn't shackle me?"

"When you went limp the big one kept stomping you. Carver and the rest of his goons had to grab him to stop him from killin' you. They fought with him all the way out into the stairwell. Sergeant Phillips only had time to clean off your window and lock you in. You ought'a file charges on that fat cracker, is what you ought'a do."

"Well, Bobo, right now, I'd like to just make it to bed."

Inch by inch, I crawled to my cot. Found the least painful position I could and fell asleep.

I woke up the next morning to sun coming through the slats covering my window. More light was coming from my cell door. I realized it was open. Slowly and painfully I rolled over. There was a young guard I'd not seen before standing there holding his keys, and an older woman who looked a bit like Aunt Bee from the Andy Griffin Show holding a food tray. They both gasped and involuntarily took a step backward at the sight of me.

I must look as bad as I feel, I thought.

"My God—Frank, what the Jesus is going on here? He looks like he's been beat to hell!"

The guard, Frank, I gathered, squirmed and looked sheepish as he pushed his dark hair back from his forehead and looked at the woman. "It was Kyle's boys. Well mostly Walter. Said the kid attacked them. Who knows with that bunch. But Maxine, I didn't know he was this bad off."

Frank was looking at his shoes. Maxine waved him aside and pushed into the room. "Take these cuffs off him." She came over and gave me a closer inspection. "I am guessing medical hasn't even been to see him yet?"

"No. After what Walter did they decided to wait on involving the doc. He knows he could get some heat over this one."

Maxine leveled a disgusted stare at the young officer who seemed to shrink into himself even more. "Well I don't give a gosh damn about him getting in trouble. You clean this boy up and wash that boot print off his face. Then you will call the doctor in here and have him checked out. Or I'll go straight to the director! Do you hear me Franklin?"

"Yes, ma'am," he said.

She looked at me. "Do you feel like anything is broken?"

"I don't know. I haven't moved around enough yet to tell." I reached to rub at the fiery, tingling purple rings around my wrists left by the cuffs and felt a sharp pain knife through my ribcage. It wasn't as bad as the night before, but I still grimaced.

"Well, we are going to have someone check you."

"Who are you, anyway? Do you run this place?"

"Oh, heavens no. I am Mrs. Fullerton. The laundry lady for Mustang and Cadillac. I work in the kitchen sometimes and help out where I can. But, other than working here forever I've got a nephew"—she waved her hand toward the young officer—"and two grandsons who work here. Plus, a good many of the others I've known since they were old enough to trick-or-treat. They know I will whip their asses good if they buck me." Her smile reminded me of my grandmother's.

I laid back with a groan. "Well thank you for caring. But I am sure I will be alright."

"Yes, you probably will be. But this is wrong. It is far from the first time this has happened, and I am tired of it." Mrs. Fullerton shook her head as she shooed her nephew ahead of her and followed him out.

I laid back and rubbed my wrists again. *She was nice, but what's a laundry lady going to do? At least she got my cuffs off,* I thought.

True to her word, an hour later a nurse showed up. She also seemed pretty upset over how I looked. The medic had the guard move me to a clean cell with a working light and then cleaned me up and bandaged my ribs.

After they left I waddled over to the sink and looked at myself in the mirror. The nurse had cleaned my face up and wiped most of the blood out of my nose, but one side of my head was swollen beyond belief. And the white of that eye was blood red. No wonder they were trippin'. I wasn't positive, but I was pretty sure if pictures of the way I looked right then were to get out somebody's head would roll. At least it was nice to think I was that important. The reality was they just kept me tucked away for three weeks until the bruises faded and I was able to get around without holding onto something to support me.

I will say this—heard it from a guard who said he was one of Mrs. Fullerton's grandsons—she raised hell. Carver, Walter and their whole crew got reamed-out by the warden.

That explained why we hadn't seen any of them since then.

Apparently, she was also responsible for getting us the use of the dayroom. Suddenly, they just started letting everyone out of their cells during the day. Well almost everyone. Me and a couple of real nuts, or at least kids who were still in trouble, they left locked down. Tracy and a few others I got to know would come by and visit me at my door. They seemed to be pretty happy with the improvements which appeared to have manifested from my misfortune. However, a little something is better than a lot of nothing.

When no one was visiting with me I whiled away my days reading books, writing letters, and people watching through the little window in my door. You can learn a lot just observing others as they go about their daily lives.

I counted about twenty-five kids in LTD. It didn't take long to figure out that more of the kids up here were mental cases, than weren't. What some of them were supposedly charged with left very little doubt of that. But kids talk, and sometimes they embellish a story. And Tracy was the king of bullshit. Considering he is where I got a lot of the details on the others up there I took the information in with a fair amount of skepticism. Though, in retrospect, I learned some of it was all too true.

For example, one long boring afternoon Tracy, and Curtis Whitesel—a white kid from Tulsa, Oklahoma, who looked like a muscled-up seventeen year old neo-Nazi, blonde-hair, blue-eyes, the whole nine yards—were at my door shooting the shit with me while we ate lunch, when Tracy pointed out this two hundred and eighty pound, moon-faced kid named Dominick Poochelli. He was about five feet ten inches tall and pale as a farm fresh egg. He had positioned himself by the trash can that doubled as a slop bucket.

Tracy grinned like he knew something funny. "Watch what he does."

Curtis and I watched Dominick as he eyeballed the thumb-sucker I'd noticed my first night up there take his tray to the slop bucket. He had been eating his lunch and having a conversation with himself. Dominick's piggish eyes tracked the cornbread on the black kids tray. As soon as the black kid, whose name turned out to be Lamont, went to dump his tray, Dominick leaned forward and reached for Lamont's leftover bread. Lamont jumped back like he thought Dominick was going to take a bite out of his arm.

"Don't touch me, cracker! What you want?"

Fat boy cut his eyes looking to see who was watching. Dominick didn't see us, but still kept his voice too low for us to hear, although he must have asked Lamont for his cornbread because we could hear Lamont's reply plain enough.

"You don't want my cornbread, you white hog. Someone done spit on it." With that he hawked up a nice lougie and spat it on the cornbread in question. "Do you still want it, honky?"

Dominick didn't bat an eye, he just nodded his round doughy face and plucked the bread right off Lamont's tray. He flicked off the top crust that the snot-ball sat on, and with a thankful nod toward Lamont, took a bite of what was left.

Me, Curtis, and Tracy all about lost our lunches right then and there.

"Ugh..." I choked and had to swallow the bile that rose in my throat.

"Oh man!" Curtis was green, but had a big grin on his face, clearly enjoying the show.

"What a sick bastard," Tracy followed up. Clearly he hadn't expected Dominick's gluttony to be so extreme.

Lamont's dark skin looked blue, were he white my guess was he would be as green as us. "Crazy ass white boy! White people are devils!" He shook his head as he walked off. Soon he was in the corner talking to himself again. I'd noticed he did that a lot. This time, it appeared he was having quite an animated conversation with what ever ghosts haunted him. Once in awhile I could hear a snatch of a sentence or two "...hate white people..." "...keepin me locked down wit crazy white people..."

Tracy drew our attention back to Dominick who was now waddling back toward his cell. "That fat bastard is sick in more ways than one. I heard the reason he's here in Hotel Hell is cause he raped his sixty year old mom."

My face lost all its color. "What! How could someone even think to do something like that to their mother!?"

"Well I guess it wasn't his blood mother. He was adopted."

"Still...." I didn't even know what else to say, just shook my head.

"We ought to fuck him up," Curtis declared, his blue eyes flashed with disgust. "I heard the reason he is up here in LTD was 'cause he worked out on the farm crew and got caught letting a calf suck on his little gnarly." Curtis ran his hands back through his short blond hair, and laughed. "The kid that told me about it, said Dominick was screaming like a little girl for someone to get the calf off him. Apparently, calves have very rough tongues and a lot of suction. He couldn't get it to let go and squealed like the pig he is until the foreman came and helped him."

I scowled through my window. "Sounds like the cop should have just let the little cow pull it off!"

They laughed a strained laugh at that. Although I had meant what I said. When they were chuckled out, Curtis repeated his desire to beat him up.

"You'd better wait till I get out of this cell before you do. That sow-belly is big enough he's liable to be dangerous and not even know it," I said.

Bobo had been sitting in a chair not far from us. He got up and came over. We all liked Bobo. And he seemed to take to me after bearing silent witness to my ass-whipping by the police. He had been there before, and I guess it bonded us in a weird way.

He looked at Curtis. "If you jump on him you may as well jump on half these other whackos too. There are some seriously screwed up people on this unit." He pointed at a little bitty black kid—couldn't have been more than fourteen. "Floyd killed his eighty-seven year old grand-pappy cause he wanted to use his car to go to the store and steal some Gummy Bears!" He shook his head. Then he pointed at another black kid. He was much bigger. Square headed, with short hair. I'd seen him walking around the dayroom, but never saw him talking to anyone that I could recall. "That's Keith Armstrong. He beat some thirteen or fourteen year old girl almost to death and raped her, or tried to. Who knows."

"Jesus Christ!" I said. Then I pointed toward Lamont. "What about him? What's his deal?"

"Lamont? Oh, he's just thrown off. He has been jacked over his whole life. First his parents abandoned him, then his foster parents did some weird shit to him; he started getting angry and hard to deal with so they sent him to different places and now here. He rants and raves and blames everything on white people but he's really harmless, and ain't never actually done anything bad."

Tracy jumped in: "I heard Big Chief over there killed a grown man with his bare hands!" He waved a hand in the direction of a big Indian who looked like Chief in the Jack Nicholson movie *One Flew Over the Coockoos Nest*.

Hell, the more I heard the more I felt like Jack Nicholson trapped on a nut ward.

Bobo nodded. "I heard that too."

We broke up our little con-fab, and I went back to the book I was reading. Bored out of my mind once again. The whole place was one big borefest after another.

A few weeks later they let me out of my cell. Even though my ribs still ached—no doubt one or more was cracked—Tracy and I immediately began planning our next escape.

Unfortunately, two days later they moved Tracy to a different unit.

Now out of my cell where I could mingle, I was able to get a better lay of the land. It seemed that even the kids I hadn't learned anything about from my cell were at least questionable, right on the cusp of having seriously crazy issues, if not right out psychotic. Which left me wondering what category I fell into. At least as far as "the man" was concerned.

As it turned out, I didn't have to wonder for very long. Not only had Mrs. Fullerton got the hatchet-crew off our asses, and brought an end to the never-ending lockdown we were on, but apparently she had also went to the warden's boss about the conditions in LTD. And the word was they were to move all the kids who didn't have specific mental health problems off the unit. Even discussing closing it down completely.

Soon my friend Curtis was moved. Next they moved Bobo. I saw a couple go who I was pretty sure were qualified to stay, leaving me wondering what their plans were for me. Two days later, my number came up and I also was told to pack my things—I was being sent to Corvette.

I'll be damned, I thought, *that little old laundry lady turned out to be quite the paragon of rectitude.*

CHAPTER 11

CORVETTE

Corvette was above Thunderbird. The building that housed the two units ran east to west like a two-story, red-brick battle ship. It was tucked end to end behind its twin brothers, Mustang and Cadillac.

The first floor unit, Thunderbird, sat with its landscaped, shrubbery enshrouded, concrete and brick porch facing the kitchen and institutional dining hall. "Dining hall" in name only since we only used it for the weekly AA and NA meetings. The kitchen complex was the *true* center of the compound. The enormous north and south running Impala/LTD/Administration building blocked off its east end, and the school and auditorium its west end. A hundred yards, northwest, past the school down the same sidewalk that lay between the messhall and Thunderbird was the Dodge House and medical unit. South of the chowhall strung Camaro, visitation, vo-tech, and the gym. The buildings I weaved my way through in my fist escape attempt. The tall fences surrounded it all.

Corvette was generally accessed by inmates through a door to the back stairwell on the north side of the building. There was no fuss nor muss like Thunderbird's ornate patio back there, just a little awning sticking out over a small concrete pad that stepped up to a big, secure, metal door.

However, my first time up to Corvette was through the front, escorted by a guard. He took me in through T-Bird where we accessed the stairwell by way of a locked door beside the day cop's desk. On my way through Wayne Womble came running toward me with a big grin plastered across his over-large, oval-shaped face.

"Hey brother how are you doi—"

The guard stuck his hand palm out and shut him down.

I laughed at the way Wayne's happy expression folded in on itself. His uni-brow scrunching together between his eyes. He was instantly fire-engine red from the low neckline of his white wife-beater t-shirt to the top of his high forehead, no doubt, fixing to launch himself into a cursing tirade which was sure to land him in the Dodge House. "It's alright bro. I'm out of LTD and on my way upstairs. I'll see you in school, we'll catch up then."

The guard who strongly resembled Mr. T without the haircut or chains, grunted and allowed if I didn't get moving that I could end-up back in LTD before we ever made it upstairs.

I shrugged and stepped through the door into the stairwell.

Once on the stairs I saw that a set of the pea-green painted, concrete steps led up to Corvette above and another to the basement level and general domain of the laundress, below.

I glanced down towards the house mother's subterranean world wondering how Mrs. Fullerton was making out and wishing she worked in this building instead of Mustang and Cadillac.

She'd kind of become my hero. And not just mine, I'd found out that she had helped many other kids, too. For my part I really wanted to thank her for getting me out of LTD.

With a shove, my escort snapped my attention back to the moment and we continued up to Corvette; ever curious to what I would find around the next corner of my life.

Mr. T checked me in, turning me over to the unit staff who quickly penciled my immediate future into a vacant double cubicle. As the house parent walked me to it I could feel the eyes of the other kids focused on me. Checking out the new fish. Normally I would have felt a little self-conscious; new place, new kids, new cliques and power struggles. But coming out of the war zone I'd just been through the previous couple months made me feel hardened beyond the normal concerns. I was a veteran of the worst Helena had to throw at me, anything else this place had would be mild in comparison. I thought.

I could see at a glance that Corvette was lain out pretty much the same as Mustang had been. The biggest and best difference (in my humble opinion) was that here we had a pool table instead of foosball.

No sooner than I'd set my little bag of books, clothes, and toiletries on the lower bunk than Timmy the nose picker popped up smiling from ear to ear: "Damn Jimmy, I can't believe you're here!" He looked at a medium-built, dark haired kid of about sixteen, who was trailing him. "Cecil, this is Jimmy Maxwell. One of the friends from Impala I told you about." Timmy turned back to me, his shaggy blond hair sticking out like straw from a hay bale, "This is Cecil Drake, he's from Ardmore."

I nodded. "Cecil."

"Jimmy," Cecil said, nodding back. "Good to meet'cha. As much as Timmy talks about you, Wayne, and Billy I feel like I already know you."

I smiled knowing that our little broom-wielding, nose-picking mascot had been bragging. "Yeah? Well ol' Timmy here will come through in a pinch, himself." I clapped Timmy on the shoulder and watched him light up like Times Square on New Year's Eve. "Hell, Timmy, I thought you were downstairs in Thunderbird?"

"Was. Got in trouble."

"No surprise there. What happened?" I asked.

Timmy gave me a sheepish look. "Well...Wayne bet me a pack of cigarettes I wouldn't eat a worm. It spread around and I got a few others to go up to a whole carton to see me eat a worm sandwich. The guys dug up a cup full of fat-assed night crawlers and I made good on my bet. I had to eat the entire thing though, or lose. It got harder and started grossin' me out when I got to the middle, and worm parts were hangin' out of the bread bit in half and still squirmin'."

I snorted almost blowing a booger. "It took a half a sandwich to start grossing you out, did it?"

Timmy continued: "It was more the look on Womble's face and the other guys hootin' and hollerin' and pretendin' to vomit that was getting to me." He was beginning to look a little green just re-telling the story. "That's when Compton, the house parent, saw us. He came runnin'. I only had a couple bites left and I knew he would stop me if he saw and I wouldn't get my cigarettes. So I shoved the last of the sandwich in my mouth before he got to me. Was tryin' to get it chewed and swallowed but he caught me and wanted to know what I was hidin'." Timmy looked at the ground and squeaked his low-top Converses against the tiled floor. "Compton made me open up and show him. When I opened my mouth and he saw all those half chewed worm guts, his eyes bugged and he gagged. I couldn't hold it no more. My innards just seemed to explode up out of me. I spewed all over him! Then he spewed too!" Timmy looked at me with an embarrassed half-smile on his face. "He was so mad! Cussin' and throwin' up at the same time."

I busted-up and laughed so hard I cried. Cecil doubled over too, even though he had heard the story before. Wiping the tears from my eyes, I said: "Wish I could have seen that."

"Anyway, Compton, said he didn't want my weird little ass anywhere near where he was workin' no more. So…they moved me up here." Now that he had us laughing at his gross little tale Timmy's smile was on full shine.

We talked a while and I warmed up to Cecil a bit after Timmy told me a couple of his recent, reform school, battle stories. Before they left me to unpack and make my bed, Cecil leant in and whispered: "What I am really interested in is your escapes. I heard you might know the lay of the land around here." Cecil looked at me in a meaningful way, as in, 'I intend to get the fuck out of here at the next opportunity,' meaningful. "But, we can talk about that after you've settled in."

Over the course of the next couple weeks I did get settled in. I started going to school, AA classes, and working maintenance in a semi-vocational capacity.

My reputation among the staff as a fighter hadn't gone unnoticed. I along with a few others who had stood out significantly in that regard were approached by Mr. Shwab, the boxing coach. I was happy to see Bobo was one of them. Pretty soon my days were filled with school, work, and training. It wasn't long and we were having matches in Enid and Woodward. It was nice to get out. And more often than not it was either Bobo or myself that stole the show. I thought about escaping again, after all it was May and summer days were upon us, but I liked our coach and didn't want to let him down. Besides what was there to go back to anyway; Tina surely had put the law on me, and word had it that Trish was back with Larry.

Cecil and I became pretty good friends. He was a drug dealer and a car thief—not a very good one it turned out—who had a pile of trouble at home not unlike I did down in El Paso. Cecil seemed to think it toughened him up. At least that was what his stepdad told him when he was beating his ass. I could relate.

We were playing pool one night after we'd came in from our weekly AA meeting when Cecil finally got around to telling me he wanted to run off.

"Come with me, man. You know the area, and, they would never find you down in Ardmore. Plus, I know a bunch of fine ass girls down there, too." He talked low as he lined up a shot off the rail.

I waited for him to shoot. He missed. I walked around the table taking in what he'd left me before answering. "Ain't no doubt we'd have a blast, but if I was going to go I'd of went when I was fighting in Woodward last week. Hell, Coach Shwab don't even watch us...well, not like he's, 'Watchin' us. Anyway, I'm learning a lot from that short, bald, fucker," I grinned. "I like it. People treat you like you are somebody when you win a fight."

I had found my shot, but was going to have to bank it. "Six. Corner pocket," I announced trying to sound confident.

Cecil took the opportunity to pop-off. "Seen you sparing with Bobo the other day. Didn't look like you were winning, that fight." He chuckled lightheartedly.

"Some days you're the bug, and some days you're the windshield," I said, thinking about that teeth jarring over-hand right that Bobo caught me with and Cecil thought was so amusing. Then I sunk the six-ball. It was a lucky shot, but it looked good. So I arched my eyebrows at him, to emphasize, that today was his day to be the bug. "Besides, Bobo is tough, he might've even had a rougher time of it than us. He's got scars where I only had bruises."

I made two more balls before scratching on the eight. We gave the table up to the next kids in line and I waved Cecil over to my cubicle.

I still had no bunk-mate, so before I stepped into my little space I glanced into the cubicles on either side of mine to make sure no one was loitering around in them. Even though the double cubes had six-foot-tall partitions on either side of the bunk beds and dresser-locker combos, they were still made of thin particle board. Privacy was a mere illusion. You could hear someone fart three bunks over. And pounding your pud, fuggitaboutit. Someone was sure to hear and front you out in the dead quiet of the night.

"Hey Jarrel! Let that thing go before it goes off in your hand and explodes all over your face!" The place would erupt in laughter.

Masturbation was reserved for the bathroom or the shower, when you could get in it by yourself. Hopefully, you didn't run into Lumpkin. He was a little black homo-sexual, ugly as all get out. He was harmless, but he would pester, pay, and plead with every kid who'd listen to let him suck on their stick.

The time he got caught was hilarious: Taking turns, three different kids stepped from the shower to stand in front the same toilet, "to take a leak." Smiling out the window at anyone who happen to look their way. There was a half-wall with glass above it to give the shitters and the showers some privacy.

The cranky old woman who was working the unit that night must have been watching the boys closely, because after the last one returned to the shower and Lumpkin's black arm reached up for toilet paper the lady realized that he'd been sitting there in the same stall, all along! and about blew a heart valve. She threw what Cecil called a, "conniption fit". Threatened to write all their families about it. The whole dormitory choked laughing so hard.

An-ee-wayz, I'm getting off topic. I checked all the other cubicles to make sure no one would be eavesdropping on mine and Cecil's conversation. When I saw it was clear, I said: "Listen Cecil, I'm not going to run off right now. Coach says I'll probably be gettin' a four or five day pass home to Guymon in the next couple months. Plus, Robert Harris, a homeboy from there just landed in Impala. I'm not lookin' to leave him high and dry with no pals here. But...I will help *you*. And, just so happens, I got a plan that requires a little help from someone just like, me." I gave him a smile the Cheshire cat from *Alice in Wonderland* would envy.

He lit a cigarette and blew a stream of smoke over my head, staring into space as he thought about it. Then he looked back at me. "I really wish you were coming, but even if I got to go by myself, I am still going to go. Tell me what you have in mind."

I *had* thought of taking off again, many times, since the powers to be had hauled my ass back to Helena. Especially when I was still in LTD. However, things were different now. Shit, I was young and didn't really know what I wanted to do, or, where I wanted to go. I did want to be free, just to be free, but my last experience had been some what of a let down. I glanced at the grates covering my window. Their whole construction had been dissected in my mind, more than once. They were nothing like the ones I had circumvented in that group home back in El Paso. These were made from hardened steel and were secured with heavy-duty hinges and locks. The only similarity between the two was they both provided a nice view of the ground.

Waving my hand at the thick metal slats, I said: "Well, there is no way to get out of the building with out being seen once your in it. But, what if, you could just disappear....

I rolled out my plan for Cecil, and the more I spoke, the bigger his grin got.

The AA and NA meetings were held at night. Usually it was still light out when we left the unit and dark by the time we were brought back.

First, one, or occasionally two, staff members would come and get the kids who wanted to participate. We each had to sign out on a sheet of paper the housing fuzz had on his desk. There was a column for out-going, and another for in-coming. Theoretically, the officer could check at a glance who was in or out.

Cecil was all nerves and excitement as we headed down the stairs and out the backdoor.

It was a mild evening, but smelled like rain could be in the forecast. The sun reflected orange fire off the bottom of the low hanging clouds as it sank in the western horizon.

We could clearly see the north fence thirty feet away, and the modest scattering of trailer houses that boxed in this northwest edge of the small town. However, it wasn't more than the length of a football field straight down the perimeter road before all signs of life petered out and you were in the fields. I had filled Cecil in on my previous cross-country experience. And, what I had learned since then during my various road trips. He had a couple eight-inch, spike nails that we had smuggled from the maintenance shop. We fashioned handles made from wrapped pieces of sheet to help him get over the tight weave of chain-link in the top half of the fence. He was as prepared as he could be. And in the light of day, I think his confidence was out weighing his nerves.

"Listen up," Mr. Pennick, the counselor who had come to escort us, said. He was one of these educator types with the tweed-jacket that has leather patches on the elbows, and spoke with a nasal twang. Though his country accent spoiled the Ivy League impression he was going for. "I've been catching some flack about letting y'all run around to the back door un-escorted when the meeting is adjourned. Tonight, you will wait for me, and we will return in through Thunderbird." He peered down his long equine nose at the ten or so of us who were standing in front of him, shuffling, already bored out of our minds, "Is that understood?"

"Yeah, yeah. Whatever man," a tall black kid replied. There were a few other grunts of acknowledgment as we filed around the building headed to the meeting.

Cecil sidled up to me with a worried look in his mud-colored eyes. "What the hell, why would they start that now?"

I shrugged. "Somebody must have complained that we were leaving him behind, running wild, and piling up at the back door 'til he caught up. I don't know, but I will make sure Clyde, Mac, and Timmy know to follow our lead when AA is over. Our plan will still work, I think. And if not we'll wait for another day, its probably going to rain anyway."

He appeared a little more relaxed after that.

Timmy fell back to us and asked, "Is this going to mess everything up?" He was the only one we had told since I would need his help to pull off my part of the operation.

"Naw, screw Pennick. We got this," Cecil said.

I clapped him on the back. He was getting his confidence back.

The meeting was your standard AA meeting: "Hi, I'm so and so. I'm a fifteen year-old alcoholic who has lived such a long, hard life...Yada...Yada...Yada..." Although, in reality, we were all pretty screwed-up in our own ways. Some of the kids had even been pretty deep into hard drugs by then. I had been lucky enough not to have had drug addicted parents. Regardless of the rest of their faults. Anyway, if I got nothing else out of these meetings I learned that I was not the victim I thought I was. I heard stories far worse than my own; and then, I'd hear a story even worse than them. For a kid of fifteen or sixteen who can't see past his own horizon it brings on a more enlightened perspective. And in retrospect, probably not a bad lesson to learn in life.

When the meeting broke up, we all mobbed the door like we always did.

"Remember," Mr. Pennick said, as he pushed his way through us to unlock the aluminum and glass cafeteria door. "Wait until I have everyone from Corvette together before you take off,"

We all nodded our intention to adhere to his wishes, and when he let go of the door me, Cecil, Clyde, Mac, and Timmy all shot off down the sidewalk laughing. We left him trying to rein in the rest of the kids from bolting, too. We could hear Mr. Pennick as we rounded the building yelling for us to come back and not to run.

Mac and Clyde were just messing around, they ambled to a stop and turned around, but were still hootin' and hollerin'. Timmy stopped a few feet later at the back corner of the building. It was full on dark now, you couldn't even see the stars for the clouds overhead and the lighting back here was intermittent. I took Cecil all the way to the darkest part of the fence.

"Still have time to change your mind and come with me," Cecil said. He was smiling but visibly shaking from the adrenaline starting to course through his veins.

"Wish I could, bro." I was bouncing from foot to foot. My blood was pumping also and I was tempted, but I shook it off. "Even if I didn't have other plans, I am still the only person I trust to take care of the rest of this for you."

"I know. Take care Max. And thanks—"

"Come on Jimmy," Timmy yelled from the corner of the building. "Pennick's comin'. He wants us to go in the front."

With that I turned and sprinted to join Timmy. Cecil hit the fence. I could hear the metal spikes biting into the tight chain-link as I rounded the corner.

Timmy and I met Mr. Pennick on his way around to get us. "Is that all of you?" he demanded.

We both nodded.

"What about me saying we were going in the front didn't you understand?"

"I'm sorry Mr. Pennick," I said. "We were just so used to racing each other to the back door that we forgot."

"More like you delinquents just like to pull my chain." With that he herded us onto the porch with the rest of the kids from Corvette.

The man escorted us through Thunderbird, the same way I went the first time. Past the desk and into the stairwell. Upstairs we crowded around the clip-board and all took our turn signing ourselves back into the unit. I did the best I could at forging Cecil's name and then my own, hoping that the officer would not be alerted to anyone's absence. My theory was they would not pay attention to the sheet as long as the incoming matched the outgoing—first hurdle cleared.

Next, I located the wooden count board hanging on a pair of hooks behind the house parent's desk. It was an eighteen inch square floor-plan of the unit. It had little name tags for each boy hanging in the slot that marked their bunk location. When the guard was counting, he or she, pulled it off the hooks and carried it with them, matching name tags with warm bodies. If the two matched, as far as I could tell, they called count good. So, with a little help from Timmy causing a distraction—slipping coming out of the shower, then laying on the floor moaning until the guard got up to check on him—I reached over and filched Cecil Drake's name tag right off the board.

After Timmy's theatrical debut I went to Cecil's cubicle. He lived in a single. No high walls here. I quickly stripped his bed throwing his sheets and blankets into his locker. Then folded his bare, blue and white, pee-stained mattress in half and left it at the foot of the bed; just the way we were supposed to leave a vacant cube. Finally, I swiped a couple of loose items off his desk into a drawer. After a quick once over I was satisfied that it looked like any other unoccupied slot. I was just turning away when I heard....

"What happened to Cecil?"

In the bunk over from Cecil's was his neighbor. A little Mexican kid looking right at me. Sitting all quiet and creepy in the shadows. I didn't even see him.

"Ummm... Well..." I hadn't prepared for this. So I threw out the first thing that came to mind. "They took him out on a medical run." I knew it was stupid when I said it.

"At night?"

"What the hell do I know." I grunted and shuffled uncomfortably under this kids scrutiny. "Just mind your business."

"He ran off didn't he? Cecil told me he was going to." The kid turned away from me and laid down. "Don't worry, I won't tell nobody."

With that I relaxed. I mumbled, "Thanks," under my breath and went back to my end of the unit. I hoped the kid was good to his word. Something told me he would be, but you never knew. And as I lay in my own bed waiting for the guard to do his first bed check I was well aware that if I was connected to Cecil's disappearance I might as well have left with him, because I would lose my up-coming pass, boxing trips, and probably my maintenance vo-tech, anyway.

When the guard passed my bunk, where I was feigning sleep, I quietly rolled out of bed and peered down the run after him. It was about ten o'clock and the lights had been out for thirty minutes. It was dead enough for the officer's footsteps to echo off the tiles. Timmy was still awake too, I could see his shadow moving across from me. I watched the key-man shuffle from one cubicle to the next, comparing his board to the lumpy outline of a kid in his bed. Cecil lived quite a ways down. The guard's body language was; pause, look down at the board, look up at the beds, move a couple steps, then do it again. Occasionally, he would shine a little flashlight in one of the cubicles.

I held my breath as I watched him. I couldn't tell where Cecil's bed was from my vantage point. My nerves stayed stretched tight as piano wire until he hit the end of the row and turned to cross to the other side.

With a sigh of relief I returned to my bed. I laid in the dark smiling. *We pulled it off!* It occurred to me that it might be a good long while before they even discovered Cecil was gone. There was pattering on the slats covering my window. It had begun to rain. *Oh well,* I thought, *it can't be as bad as the bone chilling cold I had to deal with back in November.* I fell asleep feeling self-satisfied and wishing Cecil well.

Cecil watched his friends round the corner of the building. Alone. There was no turning back. He stretched his hands above the common chain-link and stabbed his climbing spikes through the tightly woven security-mesh making up the top half of the fence. He was young and strong and made short work of the obstacle, surprising himself how easy it was.

The year before a kid had tried to get over the security-wire with tooth brushes. The wanna-be escape artist got nine feet off the ground before falling and hurting himself. He ended up hiding inside an AC unit, where he was overheard scuffling around and consequently caught.

Once on the other side of the fence Cecil ran west down the perimeter road. He didn't have far to go before clearing the last trailer house across from the reformatory. There left the lights of civilization behind him and cut across a wheat field.

I made it without anyone seeing me, he boasted to himself. *And, if the fellas do their part, I may not be missed for hours!* He jumped in the air and punched the sky, hardly believing he'd made it that far. *This is great!*

The only thing bothering him was the heavy clouds smothering the moonlight. It made it hard to see and smelled more and more like rain. No sooner than it entered his mind, he felt a drop hit his cheek. *At least it's not cold.*

With that thought, somewhat, comforting him, Cecil trudged through one wheat field and cattle pasture after another. When his heart slowed down and he felt confident no one was after him he took to a section road. He was well aware that his northwest trek was taking him the opposite direction he wanted to go. However, he decided to circle around later; for the time being, Cecil was just determined to put a few more miles between himself and Helena. And, if fate was with him, find a car or truck to steal along the way.

The boy walked, sometimes trotted, down the dirt road for an hour before the small rain drops turned into big ones. And suddenly, just like God flipped on his backyard whirl-pool, the wind picked up and the rain came pouring down. Within minutes Cecil was drenched. A half hour of that, with his hair plastered to his forehead and his clothes clinging to him like Reynolds Wrap, he was officially miserable. Finding a vehicle was now priority one.

As time passed, his concern over how long he actually had before the reformatory started looking for him, drove him off road. He turned east and cut through a section of forest, hoping the trees would give him some shelter from the wind and rain. It did, but getting through the wooded tract in the dark was slow and tricky.

Luckily, he had only to pick his way through thirty yards of invisible, sharp, pointy branches and twigs before he came to a freshly tilled field. Across the furrowed rows was a dark, two-story house, barn, and garage backed up to another section of forested land. Cecil couldn't see what was in the garage—if anything—but parked next to a combine, in front of the barn, was an older model Dodge pickup.

Visions of getting out of the rain and down the road sent him plowing through the field, where he immediately sank past his ankles in the upturned muddy soil. Each step sinking deeper than the last and accumulating heavier and heavier clods of mud on his feet. Halfway across he pulled his foot from the oozing, sucking muck to find his boot missing. Digging in the water filled depression his foot had came out of, he found the big leather brogan. By the time he'd fought it to the surface the AWOL boot was full of mud and weighed an extra ten pounds.

Not wanting to go through the same thing again, he took his other boot off and carried it with him. Cutting through the rain soaked field had been a mistake, he acknowledged, but he eventually made it to the other side. When he went to wipe the clinging muck from his feet he discovered his socks were also gone. Saddened by the loss, he consoled himself thinking if he could get the truck he wouldn't be on foot much longer.

Carrying his boots he padded bare footed up the long dirt drive. He circled through a flooded bar-ditch and came out on the far side of the barn near the truck.

The rain let up, somewhat. At least it wasn't coming down in horizontal sheets anymore. *Maybe luck is turning in my favor and I will get through this.* With that idea in his head he crossed his fingers and ran the twenty feet of open space to the passenger side of the pickup. When he grabbed the handle it came open. His spirits cheered as he slid in out of the rain. The interior lights were dim, but he didn't think anyone would notice in the downpour. Still, he stayed low and got the door latched quickly as possible.

When the light went out Cecil sat up, tossing his boots in the passenger floorboard, then sliding over into the driver's seat. He wiped the wet hair clinging to his face out of his eyes and examined the dashboard. A smile burst across his mug like the first seconds of a sunrise. *Somebody is watching over me tonight,* he said to himself. Right in the key-hole was the solitary Dodge key already in it.

He reached for it—then hesitated looking at the house. If the truck had only been a couple dozen feet further down the drive it would be blocked by the barn. After studying the muddy lane the truck was on he knew, alone, there was no way he could push it. *To hell with it!* Throwing caution to the wind, Cecil pumped the gas twice and turned the key.

RRRR-RRRr-RRrr, again, *RRRr-RRrr-Rrrr.*

Lights came on in the house. *Oh shit!* Cecil turned the key again, *Rrr-rrr-rrr.* Next, the front porch light came on. Frantically pumping the gas he turned the key again at the same time the front door opened and a man sent three dogs out. *Rrrrr-rr....*

"Dammit! The battery's dead," he growled outloud. Fate he realized had been playing a cruel joke on him.

Baroowa, woof...woof, Baroowa, woof, Baroowa, bark, bark, the dogs were coming. It was a thirty yard span between them, and him. He was reaching in the floorboards for his boots when he heard the first shot. *BOOM!* Cecil looked up to see the man jumping off his porch with a pump shotgun in his hands. *BOOM!* The side window of the truck blew in. *This guy is shooting up his own shit. He is trying to kill me!* he thought. Time lurched—skipped, like the needle on a phonograph. Abandoning any other thought that didn't concern surviving the next few moments, Cecil jerked open the passenger door, and staying low as possible, *threw himself* out onto the ground; where he rolled to his feet and ran fast as he could behind the barn. *BOOM!* The barn was sheet metal and the buckshot made a distinctive sound as it tore into its corner.

Baroowa, bark bark, Baroowa...Baroowa, woof, bark.

The dogs rounded the corner as he was running for the woods. He dived over the top strand of barbed-wire that marked the timber line, but the dogs were on him before he could get back to his feet. They attacked, biting his legs and arms. Cecil could hear the man yelling at his dogs, "Bessy. Hank. Blue. Get that thieving' bastard!" and knew he would be coming around the barn any second.

In the waning light, Cecil could see he was fighting a blue heeler, another cow dog, and a hound mix. He grabbed a big stick and stabbed the hound in the side with it. Even though it barely broke the skin the screeching yelp it let out gave the other dogs pause. Cecil came up swinging the branch like he was Babe Ruth, hitting the cow dog across the snout. All three dogs backed away a few feet snarling, growling, and barking. Cecil took the opportunity and ran, tearing through brambles and thorns, branches and twigs, and springing over rocks and fallen logs as still another gun shot exploded in the night behind him.

His flight was so panicked it took him over the edge of a gully, where he went sliding down its muddy bank into a creek. He ran, stumbling, twenty yards down stream before stepping on a sharp rock and gashing open his foot....

I woke up the next morning to find three officers and a case manager in Cecil's area; going through his stuff, finding his sheets and blankets in his locker. One of them had the count board and another the sign-in sheet. Apparently, they knew he was gone.

I discovered later, the reason they found out was because Cecil had went to the main gate looking for help. It had rained all night. He had gotten lost and walked in a big circle. The cops said he'd been bitten up pretty bad by a dog, his feet were cut to pieces, and he was covered in stickers and brambles. I was told he had to argue with the gate guards to convince them that he was from the reform school, as they hadn't had any reports of anyone missing.

I was extremely disappointed, but there was no telling what Cecil had went through to drive him back to the gates. From the sounds of it, it must have been a hell of a night.

There was some confusion, and some speculation as to how he had managed to get his name tag, sign-in, and roll up his bed-roll, all before he left; but in the end, everyone held their mud. Cecil went to the Dodge House, and the mystery faded and finally blew over.

At least I think it did. I was moved a couple weeks later when the people in charge decided to reopen the Camaro unit. It was another unit with rooms, so maybe there was a little residual blow back.

CHAPTER 12

CAMARO

I really don't know why "the man" moved me from Corvette to Camaro. Corvette's unit staff never out right accused me of anything. They questioned several people, me included. In the process I did receive the 'We know what you did eyebrows', and some pointed conjecture, but I figured it was just part of their interrogation technique—probably aimed the same looks and innuendoes at everyone they spoke to.

Anyway, no big deal. But, I did move for whatever reason. The whole thing upset Timmy more than me. I was actually happy about it when I discovered Robert, my homeboy from Guymon, would be assigned to Camaro after he finished his orientation in Impala.

Camaro capped off the south end of the institutional complex, the same as Mustang did on the north end. The prodigious Impala/Admin. building stretched length-wise in between. It was a little different than the rest of the units. For one it was only one unit and had an annex built in the back which gave it even more floor space. Made it look more like a country manor than the medieval sanitarium vibe of its brother buildings. Like maybe it had been adopted into the family, after the fact.

Inside, if the first floor ever had cubicles they had long ago been stripped out and in there places put a Universal weight machine, a TV room, and several offices.

The second floor was a long hallway with seven or eight doorless rooms lining both sides. It had a communal shower on one end and an officer station on the other. The unit had sat idle so long that the new unit staff had to bring in beds and dressers for us. On the bright side during certain hours we had access to the whole building, including the weights and TV room. We were only locked upstairs at night.

Robert and I got a cell—room—whatever you want to call it, by the shower on the east end of the building. I knew a few of the other kids that they stocked the rooms with, but not many. However, one of them was Keith Armstrong, the big black kid, supposedly in for rape, who had been with me in LTD. He was still just as creepy, but he stayed to himself so we paid little attention to him.

Things rolled pretty much the same for me as they did in Corvette; school, work, training. Though Robert and I hadn't really known each other before Helena, we bonded quickly. Not very many kids came through there from Guymon. Soon we were best friends.

Robert was thirteen or fourteen months older than me. He had short, sandy brown hair, and brown eyes. Tall as me, if not a little slimmer. A pretty good looking kid as far as that went, and one of those boys who handled things with humor instead of his fists. He was more beta to my alpha so he made the perfect wing man for a sixteen year old who thought the world was only a dream he was having when he was awake.

Robert kept me laughing with stories from home, about his sister, Angela, and an older brother he'd had who died in a car accident. When his big brother passed it effected Robert deeply, and that is when his life took its nose-dive into crime, disruption, and rebelliousness. He was sentenced to Helena for "Arson". Robert told me he was angry and started lighting trash cans on fire as he walked down a deserted alley. He'd got a half dozen cans going on each side before some flames jumped to a storage building. By the time the Fire Department put out the blaze the shed was destroyed, along with all the property in it. Naturally someone told on Robert and Judge Ogden sent him up the river. To make the point, that if a house had caught fire instead of a storage shed someone might have been seriously injured, or even killed. Rob might have been lashing out, but he was sincerely ashamed of what he'd done when it was put like that, and very glad no one was hurt. He was just like that; not a bad kid at heart.

One warm June morning, about a week into our new digs, Robert and I were sitting out on the front porch rail smoking a cigarette and dangling our feet above the bushes below. Our reward after a half-ass workout on the Universal machine. Coach Shwab wanted me to quit with the cancer-sticks, said I need my wind, but back then even us kids could have cartons sent in, and it was the cool thing to do...just ask Joe Camel, or the Marlboro Man. Robert was chiding me about the beginnings of a shiner that was spreading under my left eye. Bobo and his damned over-hand right, again. I was starting to wonder if the only way I was going to beat him was to take a two-foot piece of steel pipe into the ring with me. Right in the middle of Robert poking fun at me, he jumped up and pointed across the yard toward Mustang.

"Look over there!"

I followed where he was pointing. It was obvious something serious was happening. Staff members were coming out of buildings everywhere and running toward two people who were almost falling down Mustang's front steps. One was a woman (case manager, I think), her face was in her hands and I could now hear her shrieking sobs from where we were. The other was a hard-nosed guard I recognized from LTD. Although, he didn't look so hard-nosed right then. He looked lost; stumbling into the grass as if he had been hit between the eyes with an ax-handle. The approaching staff were surrounding them, questions flying through the air.

Me and Robert jumped up to stand on the rail, trying to get a better look and possibly hear what was being said. All of a sudden two or three police cars came roaring up to the front guard shack. Lights flashing.

"What the hell is going on?" I didn't even realize I'd spoke my thought out loud until I saw Robert, shrug. He had the same dumb-founded expression on his face as I'm sure was on mine.

It was evident something bad had went down and someone was

probably hurt. But even the time Billy Beasley hit a kid in the head with a weight and the kid had to be air-lifted to Oklahoma City, they didn't panic like this. At least I didn't think they did, I was in LTD at the time. But this...this had a personal feel to it. By now a crowd had gathered in front of Mustang, and all the female staff among them were crying...along with a few of the men.

Robert was staring at them. "Have you ever seen the staff act like this before?"

"No. No I haven't," I answered.

All of a sudden the alarm went off, sounding eerily like all the angels in heaven lamenting at once. The alarm meant for everyone to return to their housing units. As soon as it started its high-pitched whine guards on the yard began yelling for us to get off the porch and get to our rooms. We could assume similar instructions were being given throughout the institution, because guards and administrative staff were running for every building.

Still totally oblivious as to what all the commotion was about, I glanced over toward Mustang again, my fingers crossed that Nate, Bobo, Shifter, or anyone else I knew over there were not involved in whatever it was. I even thought of Mrs. Fullerton, hoping she wasn't as upset as the other ladies obviously were.

A couple kids coming from school were being hustled up the sidewalk. When they caught up with us one of them blurted out they'd heard someone had been killed! The officer who was now herding me and Robert up the steps with them, snapped: "Shut that stuff up and get to your rooms."

Our house parent who had already been trying to corral us looked at the officer. "Is that true?"

The officer nodded ever so slightly. "In a minute. First lets get these kids secured."

On our way down the hall the boys who had been stuck in the building were trying to interrogate us about what was going on. In a rare moment of aggravation, nerves, or more likely fear, Robert barked at the group of kids bunched up blocking our way. "How the fuck would we know. Something bad!" He shoved his way past the mob.

Normally, I was the one with the quick temper, but I could see Robert was shaken up. I patted him on the shoulder; he was trembling. We walked to our room. By then we were being ordered into them anyway, and instructed not to even stick our heads out; under penalty of a trip to the Dodge House.

The east end of Camaro jutted out past Impala and faced the east end of Mustang. It was a straight shot across, like two weights on the ends of a barbell. However, me and Robert were in the southeast corner facing away from the action.

"Armstrong," I whispered over to him. He had north facing windows. "We're comin' over there so we can see."

He didn't answer me.

"That's weird. They got the whole place locked down by now. Everyone ought to be back in." I scratched my head. "Come on Robert, the creep ain't over there."

Robert and me picked our moment and sneaked across the hall where we peered over Armstrong's window sill trying to get a view between the metal slats. It was a crazy scene, the few squad cars that had pulled up to the gates earlier had multiplied into a mass of metal and flashing red and blue lights. Law enforcement vehicles were lined up along the perimeter road as far around it as I could see from my limited vantage point. *Where did all these cops come from,* I wondered to myself. There were different makes and models, colors and insignias; everything from city patrol cars to county SUVs—state troopers and a few unmarked ones as well. They all, however, had some form of flashers going on. If it had been dark astronauts would have been able to spot Helena from outer space.

Peering through slitted eyes, between narrow spaces in the door slats. The predator could still smell the blood, fear, and sex of his victim. The reek seemed to seep right out of his skin. It covered him like a haunting spirit.

He watched as the two kids who lived across the hall crept into the room. He'd heard them coming and hid. He was terrified, and also thrilled, by what he'd done. He'd gave into his urges. He felt like a wild animal, a beast, it made him feel powerful and in control. Although, now he was on the run and scared. He'd always been a coward at heart, he couldn't get away from it no matter what he did. *What to do now? Where to run? Where to hide....*

The two kids were looking out the window, talking. He couldn't hear what they were saying. Maybe he should attack them. Kill them too. He was bigger than either of them, they looked like fighters though—too hard, they might hurt him instead. Best to stay hidden.

Ahhh, they're leaving. The monster in the closet breathed a sigh of relief.

There wasn't much else to see—especially since we didn't know what to look for. When we saw a group of guards and policemen storming out of Mustang and heading down the sidewalk straight toward us, Robert and I skulked back across the hall into our own room. The house parent at the end of the run had his head down whispering urgently into the phone and never saw us.

The goon-squad had definitely been coming to Camaro. We heard them tramp through the front doors, and climb the stairs. Their footfalls were heavy and full of purpose. There was anger in the sound. Once they poured onto the range the officers immediately paired off to different cells. Two of the jerks I had fought with up in LTD came to ours.

Lieutenant Carver came through the door first. "Where have you been for the last two hours?" he demanded.

"Right here..." Me and Robert echoed at the same time.

"Open your pants and turn the inside of your underwear out," his sidekick ordered.

"What!?" I stepped back, tensing up.

Robert stepped back, too.

"Just fucking do it," Carver barked. "We are looking for blood and semen." It was apparent he was stressed-out, and it was just as apparent that it wasn't necessarily aimed at us. He had a wounded look in his eyes, and seemed to have aged ten years since I had last seen him.

For me the whole thing had just taken on a completely new dimension. The words "blood and semen" were ringing in my head. In a distant part of my mind I heard an officer across the hall ask our day officer where the kid who lived in that cell was. Our housing staff didn't know where Armstrong was, and allowed that he wasn't signed out for anywhere.

Still shaken by Carver's words, I complied, opening my jeans and flipping the elastic of my boxers out so they could see it. Robert followed my lead.

The lieutenant waved at us to button back up as if he knew he wasn't going to find any evidence in our pants, anyway.

The other goon had just glanced under our beds when an officer across the hall yelled: "Hey this kid over here is hiding in his closet!"

Both men in our room immediately bolted across the hall.

"What were you doing in there? Why were you hiding?" You could hear the officer's questions. "Where have you been the last two hours?" That was Lieutenant Carver, I was sure.

I couldn't hear Armstrong's response due to the two officers in the hall between ours and Kieth's cell muttering to each other. "...this is the sick bastard right here. I fucking know it!" one of them said. But, I heard the Lieutenant's next words loud and clear.

"Oh yeah? Are you sure you weren't down in Mustang's basement raping and stabbing Maxine Fullerton to death with a pair of scissors!"

The earth seemed to stop turning on its axis for a few seconds. I couldn't believe I heard him right—someone hurt sweet, kind, helpful, grandmotherly Mrs. Fullerton!? Tears sprang to my eyes; suddenly I understood all the weeping, shock, and despondency that me and Robert had witnessed from the porch.

Robert asked, "Was that the lady who helped you guys when the police beat you up?"

I nodded. But couldn't get my throat to work in order to answer him.

Armstrong's underwear was examined, and it was instant anarchy in the room across the hall. The whole goon-squad converged on the ten by twelve-foot cell. It was obvious they had discovered the evidence they were looking for. Soon some bloody cloths were found hidden away, too. The tension was so intense that you could feel it like electricity cracking through the air, and if a couple of actual state troopers hadn't been in the room I don't know if Armstrong would have made it out of that cell alive.

I know even with the two officers blocking Robert and I in, if I'd had a pipe or a knife they couldn't have stopped me from going after him myself.

The police handcuffed Kieth, and then they, the guards, house parents, admin staff, and even a school teacher who had piled into his room surrounded him and marched him out and down the hall.

I was stone cold. Streams of tears ran down my face and were dripping off my chin. I couldn't help but see Maxine's kind, smiling face turn to terror and pain. It was Robert's turn to put a hand on my shoulder. He said something, but my mind was too far away to hear.

"What did you say?" I asked without looking over at him.

"I said. That freak was hiding in the closet all bloody the whole time we were over there." He shuddered.

I balled my fists. "Yeah. If only we had known what we know now we could have fucked him up ourselves before the cops ever got to him."

Robert stared me in my eyes—then looked away and stepped back. He had just met my demons.

The media came next. The skies in that area which had rarely seen so much as a crop-duster, were now awash with helicopter rotors. News 9; Channel 4; On the Scene News. There were vans and film crews taking pictures and video from the other side of the fences. I remember seeing one pointed in my direction and wondering how they could see anything through the chain link fencing from that far away. But, later that night, Boom, there I was—a short clip of me smoking a cigarette. The picture so clear and close-up that you could almost make out what brand I smoked.

My nightmares came back and now had new faces in them, along with the smelly ghouls I'd brought with me from El Paso. That little club was a hard one to get into, but Kieth made it. Except he didn't look like Kieth. He had morphed into a dark, scarred, puss-oozing, Freddy Kruger looking freak with bloody scissor shanks for fingers. He was right there with the claw-hammer-handed hoboes, chasing me through the thick disabling molasses of my dreams. But the worst were when Mrs. Fullerton was in them full of terror, tears, and blood. She would look to me for help through my grandmother's eyes. Sometimes their faces over-lapped and flipped back and forth. The harder I struggled to reach Armstrong to stop his attack the weaker and more debilitated I would become, and the ghouls would drag me down and tear me apart with their claw-hammers. I was forced to see in my nightmarish dream-scape the destruction of a sweet soul. It was so unfair and tragic that it tore away what little was left of my youthful innocence.

The horrific crimes against Mrs. Fullerton without a doubt was the closest to true evil I had come to at that time in my life. Not that it had anything to do with me at all, but pure evil is like a black hole; the gravitational forces can unravel the realities of any number of worlds, even though they may be from the other side of the galaxy. I can only imagine what impact it had on those whose worlds were directly effected. My heart still goes out to her family.

It was a terrible tragedy and devastating for the whole town. They needed time to recuperate so by the end of the month the forces who were in control of our lives put everyone six months or less from parole in for it. The idea was to thin the population down long enough for the Administration, employees, Maxine's family, and the town to get their feet back under them.

I fell into that category and was paroled into the custody of my aunt Cheryl, and uncle Jimmy. Next thing I knew, I was being dropped off at the Greyhound Station on my way home.

Robert was scheduled for the following month. He was going to turn eighteen in August, anyway.

CHAPTER 13

EL DORADO

The bus station was a one-room shoebox in Cherokee, Oklahoma, fifteen miles north of Helena. A place where buses stopped maybe once or twice a day; a place where people might get on to leave, but rarely got off to stay. It was small. The town was small; hot; flat; and dry. Although, I couldn't have been more excited if it had been Grand Central Station in New York City. I was *going home!*

"Going home" after being locked-down awhile is a hard feeling to describe. It starts in your stomach and rises up through your chest with a mixture of joyous anticipation, unexplored potential, and not a small amount of relief that the painful part has passed and you are still standing. Like how you feel *after* the root canal. All these years later— it's still the same. And *it's summertime!* You can't beat it. It's right up there with getting laid by the Double-Mint twins. Which by the way was at the top of my sixteen year old bucket list.

Coach Shwab drove me to the depot in his own car. Normally it would have fallen to transport officers like Cal and Will. But since they were still mad at me, and the coach requested the duty it fell to him.

On the way he tried to encourage me to stay out of trouble, keep boxing, and stop smoking. Even though, the ashtray in his big purple El Dorado was overflowing with cigarette butts like a slot machine's coin-tray after a jack-pot. He also suggested I consider joining the military when I was old enough. He believed structure and something to give me a sense of accomplishment was all I needed.

Okay coach. All I'm thinking about right now is getting drunk and getting laid. In which ever order they come. Of course I didn't say any of that, that would have spoiled the fatherly coaching moment he was going for, but it was what I was thinking as I sat in the passenger seat of his comfortable Cadillac nodding my agreement to everything he said.

We talked a little about Mrs. Fullerton. A month later and the town was still mourning her loss as if it had happened only the day before. "They ought to fry Armstrong," he said, "but he'll probably get off with Life. Be'n he's only sixteen." I told him I felt bad for Maxine's family and that I'd liked her a lot the little I knew her.

Before he left me to catch my bus he dug in his pocket and came out with a five-dollar bill. "I'm not supposed to do this, but the warden can't tell me what to do with my own money." He chuckled like he had made a joke. "Take this. I looked at your bus route, it goes up toward Kansas, then straight down the panhandle; stops a couple hours down the road in some po-dunk town a few miles past Buffalo for lunch. You're going to need this to get a burger, or something."

"Thanks Coach."

I meant what I said, though knew I wouldn't be buying food with it. If there was any way possible, when the bus stopped, beer would be what I went for. I already had a couple dollars in loose change I'd picked-up and hoarded back when I was anticipating getting a pass; hoping to get an opportunity on my way home to snag some form of cheap liquor to distract me from the long bus ride. *Shit! With an extra fin,* I thought, *I could go for a six-er, possibly even two!* It occurred to me that maybe *I was* a teenage alcoholic. I would have to ask someone at my next AA meeting.

Thankfully, my bus was on time. As much as I liked the coach, I wasn't going to feel truly free until I was shy of everything to do with, Helena. The baggage handler put the small box of things I couldn't part with: letters, pictures, and a few clothes into the undercarriage storage compartment. Then the driver took my ticket and I climbed the three rubber and chrome treaded steps into the confines of the big bus.

Buses have a certain feel, sound, and smell to them. At least while idling, vibrating in time with the deep rattling rumble of its diesel engine. The scent of exhaust and big rubber tires always finds its way into the coach to mix with the stale smell of cigarettes and old used-up chewing gum, all of which never fails to stir in me nostalgic images of freedom, travel, and the open road. Color me weird, but I like buses.

After climbing past the shiny poles that separates the driver's area from the passengers I saw about a third of the seats were occupied. Of that only half of the occupants were curious enough to look up and check-out who, or what, was climbing aboard to share their cross-country journey. Fewer still met me, eye to eye.

You can tell a lot about people in such close quarters. Some smile and look hopeful, some frown finding distaste in what they see, some jerk their eyes away as soon as they see you looking at them. Fear? Guilt? Bashfulness? I don't relate very well so I couldn't begin to say. Most, who just glance up or not at all, are merely too busy, too preoccupied, or too bored to give a damn unless you interject yourself into their bubble, by saying something like, "Excuse me is this seat taken?" But, why would you when two thirds of the seats are empty? One guy, in the middle, scooted over as if to offer me a place to sit— one of the smilers. *Ahhh...No thank you.* If there is a choice I am more of a single-seat, back of the bus kind of guy. Then I turn into the bored preoccupied type. At least until I get a couple beers in me.

Don't get me wrong, I'm always looking for a hot chick to talk to. Generally, if they were my age and on a bus, or a plane by themselves, or hanging out at the truck stop hitchhiking through, there was a good chance we were kindred spirits and would hit it off. But, there were no age-appropriate girls on this ride.

There were two women up front, who could have passed for sisters. They had three kids in tow and looked like they were running from something. I definitely saw fear in their glance as I climbed on, and relief, before their eyes darted away.

There were a few men scattered around; one with an open briefcase on his lap; another, had a huge backpack sitting next to him; several farmer types, John Deere hats and overalls; and a couple uniformed guys who looked like they were on leave from the military. There were two middle-aged couples, a pair holding hands and whispering together, seemed happy, the other pair looked frustrated and were staring out opposite windows; the smiling guy was the only long-hair on board (another demographic I relate too, since my hair hung to my shoulders); and one older lady, knitting what appeared to be a shawl, who was most likely someone's mom or grandmother, coming from, or going to, a visit.

The three rows behind the long-hair were empty. I picked the last before the bathroom and slid across the blue-gray cushioned seat. Soon we were rolling down the road and everyone had withdrawn into their own inner-worlds, myself included. The scenery passed by through the big, tinted, passenger-side window. It was a beautiful day.

I sat watching the fields and trees glide by, daydreaming about the last few letters I'd received from Rhonda. Arley had finally given her my address. Apparently she'd gotten tired of living with the pervert she married and left him. From what she'd written it hadn't lasted long. I was extremely happy about that, more than I realized I would be. I liked Rhonda and that whole situation bothered me. Anyway, maybe I wouldn't be girlfriendless when I got back home. She was definitely pretty, she had heart, and she fit in with the fellas. Along with the mile-wide bad-girl streak she had running through her made her just about the perfect girl in my eyes. Moreover, unlike Tina, she was trustworthy. Although, I wasn't so sure I was good boyfriend material, anymore. Tina had taught me some hard and painful lessons.

Coach Shwab was wrong about my lunch stop being after Buffalo. Just thirty minutes in and the bus driver announced, to my utter delight, that we would be pulling over at a up-coming diner. He gave more instructions when we got there; how long we had, and what was good on the menu—according to his experience. I didn't catch much of it, because I was eye-balling a little quickie-mart that was half a block away.

I waited, impatiently, for everyone to get off the bus, and the driver to go in the diner before I made my move. Pretty sure the driver had rules against letting some sixteen year-old delinquent smuggle beer onto his coach. The people off-loaded. The hippie was last. When he stood I could see his brown hair hung to the middle of his back. There was something awkward about him, though I couldn't put my finger on it. And honestly, I didn't put much into it. It was time to go.

My concerns now turned to my chances of getting carded at the store. I rarely got ID'd and had looked old enough to have frequented a few loose and unsavory bars from as early as fourteen. But, it still occasionally happened. And, something like that would land my ship in dry dock before it ever set sail.

As things went, I made it there and back with two six-packs and change to spare. I was sitting on the bus like I'd never even moved when the passengers started climbing back on and shuffling to their spots.

"You weren't hungry?"

I looked up from the Stephen King novel I'd brought along. The hippie was in his seat looking back at me. He appeared to be in his mid-twenties. I took a chance he was cool and raised my can of Pabst. "Other priorities," I said.

"You got beer? Can I have one?"

Hell, I'm not a complete dick, and honestly, as dried-out as I was, it wouldn't have been a good idea anyway to drink a whole twelve-pack by myself. My Aunt Cheryl was picking me up in Liberal, Kansas, and she wouldn't appreciate me being shit faced when I got there. Though it wouldn't be the first time I'd let her down...nor, would it probably be the last.

"Sure man." I leant up and handed him a beer.

He smiled. "My name is Jerry Reis. What's yours?"

I told him, and since I could tell we were going to continue our conversation—and because I'd already slammed a beer when I got back onboard, making me Mr. Friendly—I moved up to the seat right behind Jerry, and handed him two more beers.

Ole, Jerry, was a pretty open person. He allowed he was from Washington. "The state. Not the Washington where the fascists try to rule the world from," he said. *What the hell is a facist?* I mused. He went on to tell me he was a game warden in some national forest up there.

My bullshit meter was going off. I really didn't know anything about being a "Game Warden of a national forest", but the picture those few words bring to mind certainly didn't match with the long-haired, clean-shaven, hippie-looking dude sitting in front of me. Although, what the hell do I know.

"So," I asked opening another beer, "what are you doing on a bus traveling through Oklahoma?"

"I'm on vacation. Riding a bus is a great way to get away from it all and see the country at the same time. Do you, by chance, drop acid?"

"Not for awhile. I haven't been doing anything for awhile, including drink beer," admitting by my facial expression that I was already catching a buzz. He offered me a couple hits of Purple Microdot for another can of Pabst. Jerry had a small bottle full. Thinking it would be a nice surprise for my buddy David back home, I got the hippie game warden to give me two more hits for another beer and the change I had left in my pocket.

"So tell me why you haven't been able to do anything for so long."

There was no reason not to tell him, he was obviously cool. I glanced at the old woman across from me, and a few of the other passengers who were near. It wasn't that I was embarrassed, I just didn't want those around me to start watching their purses and wallets the way people do when there is a perceived criminal in their midst. I liked to believe I wasn't a scumbag, and if I could help it, didn't want to be made to feel like one. Regardless, it didn't matter, as far as I could tell, no one was paying any attention to mine and Jerry's conversation.

"I just got paroled from a reformatory and I am on my way home. I've been gone nine months."

Feeling self-conscious I looked out my window. The world was bright out there. Probably getting hotter too as the day wore on, being it was July. From where I was sitting though it looked pretty damn good to me.

Jerry brought me back. "Nine months! My God that seems like a long time. What did you do kill the Pope?"

I smoked a cigarette and finished the beer I was drinking while I regaled him with my harrowing tire-heist tale.

"Wow. Excessive. The judge wouldn't just let you pay for the tires? Maybe do some community service?"

"Naw, it was straight to the clink for me. And trust me, parts of it was hard time." I reached in my paper sack and fished out my last beer.

He shook his head at the injustice of it all. "What was it like? Was it rough? What did you guys do for that long, for say, sex?"

I laughed. "Well there was the Swimsuit Issue of Sports Illustrated. I can't tell you how many times I whacked off to Christy Brinkly's bikini covered muff." I belched, and thought: *I must be drunk bragging about jacking off to Sports Illustrated.*

"That's it! That's all you can do in there for months, or years at a time?" He sipped his beer and stared at me.

"Well...I guess there are a few gay dudes around who will gladly blow you. If you are into that kind of thing."

"Oklahoma is so conservative, what do people in this part of the country think about, *'that kind of thing'*?" Jerry leant forward appearing very interested.

"Hell, it's illegal, as far as I know."

He rocked back as if I had just slapped him. "Illegal! Are you kidding me?"

I shrugged. I really didn't know, but that is what I sincerely believed at the time.

Jerry regained his composure. "Well, I have been with several men...and I don't see anything wrong with it." Then he winked at me.

Whooosh-all the air was suddenly vacuumed out of the passenger compartment, and time stood still while a cartoonist drew "*HE'S GAY!*" in big dark cartoon letters over my head. Like the proverbial light bulb moment.

I'm sure the shock showed on my face. I didn't try to hide it, couldn't have if I'd wanted too. Hell, I didn't really care that he was a pole smoker. It was just funny to me how blind-sided I was. Now, the awkwardness I'd noticed when he got off the bus made perfect sense. He had a little too much jiggle in his jello.

I chuckled; told him I wasn't interested; chugged the rest of my beer; stubbed out my cigarette, and then kicked my feet out across the aisle to the other arm rest and got as comfortable as I could. Two minutes later I was asleep. My last thought was that, *David and Lisa are going to give me hell when they hear this story.*

I woke up to someone softly squeezing my leg right above my knee. Anger washed through me like a flash flood. I could see Jerry in my minds-eye making his move! He had obviously turned into the aisle to wake me, and was being way to familiar about it. Touching me is going, far too far. No. Means No, pal.

All this registered in an instant before even opening my eyes. Purely on instinct I shot up from my reclined position with my left fist already moving, fully intent on breaking this gay game warden's beak. Halfway into the bone crushing punch my eyelids caught up to the rest of my body and flew open. I was right on target to the middle of the mug framed by that long, brown hair.

Only, it wasn't his mug I was looking at. My aunt squealed and jumped back as if she'd stepped on a land mine. The lady across from me squealed too, dropping her knitting needles and throwing her hands over her face. She didn't want to see the train wreck that was happening in front of her. When I realized it was my aunt who had squeezed my knee I reigned-in my blind assault, quickly looking at both her and the lady across from me then jerking my head around still confused by the conflicting images in my mind, and stared at Jerry. He was sitting with his back against the windows of the bus; feet innocently stretched out atop his own seats. My eyes penetrated his soul like an air to air missile. He knew that loaded left was meant for him. My body, my senses, and my awareness all finally caught up with each other, and looking abashed at all the people staring at me I jumped up and helped my aunt before she fell.

"Cheryl! Are you alright? What are you doing here?"

"I'm alright. You just scared me," she said fanning her face with her hands. "I'm sorry I startled you, but when you didn't get off the bus the driver let me get on to look for you."

"We're in Liberal, already?" I peered out the window, still a little dazed, and maybe still a little hungover.

"Yes." She turned to get off the bus, "That place you were in must have been just awful. Do you wake up like that all the time, now?"

Jerry was looking at me. I nodded. "Yep...pretty much." Then I followed her off the bus.

CHAPTER 14

JEEP CHEROKEE

My aunt Cheryl and uncle Jimmy Oaks are truly awesome people, and they deserve a better nephew than me. At this time, my uncle was an up and coming certified public accountant working at his dad's firm. He was a big, intelligent, athletic man who earned his college scholarship cross-country running for the University of Arkansas. "*Go Razorbacks!*" Always wearing that stupid hat shaped like a hog's head. Personally, I'm more of a Sooner fan, but we didn't hold that against each other. My, Aunt Cheryl, mom's younger sister, was sweet, pretty, sort of innocent, and full of good intentions. Her and my uncle both were funny and had the hearts of saints. Nevertheless, being a rebellious teenage kid who has previously had zero, or next to zero, positive adult relationships, I was better off, I thought, just bucking them all.

After a short visit to my grandmother's to let her see my smiling liberated face, we headed to Jim and Cheryl's house, where according to the terms of my parole I would be staying and attending school from. Apparently, my uncle in accordance with someone on the school board worked out a deal to skip me a year and some change, ahead. In return, I would play football for the Guymon Tigers. I was to become a regular kid, like the last sixteen years of a struggling, chaotic, and violent childhood never even happened. They had it all planned out for me. It's too bad I couldn't see it for the opportunity that it was.

While I had been away Jim and Cheryl moved to a new housing edition on the northwest side of town that was only being developed before, I'd left. I'd been away, "at school", is what we told my cousins Jamie and Jason. They were very young, and didn't need to know their *Uncle Jimmy*, as they called me, was a highly troubled youth with a proclivity for mayhem and general wrongdoing.

Although I loved my aunt, uncle, cousins, and grandparents very much, I was chomping at the bit to get away and visit with my friends, Arley and David. To see and be seen. To find out what had been happening in the big town of Guymon, Oklahoma, USA, in my absence. And, of course, see Rhonda, since she had been the only girl writing me lately. Cheryl had won a little Vespa scooter in a raffle at the fair, and said she didn't mind if I used it to get around town. Just another thing for David to clown me over when he saw it. The thought of him and Lisa laughing and teasing me made me smile to myself, and I headed in their direction.

Sure enough, when I pulled down his gravel drive, David came running out hooting and hollering about it. "I spotted you all the way from Main Street on that chick magnet. The bad-ass escaped convict, riding across the country on his iron horse." He cracked up laughing at his own half-drunk humor. As soon as I set the scooter on its kickstand, however, David was grabbing me in a bear hug, "Sorry you got caught little brother. It's all over town that Tina put the cops on you."

"Yeah. I figured."

Lisa, looking as lovely as ever, was on the front porch leaning against the trailer's door frame, smoking a cigarette, and smiling at us.

"Lisa," David said, "show Jimmy your boobs. It will make him feel better."

"Hi Lisa. I see you still haven't got this fool under control. I'll just settle for a beer, if you don't mind."

"Sure, let me get you one." She gave me a hug when I stepped up on the small metal-framed porch. "I'm sorry I haven't written in a while. I'm working at a diner now, and it wears me out."

"That's alright, Rhonda Redmond has been writing the last two or three months. Between her and my grandmother they've kept me in touch."

We went inside. After popping the cap off a bottle of Bud, I told them what had been going on in my world since, months earlier, I'd taken off from the cops out their front door. David said we should load up, drive to Helena, and beat the shit out of Walter, Lieutenant Carver, and the whole bunch who had a hand, or foot, in stomping me. However, when I got to the part about Mrs. Fullerton being murdered, he agreed their little community didn't need any more troubles right then.

"Besides," I said, "I am pretty sure that would be a parole violation." David laughed, snorting beer out of his nose at that. "Anyway," I went on, "Karma has a way of evening things out. I'm sure Walter and that little crew will get theirs eventually."

David and Lisa, both, almost spit their beer out when I told them about the gay park ranger hitting on me on the bus.

"Fucking fag. You should have smoked that dude, anyway," David said. He changed his tune after I gave him the two hits of acid, I'd gotten for him from the guy. Then it was, "Well...maybe he wasn't *all bad*." He popped the tiny purple pills in his mouth and, seductively, wiggled his eyebrows.

Lisa slapped him on the shoulder. "You, wouldn't!" she huffed at him. We all got a good laugh out of that.

I dropped my hits and decided to split before they took effect and added to the beer buzz I'd been milking all day. It was getting dark and I didn't want Cheryl to worry that I was going to screw up my first night out. Not to mention, being pulled over for wobbling around on a Vespa would be more humiliation than I could bear.

Taking the long way—actually the opposite way—I rode over to the southside to cruise by Rhonda's parent's house. As luck would have it Rhonda's older brother, Bryan, who everybody called Red, because, you guessed it, he had red hair, was screwing around in the garage.

"Hey Jimmy, nice ride. You got out I see." He stood up from a lawn mower that had the rope-pull housing off of it with a grin on his freckled-face, and wiped his hands on a shop rag. "Rhonda will be happy to see you. Says you guys are going together now, huh?"

I shrugged. That was news to me, but I could do a lot worse. Rhonda was a year younger than me, semi-flat-chested, and tomboyish in a drinking, fighting kind of way. She had long, sandy-brown hair that framed an extremely pretty face, along with a set of legs and an ass filling her jeans that you could put on the cover of a magazine. The best thing about her, though, was she was real and down to earth, and despite the times we'd gotten together to beat the stuffing out of a mattress she was more than just a piece of tail, she was a friend. The only thing that held me back from staking claim to her as a serious relationship before, was Tina. "Can you go get her?"

"What are you going to do, whisk her away on your road hog, there?" he chided, pointing at the Vespa.

"How about you just get her before I punch you in the face," I said, not entirely kidding.

"Alright, alright," he held his hands up in surrender, and laughed. "That place didn't do anything for your sense of humor, I see."

He was halfway up the steps to their back door when Rhonda came out. "Your boyfriend is here." He pointed his thumb over his shoulder at me.

"Jimmy!" she squealed. Shooting past him, Rhonda jumped off the last step into my arms and wrapped her legs around my waist. Then she planted a passionate kiss right on my mouth.

Guess we are "going together", I thought.

She smiled at the scooter. "Is that what you're ridin'?"

"Yeah. My aunt won it in a raffle."

"I love it. Give me a ride."

And that—is when I fell in love with her. Or, maybe it was the acid.

We tooled around, talking and laughing, for about twenty minutes before I told her I had to head home and spend some time with my aunt. We made plans to sneak out later so we could catch up on other things we'd been missing out on while I was gone. The acid was kicking in and it was time to go.

Colorful star-bursts were shooting off the street lights as I passed them, and tracers were stretching from light-post to light-post by the time I got back to Jim and Cheryl's. I parked the Vespa inside the wooden stockade fence that surrounded their backyard, and went in.

My little cousins were already in bed and my uncle had some business meeting out of town. So it was just me and Cheryl, and of course, the little caterpillar from *Alice in Wonderland* sitting on the corner lamp, smoking a hookah.

My aunt and I were close back then. Well, sort of. Although we rarely ever just sat and talked and laughed like we did that first night back. She played a cassette tape my uncle made while he and Cheryl, and the boys, were driving through downtown Oklahoma City. Jim riding in the back with Jamie and Jason, giving a humorous play by play of the people they saw out the windows.

"...we're here in the urban jungle watching the common double-breasted, button-downed, businessman in his natural habitat. Oh, look! See how he flaunts himself, puffing up like a peacock when he spots the female of the species having lunch at an open-air diner. Observe, how he preens himself in the reflection of a shop window—chest out, shoulders back—hoping to attract the female's eye..."

The tape went on and on and got funnier and funnier. And, it wasn't just the acid, either, I mean—the pipe smoking caterpillar on the lamp was even rolling in laughter.

We had rarely enjoyed each other's company so much. She hugged me before I went to bed, and said, "I know you don't like living with *anyone* like this, but I hope you give it a chance. Good things can happen for you, if you will just let them. You are not a bad kid. You only need an opportunity to *be* a kid." Remembering this story makes me really wish I hadn't stolen their Jeep a few weeks later.

After Cheryl went to bed, I snuck out, as promised; pushed the little scooter through the side gate and went to pick up Rhonda waiting in the alley between her house and the skating rink. I was actually happy that my buzz had worn off a little by then as we traveled back roads out to Sunset Lake. Sunset is a small lake as lakes go. It lays in a sheltered valley that makes up Sunset Park just down the slope from the fairgrounds. The lake and park comes complete with wild ducks, paddle boats, and a miniature train that runs on a track three-quarters the way around the lake, and back.

There were a few secluded spots where a couple could find some privacy if they knew where to look. I had a favorite. We followed a path over a little wooden bridge, and up a knoll through a small grove of trees and evergreen bushes. At the top, completely surrounded by a waist-high wall, and overgrown with shrubs was a concrete pad with a small obelisk erected in its center. The embossed plaque embedded in it said something about the founder of the park, but what exactly, I can not remember. The road below wound down and around this little wooded oasis.

Rhonda laid a blanket out she'd brought from her house. We kicked back and listened to the crickets and watched the stars. It was a beautiful night. I could smell the algae in the lake, and the musky bouquet of the trees and bushes around me. Until that moment, I didn't realize how much I had missed the smell of the fresh outdoors. There was, also, a faint hint of burnt pyrotechnics left over from the 4th of July festivities the week before.

Rhonda rolled on her side facing me, flicked a grasshopper off of my shoulder and pressed her hand against my chest. "So. Are you done with Tina?" she asked.

Rhonda had the most amazing eyes. Bluish-green. Although, it wasn't the color that made them special; it was the shape, and the no-nonsense way she looked through them. We were both mature beyond our years, in some ways at least, and it showed in the windows to our souls.

"Yeah, I'm done. What about you, and the whole marriage thing?"

Rhonda told me that she'd finally given up on me, and Chris, his name was, was a way out of her parents' house and on her own. She'd thought, anyway. But it turned bad quickly. Chris, first tried plying her with alcohol to control her, when that didn't work he beat her. Rhonda said she hated the man and vowed to someday make him pay for his abuse.

"Not if I get him first," I said before pulling her to me and kissing her long and deep.

Soon we were rolling around shedding our clothes. Rhonda couldn't get her jeans off, so she stood up to peel them down. I caught my breath, the shape of her smooth ass and bare thighs were stunning in the moonlight.

"What?" she asked.

"Nothing. You're just beautiful," I said.

She smiled and slid down on top of me. I rolled her black lace panties over the silky half-moons of her buttocks, then slapped her bottom hard enough to leave a handprint. She bit me on the neck. I pulled her head back by the hair and locked my mouth onto hers. She couldn't get me inside her fast enough. The next ten minutes went by in a blur of desperate, aggressive, raw sex. We rocked and wrestled each other to climax under the stars, to sounds of the babbling brook down below. The second round was more subdued, gentle, and sweet, but no less passionate. Rhonda was a pistol, and game for anything.

Afterward, we were laying naked, her head resting on the arm I had under her neck. She shifted to look at me. "So what are you going to do now? Are you going to live with your aunt and uncle?"

"I'm supposed to. School, also. Cheryl says my uncle has it worked out where I can skip a year and a half, and start a sophomore. The coach wants me to play football for them. Seems like a good deal. But...I don't know..."

"Wow. You'll go from *Rebel Without a Cause*, to *All American Teenager*, huh?" she poked me with her finger and smiled.

"Yeah, well that's the idea, but it's a lot of pressure. I'm not a 'normal' kid anymore. It's hard to fall back into a *Leave it to Beaver* family structure. After all I've been through, it will be like trying to scoop soapsuds back into an over-flowing washing machine. I want it to work, but..."

The sound of a car engine stopped me in mid-sentence. It was traveling slowly on the paved loop that circled our wooded hideaway. Then a spotlight showed across the bushes we were behind. Cops. There was no way they knew we were there; this was just one of those places that attract kids, winos, and late night revelers. We laid still, waiting them out.

The cruiser stopped rolling. Then the engine shut off, and car doors opened and shut. They were going to come all the way up! Panicked now, we jumped into motion and scrambled for our clothes. We were so frantic that I tried putting on one of Rhonda's socks. I gave up on them and stuck all four of our socks and Rhonda's panties in my pocket. It was hard not to laugh out loud. As it was, we were both giggling while we hopped from foot to foot trying to get our pants on.

The officers below made noise as they searched the bushes. They were working their way up the south path. As quickly and quietly as I could, I rolled the scooter down through the copse's north side path. Once we were to the asphalt, I ran pushing the light-weight bike as far up the winding road as my legs would let me before starting it. For the first time I was happy that I was driving a quiet little Vespa. It purred to life, rather than roaring into the world like any other motorcycle would have. Rhonda jumped on behind me and we busted out laughing as we puttered up the hill to the fairgrounds, like a couple of real desperados.

"Do you want me to take you home?" I asked Rhonda over my shoulder.

She wrapped her legs around my waist from behind, and her arms around my chest. She had one shoe on, half-laced; the other hanging over her shoulder by the strings. "Can't I stay with you?"

Rubbing her bare foot with one of my hands, I guided the scooter north with the other. It was a much safer trip to Cheryl's than it would be to ride all the way across to the southside in the middle of the night, anyway.

Walking beside Rhonda, I pushed the Vespa the last half block, tucked it back inside the fence, then lifted Rhonda through the window into my new room. I climbed in after her and shut out the night.

After moving a dresser in front of the bedroom door so no one could surprise us, we stripped back down and climbed into the big comfortable bed. My aunt kept it piled with pillows and blankets. I reached over her and shoved a Led Zeppelin tape into my eight-track player.

"This is n-n-n-n-ice," she said, as I slid into her for the third time that night. *Whole Lotta Love* coming over the stereo speakers.

Sunlight was shining through the east facing window when I opened my eyes, and someone was trying to open my bedroom door. *Oh shit! It's morning!*

It was my grandmother. "Jimmy. Wake-up. Something is blocking the door." She had the door open about three inches and was trying to look in. I threw the comforter over Rhonda's prone nude body. She was small at five-four, and one-ten. She literally disappeared into the pile of covers. "I'm coming Mema, give me a minute to get dressed."

"Well why is this dresser in front of the door, anyway?" she asked, frustrated as she pushed on it again.

"I don't know grandma. I'll be out in a second."

"Okay, I guess. But come join us, it's time for breakfast." She closed the door all the way and walked off.

"What do I do?" Rhonda was up. "Where are my panties?" she whispered.

Digging through my pants pockets I tossed her her panties and socks. The clock by the bed said: 7:15.

"Just get dressed and go out the window, then come around to the front door. Tell them you heard I was out and wanted to see me. They will let you in and we'll have breakfast." I smiled real big, trying to reassure her.

"They are never going to buy that." Still, she was throwing on her clothes as fast as she could.

"I am almost sure my grams even saw you. But, I'm bettin' they will roll with it anyway. Besides, I'm hungry aren't you?"

She giggled and kissed me going out the window.

As I was moving the dresser, I heard Rhonda knock. My aunt answered. They talked. A few seconds later Rhonda appeared in my bedroom door, my grandmother standing behind her with her eyebrow cocked like Dewayne Johnson.

"Mema, you said it was time for breakfast? Do you think Cheryl would mind if Rhonda eats, with us?"

Rhonda leant up on her toes and kissed me. "Your aunt asked me if I wanted to join y'all when she let me in."

My grandmother just smiled her knowing humor-driven smile, and shook her head. "I don't know how Cheryl and Jim think this is ever going to work, but I am glad you are here. Please try to stay out of trouble. For me. I love you and want you to be alright."

"I'll try." I gave her a hug and a kiss on the cheek. "I love you, too, Mema."

The judge ordered me to pay my court costs and restitution. I did that at the city police station. The first time I went in to pay I found an extremely attractive, well-built blonde working behind the front desk.

"Damn you're pretty. What's your name?" I asked when I handed her thirty dollars. A partial payment, but all I had. Well...all I could spare at the time, and still party later. "You look good in that uniform. Probably even better out of it." I gave her my most charming grin.

"Have you been drinking? Cause only someone half drunk would use such a corny line. Especially, in a police station."

"It is true, I have been drinking, and it is true it was a corny line, and it is also true that I think you are gorgeous." I wobbled a little bit when I said it.

She laughed. "You're *good*, boy. I'll give you that. And, cute. So when are you going to bring in the rest of the money you owe this month?"

"To see you, I will make a special effort."

"Oh yeah?" She smiled. "Well, I work Sunday through Thursday." With a wink, she said, "Now get out of here before someone sees you, and wants to breathalize you."

I sauntered out of the precinct house feeling pretty good about my chances of, some day, seeing her out of that uniform. She was definitely open to flirting, and by the third payment, I knew her name was Cassie Demayo; she was twenty-one and working to become a dispatcher. She liked to party on the weekends, and wasn't opposed to, maybe, running into me sometime, "out of uniform".

She was half-lit herself when I ran into her at Walmart. Tipsy enough to come right up and kiss me. She whispered her address in my ear. "Come over after I get rid of my friends, and you just might get to see me the way you've been wanting to."

It was almost midnight when I showed up at her apartment that night. She was confident I was coming and had put her uniform *back on* for me, just so she could turn around and take it back off, while I watched. I was right, as good as she looked in it, she looked even better out of it. Cassie was very sexual and taught me a few things about female anatomy that I didn't already know. It was dawn before I rolled out of there trying to get back home before Jim and Cheryl woke up.

I felt a little guilty for stepping out on Rhonda, but we hadn't been together that long and I had some time to make up for. Besides, Tina had really done a number on my belief in true love and monogamy; at that time in my life, anyway. You can only be kicked in the nuts so many times before becoming insensitive to the whole idea. I always thought it was a shame that I hadn't given my heart to Rhonda first. The succeeding years may have played out differently if I had. Right or wrong, this was just a fling that was completely on the down-low. Not only because I was still a minor, but because it wouldn't do for Guymon's hottest city cop to be caught sleeping with its most incorrigible bad boy. So as far as I was concerned, no one would ever know.

My relationship with Cassie was beneficial in other ways as well. She let me know there were a couple of officers who did not like me, and were laying in the cut to get me revoked. In retrospect, I wonder now if it wasn't my suspected relationship with her that inspired their enmity.

Regardless, I was already feeling trapped and out of place, and what Cassie told me just added to it. Cheryl and Jim knew I was not conforming well. In an effort to bond and get me away from town and the pressures of parole, Jim and Cheryl took me on a trip to their time-share, in Angel Fire, New Mexico.

Angel Fire's raison d'etre was its ski slopes. It was a regular winter wonderland, complete with ski resort; lifts; lodges; and all that goes with a snow capped mountain. However, it was a summer vacation spot as well. My grandparents had been taking Cheryl and my mom there since they were kids. Uncle Jim's parents had taken him, also. Hence, their strong attachment to it after they were married.

I broke my leg coming down one of Angel Fire's slopes the year I lived in Guymon. I found the cast buried in my grandmother's attic a few years ago. Signatures from my third-grade classmates still scrawled across it.

Even though at that elevation, the mountain's down hill season begins early in the fall and lasts deep into spring, its summer months are just as stunning. The whole Rocky Mountain chain that extends down into the northern part of New Mexico is beautiful, and the valleys, peaks, and canyons are flush at that time with green pine and fir trees and decorated with streams and lakes that sparkle in the summer sun like diamonds in the Queen of England's crown. It is incredible.

Jim and Cheryl's time-share was no more than a fancy apartment in an apartment complex. Albeit, they were very nice apartments plushed-out in a half dozen two- and three-story buildings. The complex, its condos, lodges, restaurants, and hotels, all hugged the side of the mountain at differing heights among the trees. The whole mecca was finished wood-grains and plank porches. Even the parking spaces were curbed with sawed-off log posts. The main part of the complex had several buildings placed around a quarter acre central park, that was studded with big pines, barbecue grills, and picnic tables.

We went up in the heart of the summer. Just in time to catch Angel Fire hosting a co-ed softball tournament. So...all the other condos around us were filled with college age female softball players. Which brought in every stray pussy hound within a hundred miles.

Me, Cheryl, and Jim watched a full day of games. They took place in a series of ball fields set in the bowl of a high valley between two gorgeous mountain peaks. The beer was flowing freely among the spectators, so I had a warm glow by dinner. Jim and Cheryl knew I had been drinking, but figured I was safe up in the mountains.

They, however, hadn't counted on the assholes who showed up to the keg party the winners of the tournament threw that night. The park out front of Jim and Cheryl's cozy little place filled with drunken revelers, as soon as the games ended, and the sun settled behind the peaks.

It was a come one come all party and I soon found myself drinking, laughing, and flirting with the girls like everyone else. No goal in mind, it wasn't as if I could take a girl back to *my place*, or even go to theirs. They were packed into those fancy condos like hot-dog buns, still in the package. Not to mention, the coaches and other forms of chaperons, infiltrating their ranks. I was just having fun.

That is, until some townie waltzed up starting shit with me. His mistake was to think I was just some kid he could hip-bump out of the way so he could take over the conversation I was having with a very pretty blonde from California, like I was no more than an afterthought.

Bam!

One punch, and I knocked his stupid ass out. When his friends ran over like they were mad about it—feeling under attack, I started jacking up anyone who got within reach.

I am not sure what happened after that, my uncle told me he had to knock me out, himself, to get me back in the house. I'm not sure about that, but when I came to my senses, I was in the apartment struggling with him to get back out the front door.

Apparently, the townie I had laid out was awake and yelling at my aunt and uncle to let me come back and fight. He and his crew were surrounding our end of the building. I may not have won every fight I have ever been in, but I have *always* answered the call. So I was literally fighting my uncle to get out the door.

My uncle was a big man, and he was someone I loved, and I was not willing to hit, or hurt him, so he was effectively blocking me from rejoining the party. When I heard my aunt scream, "Jimmy! They are trying to come in the back!" Forgetting that my uncle's name is also Jimmy and not realizing she was yelling for him, I ran to the rescue. The riotous crowd of townies had come around and were taunting Cheryl through the sliding glass entrance to their bedroom balcony.

I went crazy.

I shot through the bedroom door, leaving my uncle in the front foyer. My aunt was laying in bed her covers pulled up and pointing at the balcony. I bounded right across the top of her bed and out the glass slider before my uncle could stop me.

The guy who had started it all was throwing rocks at the windows and running his mouth. Up on the railing I went. The place was built on a rising incline. Our balcony was five or six feet above the neighboring parking lot, where a crowd had gathered around my nemesis. Without even thinking about it I dove off the banister and tackled the townie sack of shit. We rolled around punching and gouging each other like something out of a Johnny Cash song. A couple minutes into it he finally got me in a headlock, and we came to a momentary stand still. The guys friends declared the fight over and called for it to be broken up. My uncle, however, stepped in and told them all, to keep their hands off of us. He was determined we fight until we could not fight, anymore. He allowed that he was not going to battle with me, or them, all night because either I or their friend didn't think that we were done.

My uncle told me later, that no sooner than he said that than I slipped the hold I was in and slammed the guy to the ground where I began beating his head against one of the sawed-off log posts that bordered in the parking lot. At that point—for the townies safety and to keep me out of jail, he agreed to break it up.

Jim later admitted he was proud of me—though he made it clear it was not for getting drunk and fighting—but, proud of me for my stamina and not quitting until the job was done. However, he and my aunt were more disappointed than anything, and I could tell they were beginning to have doubts about whether they would be successful in adapting me into a normal teenage lifestyle.

I couldn't blame them, I was sneaking out almost every night, and they knew it. Came home one time to find a bucket of water under my window. Stepped right in it climbing over the sill. "Ugh. What the hell?" I cursed out loud. When I saw what they had done I had to laugh and marked it up as one for the good guys. It was just the kind of thing my aunt and uncle would do, never saying a word about it. Like I said hearts of gold.

On the surface, things were good. I was working Uncle Jim's ranch, and driving their Jeep Cherokee, or their Ford farm truck. I was working-out at the high school gym getting ready for football and school. My problem was, when things were, too good, I always seem to blow it. There should be a twelve-step program for fuck ups, like there is for alcoholics. "Hi. I'm Jimmy, and I am a habitual bad decision maker..." The more shit I had going on the more sure I was to foul it up, and the more isolated I felt. This was not the world I was used to, and I didn't belong or deserve a wholesome and easy existence. I was not good enough to fit into the all-American mold. My stepparents had told me so numerous times. And honestly, average kids, even ones older than me—especially ones older than me—resented my rebellious and jaded attitude toward the world. Perceiving it, I guess, as arrogance. Maybe it was. The only thing I can say for sure about my state of mind at the time, was that I was angry deep down in my soul, and my trust extended about three feet. Within arm's reach. I took lessons not only from *my life*, but others who I had known that toughed it out through some truly tragic circumstances, and grew a prickly hedge of thorns around myself that few could penetrate.

Rhonda understood me. She was a lot like me. She didn't relate with other kids our age, any more than I did. And was almost as quick with her fists. While I'd been in the mountains with Jim and Cheryl, Rhonda sought out and beat up her older brothers ex-girlfriend. Some senior preppy that had smeared her brother's name after they'd broken up.

Rhonda hadn't necessarily had a *rough life* or anything, she hadn't been abused that I knew of and her parents were if anything, too kicked-back, except when it concerned me. They owned a small bar a stones throw from David and Lisa's trailer. She started having trouble after her grandmother died. They had been very close. Rhonda's grams for whatever reason had been the stabilizing factor which held her on course. Without her she rebelled. Against life in general. Drinking and running wild. Her parents didn't stop her.

Then she met me.

Rhonda's mom was not my biggest fan, and really didn't want her seeing me. Somehow, I caught the blame for Rhonda dropping out of school at fourteen. Although she was having trouble fitting in with her classmates long before I entered the picture.

I was fifteen myself at the time, fresh from the streets of El Paso. Tina and I hadn't really made our thing official yet. Although, we'd lived together off and on for a couple of months. We were off at that moment, and I had a small one-bedroom trailer on the edge of town. Rhonda came home with me from the skating rink and spent the night. No sex. Not for lack of trying on my part, but her mother had told her never to give it up on the first date. You have to respect that. I did. The next morning, I rode her to school on a little Honda 250 I had.

Rhonda's mother showed up angry. She humiliated and embarrassed her daughter in front of the whole school. Rhonda walked out of class, called me to come pick her up, and never went back.

That night, with no prompting from me, she stood in front of the easy chair I was reclining in and stripped completely to the nude, then climbed on top and rode me like I was a wild bronc. For a girl so young she had specific tastes. It was as if she wanted to let all her anger and frustration towards her parents, school, and the loss of her grandmother out between the sheets. I don't know if she was like that with other boys. She told me she felt a freedom with me that allowed her to let it all go. Like we were kindred spirits, both fighting to breathe in a suffocating world. I don't know what was going on inside her mind, other than what she told me, but our internal hardships drew us together as friends, as much as lovers.

However, I was still spellbound with Tina and when she came back into the picture I pulled back from Rhonda. We had a couple other momentary trysts between then and when she started writing me at Helena, but Tina always came between us. Although now that I had finally sandblasted Tina out of my heart and mind, I was realizing how much depth I had missed in Rhonda.

Rhonda and I went to a concert out at the fairgrounds, local bands, mostly. While we were there the preppy girl Rhonda had beat up over Bryan and a couple of her friends caught Rhonda in the bathroom sitting on the commode and jumped her. She got piss and toilet water all over her. Embarrassed and angry she tried to leave without even telling me what happened. I got the gist of it and could not walk away without making it right, but Rhonda wouldn't wait and stormed off into the night. Going home to her parents' house, she'd said.

Rhonda stayed at her mom and dad's, mad and humiliated, for two days. Until I finally drove over there and pulled the farm truck into her folk's front yard and revved the engine until she came out.

Later that night Rhonda and I were laying on a blanket in our tree shrouded hide-a-way at Sunset Park. We listened to the unseen stream below burbling over stones and fallen logs. It was a hot and humid night, and the smell of the lake water was mucky. I followed a bead of sweat down Rhonda's collar bone with my finger. She was laying on her back.

"The stars seem so much brighter when we are out here, than when I look at them in town. You ever notice that, Jimmy?"

"Huh? Yeah. Cause its darker out here." I flipped on my back with a sigh.

"You're not going to make it are you?" she asked.

"No."

"Why? What do you want to do?"

"There are a lot of reasons, why, most of them you already know. But the latest problem is that shit we got into at the concert. I have not had a chance to tell you, but after the girls jumped you and you went home. I went back inside. One of Tina's little sister's, Suzy, told me she saw what happened to you. She searched the place until she found the girls and pointed them out to me. I flipped their table over and beat up two of their boyfriends. It turned into a big deal. There were only a couple handfuls of hoods there to back me, and we had them jocks and preps fired up. They held them off long enough for me to get the job done. But, I guess one of those kids went to the hospital.

"The cops didn't catch me. But they were told who I was and I have reason to believe that they are going to try and revoke my parole."

"I'm sorry I didn't stay. I had piss all over my pants. The punk ass bitches ran in on me right while I was taking a leak. I was so fucking mad I couldn't even think straight. I love you Jimmy, what ever you do I am with you."

"That's just it. I don't know *what* to do."

Rhonda laid her head in the hollow of my armpit and snuggled close. "To bad we can't leave and go live somewhere else."

"Maybe that is the answer. We could take my uncle's Jeep. It's waiting to be picked up from the mechanic's shop right now. I've still got the keys. After we got set up somewhere I could drop it in a place the cops would find it and hopefully return it to him."

"Where are we going to go?"

I smiled at her. It seemed the decision was already made. "We won't know that, until we get there, baby boo."

The next night when I snuck out, I was well aware my aunt and uncle could be watching. And this time I had a backpack full of clothes and other essentials with me. It was obvious that I was leaving. I didn't want to have a confrontation with them. They had been nothing but good to me...and they wouldn't understand. Hell, I didn't understand. "Hi. My name is Jimmy and I am a teenage fuck-up and alcoholic..." They deserved a better nephew. I wanted to be a better nephew, son, grandson, brother, cousin, boyfriend...it was almost as if the people I loved the most I pulled away from the hardest. Sigmund Freud would say: "Youst art twully a mess boy."

Anyway, out the window I went. It was another hot night and I was sweating by the time I had hauled Cheryl's scooter and my heavy laden pack the half-block I felt it necessary to go before starting it. I had taken the Jeep to the mechanic's a few days before to get the starter fixed. It was waiting to be picked up. I rode the Vespa down back streets and pulled in behind where the Jeep was parked. I left the scooter on its kick-stand right next to it. Climbed in the Cherokee and drove off.

Rhonda was waiting for me in the alley, bag in hand. When she opened the door the dome light came on and I could see excitement dancing in her bright eyes.

"I almost had to fight my mom!" she said climbing in. "She saw my bag and knew I was leaving with you. We'd better go."

"She won't call the law, will she?"

"No, she wouldn't do something like that. Besides, if she did I would never speak to her again. But if she's mad enough she might try and shoot us...well you anyway." She laughed and kissed my cheek.

We pulled out of the alley. "So, she would shoot *me*, but yet she let you marry Chris what's his name? I still don't understand that."

"I think she married me off to him to keep me away from *you*." She poked me in the ribs when she said it. "Not really. I was just getting wild, and she thought being married would settle me down." I shook my head and turned onto Highway 54, taking the nearest straight shot out of town.

Even though I didn't feel good about abandoning Jim and Cheryl, or about taking their Jeep, as soon as we hit the highway the chains that were weighing me down seemed to fall away. I felt truly free for the first time since I'd gotten out of Helena.

"So where are we going?" Rhonda lit a cigarette and looked at me.
"I don't know."
A shadow of doubt flickered through her eyes.
"Well the Jeep is big enough to sleep us in the back. It's enclosed, I have a little money, and I can wa-hoo gas until we figure it out."

"Okay but if we are always driving, we are bound to get pulled over eventually."

I'd been winging it for so long that I often ran blindly into the future without giving it a second thought. In this case, I was so determined to get away before being arrested that I hadn't planned past just, going. The story of my life.

There was a turn off coming up. It was a country road which cut across the river and connected with Highway 67, going to Boise City. I took it.

"You're right, baby. We'll go to Gene and Julie's. They are some friends that I have up in Tribune, Kansas. I don't know why I didn't think of it before, it's about a hundred and fifty miles north of here. They will put us up until we figure out what to do next."

Rhonda smiled at that and scooted over next to me. She found some Meatloaf on the radio, and we drove through the night *By the Dashboard Lights.*

CHAPTER 15

TRIBUNE

Tribune, Kansas, was less than half the size of Guymon. Too small to hide in if the people looking for you knew you were there, which at the moment, no one in the world did. After Rhonda and I pulled over into a cattle pasture to have sex and get a couple hours of sleep in the back of the Jeep, we pulled into Tribune around noon. I'd been there a few times with Gene, before he moved back, but never for long enough to check out the landscape. However, it was still hot, dry, and flat just like I remembered it.

Gene's mom was the only person I knew to ask where him and Julie were now living. The little old lady, who looked like Clint Eastwood's mother in *Every Which Way But Loose*, didn't know his address, or even the street.

"Well. You go down Main. Then turn at Martha's, go past where the old church used to be. Then turn left, no right..."

Her unorthodox directions left me more confused than before I'd asked. She did tell me, however, that Julie would be at the old folks' home, where she worked.

At least the retirement center was easy to locate. To say Julie was surprised to see me come walking up the sterile, antiseptic hallway that smelled like toenails, mothballs, and Aspercream would be an understatement. She tossed her two-foot-long, brown, ponytail back over her shoulder, which was her trademark move, and smiled real big.

"Jimmy flippin Maxwell, what the hell are you doing here?" She came and gave me a hug. She was the pretty girl-next-door type, short and slim, and filled out her white nursing uniform nicely. "I thought my eyes were lying to me! Someone said you were in prison, or juvy, or what-the-fuck-ever."

"Well I was, but now I'm not. Although, I am kind'a on the run."

She looked over my shoulder. "Who is this? You're not with Tina anymore?"

"This is Rhonda. Rhonda, Julie," I said introducing them.

After a quick sizing-up, Julie seemed to approve, and nodded to Rhonda. It didn't seem like *anyone* was a big fan of Tina. Turning her attention back to me, she said: "Gene is at work. He gets home around five. I get off at two." She gave me her keys and directions to their house.

This time I found it with no problem.

"From Main, turn west on 4th, go three blocks and turn left on Maple. It's the only white house with blue trim on the whole street."

Simple.

Their place was a quaint little one-bedroom with a big sycamore tree and a couple of evergreens in the yard. Bordered with a light-blue picket fence that could have used a coat of paint. We let ourselves in and waited.

Julie came home around two-thirty with a bag of groceries and a twelve pack of beer. By the time Gene got home at five-thirty we had already polished it off and had a warm buzz building.

"Who's fucking Jeep is that in front of the house..." He was in the middle of his tirade when he saw me through the kitchen door. He ran his fingers back through his shoulder length, dirty-dishwater colored hair. "Jimmy! Oh man, what are you doing here? When did you get out?"

Gene was tall and lanky and about six or seven years older than me. He walked with a long gait and was quick with his fists. Unfortunately, he often used them on his wife. I intervened on more than one occasion to talk him down from taking his frustrations out on Julie. He and Julie had moved back to Tribune while I'd been gone. We were close, almost as close as David and me. Him and his family of six brothers and seven sisters were originally from Kentucky. Half of them moved to Kansas, also, and lived in or around town. They were proud hillbillies. The ones I new were hard fighters, heavy drinkers, and loyal friends, if not a little thrown off.

The next day Gene, Julie, and several of their family members threw us a party. When partying is all you have to do in a place that small it doesn't take much to get everyone around involved. We drank, cooked on the grill, and when it got dark somehow the festivities moved to the high school gymnasium. Don't ask me how, all I know is I looked up and we were on the free-throw line having beer poured down our throats, with a funnel and a hose, to the chant of: "Chug it...Chug it...Chug it."

Somewhere along the way, Gene's middle sister, Lyda, walked up. She was pretty, in an eighties Jamie Lee Curtis kind of way. "Hi," she said.

"Hi, yourself." In the spirit of the moment, I swooped her up and kissed her. Someone huffed, and I looked over to see her old man stomping off. I hadn't meant anything by it, I was just *drunk kissin'*. Oh, well.

I met Bubba Luke and Conway. They were two of Gene's brothers. "I'm the youngest and best lookin' of the bunch," Bubba Luke said. He smiled flashing a chipped front tooth. Bubba was tall and lanky like Gene and wore his hair shaggy and sticking out around his ball cap like Beetle Bailey in the Sunday funny papers.

"The hell you say," Conway cut in. He was bald, with a little beard hanging off his chin like a goat with no mustache. He was thicker built than his brother and had a gut on him that he could sit his beer can on. "Just like good Kentucky bourbon, it takes a little age to make you smooth and stout."

Bubba Luke leaned in and whispered, "He's full of shit, that's why we call him, *Hogwash*." He thought that was pretty funny and laughed his ass off.

They spent a little time telling me about their lives back in Kentucky. How they used to be racing partners on some dirt or mud track event that was a big deal back home, and how much they missed it. "Not much going on around here," Conway finished up.

"So," Bubba rubbed his chin whiskers, which he kept short and rakish. "Gene says you're gonna get rid of that Jeep you got sittin' in the garage. You gonna sell it?"

"No. It's my uncle's. I'm going to take the plates off it and leave it outside the county line, so they will tow it to a different town, in a different jurisdiction. They will eventually figure out who it belongs to and hopefully return it to him."

"You think it's reported stolen, then?"

"Of course. My uncle's insurance wouldn't pay for it if it wasn't. I took it, knowing that ahead of time. That's why I'm not driving it now."

We hung out and partied for several days, until Gene's job was in jeopardy. Lyda started staying over. Said her and her old man were fighting. I gave her and Rhonda the fold-out couch while I made a pallet on the floor. Second night she was there, I woke up with her straddling me and exploring my mouth with her tongue.

I pushed her back when I realized it wasn't my girlfriend on my chest. "What the hell! Where is Rhonda?"

"She's asleep. Shut up and fuck me." She reached down my pants to find me already hard. "I've been wanting this since you kissed me in the gym."

I looked up at the fold-out bed, there was no movement and no sounds coming from there. Lyda was pretty and her body was smooth and lithe. I was worked-up before I was even awake. Before I could think what I was doing I was kissing her back. She worked her way down and took me in her mouth.

"Stop." She looked up. "Not here," I said. "I can't do that to Rhonda."

Lyda stood up, grabbed my hand and a blanket, and quietly pulled me and the cover off the floor. I followed her out through the kitchen door into the backyard.

Twenty minutes later I rolled off of her, spent. We laid in the moonlight with nothing but the sounds of crickets and the occasional throaty rumble of a distant engine. I closed my eyes, *What did I just do?* I looked at the living room window on the side of the house. *Did that curtain move, or was it my guilty conscience seeing things?*

Lyda broke into my thoughts. "What are we going to do about Rhonda?"

"What do you mean?" I stared at her. "I'm not going to do anything—and neither are you. You wanted to fuck. We fucked. But Rhonda is my girl."

"Oh.... You fucking bastard. I left my old man for you!" she said raising her voice.

"Seriously? Why would you do that over a kiss?" I sat up grabbing my pants.

"I can't believe you would string me along like this! Do you think I am some kind of plaything to be used and then discarded?!" Now she was shouting, and stomping around the yard in her panties and shirt.

She kicked the trash can over. Yelling and cursing me for a dog, getting more furious by the second.

Not having a clue *what* to say, I jumped up dumbfounded and speechless. I'd never seen a girl flip the script so dramatically before. I was real tempted, however, to knock the weird bitch out.

The living room light came on right before Gene, Julie, and Rhonda appeared in the kitchen door. Just in time to all watch Lyda storming off down the alley, carrying her shoes and dragging her pants behind her. Rhonda was looking at me standing on the blanket in nothing but my unbuttoned jeans. Her face crumpled, then she turned away from me and went back in the house.

Rhonda wouldn't talk to me, and I didn't try to make her. I wanted to justify my actions, tell her it was not my fault. I wanted to tell her I was a good guy, and that I stood up for her. But that shit sounded lame to me even as it rang through my brain.

Later I asked Gene why his sister acted that way. "Aww she's just crazy," he said. "Although, I never seen her act *like that* before. At least she's got good pussy, though, don't she?"

"Yeah, but how the hell you know?"

"Oh hell, me, Conway, and Bubba Luke used to fuck her all the time back when we were teenagers."

No wonder she's friggin' psycho, I thought.

Two days later Julie approached me. She pushed her long dark hair out of her face, one of the rare moments she didn't have it in a ponytail, before telling me that Rhonda was planning on hitchhiking home to Guymon. She had tried talking her out of it. Told her that Lyda was a whore and probably did exactly what I had said she did. Julie told Rhonda that she was sure I never meant to hurt her, but Rhonda wouldn't listen. I didn't want her hitchhiking, so I asked Julie to drive her. Julie was making plans to make the trip after lunch, however, when it was time to go, Rhonda was nowhere to be found. She had taken off on her own; I was sure not wanting to put Julie out.

I got extremely drunk. One of those 'paint the town red', bloody knuckles the next morning to prove it, but don't remember anything type drunks. I was a piece of shit, and all the alcohol in the world wouldn't wash off the stink.

The next morning, I woke up wrapped in the sheets on the fold-out couch to the sound of Julie doing dishes in the kitchen (Gene long gone to work). I needed to piss—bad. Before rolling out of bed I realized my pants were missing. And, considering I hadn't worn boxers since leaving Guymon and a regular washing machine, I was bare ass naked. I looked around the bed searching for my pants. They were nowhere to be found. My urge to pee growing by the second.

"What are you doing?" Julie asked from the kitchen door. She had heard me moving around.

"I am looking for my pants. My shirt is also missing. I can't get up without 'em, if you know what I mean?"

She chuckled. "I guess you got pretty drunk last night, huh?"

She had left early—driving all the way to the next town looking for

Rhonda. She was as concerned about her hitching as I was—and was gone before I went to the bar. Her and Gene were asleep by the time I got back. I guess they were, anyway.

"Yeah, a little bit. Honestly, I can't remember."

"Well your pants can't be far. It's not like you could have left the bar without them," she said grinning.

"Would you stop clowning me and help find them before I piss myself."

She laughed, threw her ponytail over her shoulder and started looking for them in earnest. I'd already searched under the couch, but we both looked again. She checked behind the chairs and made a pass through the bathroom——no pants. Finally, she headed off out the front door. Suddenly she was laughing so hard and loud she was screeching.

"Found your pants Jimmy!" She came in carrying my jeans, red-faced and still laughing. "I would just like to know, how *the hell* your pants got in our tree!?"

"What? In the tree?" I said totally clueless.

"Yep. Hanging from the bottom limb like you went outside took your clothes off and threw them in the air. The shirt was on the fence." Julie shook her head, still chuckling. "I love your crazy ass Jimmy, but you might have a drinking problem." She handed me my clothes and then gave me a kiss on the cheek before heading back into the kitchen. I could hear her talking to herself. "Ha. In the tree! I can't wait to tell Gene. In the tree…"

I never lost my pants again, but I stayed drunk for a week after Rhonda left.

———————————

Rhonda liked Julie, and knew if she let her Julie would insist on driving her all the way back to Guymon. There was no reason for Julie to go so far out of her way. Rhonda was fine with hitching and confident she wouldn't have any trouble getting rides. *God damn Jimmy! I can't believe he fucked that bitch, Lyda.* She ground her teeth at the thought. More than that she was frustrated because everyone knew about it. *I love Jimmy, but if I don't break him from treating me badly now, I may as well get ready for a lifetime of abuse.* So... she had to leave. *The more abrupt and final, the better,* she thought, *maybe it will snap some sense into the cheating bastard.* She took her little bag of clothes, slipped out of the house, and hoofed it down the alley.

At its widest point it was only a mile and a half hike all the way across Tribune. Soon she was on the highway heading south. She was nervous, and chewed on her nails as she walked, hoping for a ride before Julie, or Gene came looking for her. She knew Jimmy wouldn't come, he'd given up trying to plead his case after the first day. The sad thing is, she believed him. Lyda was a crazy bitch, she was definitely the aggressor (Julie even said so), but, "*She caught me off guard.*" Or the best one, "*I stuck up for you.*" Paaalease, how lame is that? Any way you slice it, she was hurt, and embarrassed. Jimmy wasn't only her boyfriend, he was supposed to be her friend, too. She'd thought so anyway. She was getting herself worked up again and started sobbing.

Rhonda was walking and crying and mulling her thoughts over when a lady in a blue, Dodge Dart, pulled over.

"Hey girly—chew—what 'cha doing—smack—out here?" The lady smacked and chewed her gum between every few words. "Don't you know—chew—it could be dangerous out here for a young girl?"

Rhonda leaned in the passenger door and saw a round faced woman in her mid-forties, with dark hair blow-dried into a fluffy, brown halo around her head. "Yeah," she said, "but I got to get home to Guymon. And I'm not stayin here one more day." Rhonda still had tears in her eyes.

"Well girlfriend—smack—you just get in this car. I'm not going all the way to Guymon, but—chew—I can drop you—smack—at my turn-off for Boise City." She threw her handbag that was in the passenger seat, in the back. "Come on. Have some gum and dry your eyes. Tell June, that's my name—smack—all about it." She patted the passenger seat. "It's about a boy, isn't it?"

Rhonda got in, wiped her eyes, and over the next ninety miles regaled June with the whole tragic, Jimmy and Rhonda, runaway, love story. June nodded, and tsk, tsked, while Rhonda talked. She cried with Rhonda, and she laughed with Rhonda, and she cursed all boys for the worthless pussy hounds that they were with Rhonda.

Rhonda had made a friend by the time they reached June's turn off. June hugged her and gave her number and some more gum. "If you are ever in Boise City—chew—look me up. You can bring your beau over and I will give him—chew—a good talking to, for you. You are a good girl—smack—stand up for yourself and take care."

Her next ride was a two-toned, tan and brown Monte Carlo, driven by a fat middle aged man. He had a dozen or so long dark hairs, which he combed over the top of his otherwise bald dome. It was five o'clock in the evening and they were ten miles out of Guymon when he pulled over into a rest area.

Rhonda was smoking a cigarette and looking out her window, thinking about how she was going to handle her parents when she got home now that her arrival was imminent. She snapped back to the moment. "What are you doing?"

The fat man had put the car in Park, and was sitting with his hands in his lap, staring at her with a glazed look in his eyes. Her alarm bells were going off even before he moved his hands and exposed her to his pink, pudgy, four-inch dick, that he had covertly worked out of his fly. It was hard. He glanced down and shook it at her with his forefinger and thumb, which made it look even smaller. "I did you a favor. Now you do me a favor."

At first, she was in total shock, then fear took over. When he looked back up at her, Rhonda punched him in the face with her left fist and ground her cigarette out on his child-sized penis with her right. The guy's head barely jarred from the punch, but his reaction to being burned was explosive. He bellowed like a castrated bull and grabbed his junk.

Rhonda took the opportunity to jerk the door handle and kick it open. She was following the swing of the door into the parking lot when the pervert caught her by the hair.

"You little bitch! I was just going to make you touch it. Now, I am going to make you suck it." He growled and grunted as he struggled with her. Rhonda's feet kicked up dust in the parking area as they scrambled for purchase. "What do you think, you can get out here and take rides for free?" He jerked her by the hair and managed to drag her back into the car.

He pushed her face into his lap. She scratched at his eyes with her left hand. She could feel his little grub worm on her cheek, it was slick like he was already cumming. Gritting through her teeth she snarled, "If you put that nasty thing in my mouth, I will bite it off!"

He hesitated, as if that thought had never occurred to him before, and his grip weakened. At that moment she sunk her thumb, with a chewed and broken nail, into his right eye. He screamed and let go of her. While he grabbed his face, she was backing out of the car. "Why'd you hurt me? I wasn't going to hurt you," he whined.

A four-door king-cab pickup pulled into the rest area The guy could see several men in the truck, panicked he threw his car in Drive and peeled out of the gravel lot holding his hand over his injured eye. The passenger door banged around and finally slammed itself shut when he swung back onto the road.

"Fuck you asshole!" Rhonda screamed after him, extending her middle finger in the air.

She was shaking and scrubbing at her face with both hands and the sleeve of her t-shirt when the pickup pulled up beside her. She stepped back when she saw four men inside. Then she saw the "Sam's Well Service - Guymon, Oklahoma" sign on its passenger door and relaxed...a little bit. At least she didn't run. Although, her feet wanted to. She remembered that Jimmy used to work for Sam's. She held her ground.

The passenger rolled his window down letting out the smell of paraffin, grease, and marijuana. "What the hell is going on, here?" The passenger said. "Why are you crying?"

She wasn't sure what to say. She was having trust issues at the moment. Finally, she said, "That fucking pig tried to force himself on me. Said I owed him for giving me a ride to Guymon."

"Is that so? Well, get in and we'll see if we can catch this guy. Maybe he would like to force himself on us." Rhonda wasn't sure what to do, she was looking at a big man in his late twenties, two-eighty if he was a pound; dark headed, round faced, with a scar running down his right cheek. The other men in the truck, also, looked strong and formidable. She knew if they turned on her too, there was no way she could fight them off like she did the fat guy.

The big man could see she was hesitant. "Really, it's okay. My name is Norman Blades. They call me Stormin Norman. These three yahoos are Eric Finley"——the driver nodded, and Norman pointed with his thumb over his shoulder into the backseat——"Jeffery Townley, better known as J Rock; and Ryan Freeburg, who we call Lucky Charms, because he looks like a Leprechaun." She could tell he was trying to make her smile and put her at ease. "We are from Guymon, too. We'll take you right home. No charge," he added with a wink.

"Do any of you know my boyfriend, Jimmy Maxwell? He used to work for Sam's."

The other three shook their heads, but Norman nodded. "Yeah, young guy. Got fired for beating up a derrick hand at the shop. For messing with his girlfriend, if I remember right. You're not her, are you?"

"No. Different girl, same guy."

"Didn't really know him, but what I did I liked. The derrick hand was a piece of shit, anyway. So where is Jimmy?"

"I'll tell you about it on our way to Guymon."

Norman got out and let her squeeze in between him and Eric. "E, let's see if we can catch up to that Monte Carlo," Norman told the driver. Then he looked at Rhonda and asked her to tell them what happened.

The guys in the back whooped and hollered when she got to the part where she burned the perv's little Vienna sausage with her cigarette, but they were all mad enough to kill the man and leave him in the bar-ditch with a rod-wrench up his ass when she told them about him forcing her face into his lap.

When she finished the story, Norman looked her in the eye. "I am proud of you, little girl. E, speed this truck up. That cock sucker can't be that far ahead of us."

J Rock and Freeburg, both reached up and patted Rhonda on the shoulder lending their support to Norman's intentions.

Sadly, they pulled into town without ever spotting the prick. All five of them were very disappointed.

Norman asked if she would be comfortable making a pit stop at Shelly Woods's house before they took her home. It was on the way, he said. He allowed he needed to pick up some speed for work the next day.

"Shelly Woods. I know Shelly, sort of, I haven't seen her in a while."

With that they pulled off the highway and drove down by the municipal swimming pool, where Shelly had a small, square, blue and white, two-bedroom house. Shelly was the town drug connection, she sold meth and marijuana. Though she has been a model citizen since then.

Shelly was standing on her porch when they pulled into her driveway. Her shoulder-length blonde hair was blowing in her face from the summer breeze that was gusting through the little valley her street was built in. Shelly was in her mid-twenties, short, pretty, and cocky as game rooster. She had to be to maintain her business. Although, she was not a woman alone. Louis Muller was her daughter, Jennifer's, father, and his buddies were Norman, and Gary Dale Bledsoe. The town's triple threat bad boy bikers.

When Norman finished telling Shelly Rhonda's story, she asked her, "What were you doing out there hitchhiking, anyway?"

That's when Rhonda told her about stealing the Jeep, leaving town, catching her boyfriend fucking some slut, etc., until she'd brought the whole tale around to where Norman had picked her up.

"Jimmy Maxwell? I know Jimmy. Didn't he used to be with that tramp Tina Jarvis?"

Rhonda nodded.

"Got yourself a handful with that kid, I'll tell ya." Shelly, grinned, and winked at Rhonda. "You know as soon as you go home the cops are going to be all over you trying to find out where Jimmy is at. They might even try to hold you accountable for something. You can hang here for a couple days and get your head prepared for it, if you want."

Rhonda took her up on her offer. Nevertheless, when she finally went home three days later, she was not at all prepared for what was thrown at her. The powers that be did not charge her with anything, but *everyone* wanted to know where Jimmy was.

I was still soaking my sorrows a week later when Bubba Luke and Conway asked me if they could borrow the Jeep to make a whiskey run. Greeley County was a dry county so to get any strong liquor you either had to know a bootlegger or go to a county that was not dry.

"A little whiskey would be nice," I said, "but there ain't no tag on the Jeep. If a cop sees you the chase will be on, and if you are caught you guys could get charged with stealing it in the first place."

Bubba scratched his head. "I'd be willin' to take the chance. We're just goin' to a moonshiner we know who lives about five miles out of town. Back roads all the way. Be there and back faster than Lyda can break up a relationship."

"That is damn fast, for sure, but it seems like you would want a legit ride if you were doing something illegal; like haulin' bootleg whiskey," I pointed out.

"He's right Bubba Luke." Conway thought for a minute, then said, "What if we pulled the tag off old blue. My broken down Chevy at the house. We could put it on the Jeep long enough to get out to Joker's and back."

"That will probably work," I agreed. Conway smiled like Thomas Edison must have when he finally got the light bulb right. "Just be careful, wouldn't want y'all to end up in jail."

Three hours later Bubba Luke and Conway came stumbling through the door. Conway had a Tampax taped to his head, and his arm in a homemade sling. Bubba was limping.

"What happened?" Gene exclaimed, jumping up to check out their injuries. "Y'all look like you been run over. And you smell like you been swimming in rotgut alcohol."

"You're pretty close. The cops got after us, and we had a wreck!" Bubba walked over to me. "I'm sorry Jimmy, but we totaled that Jeep."

"Why did the police get after you in the first place?" I was eyeing him. I knew what he was going to say when he wouldn't hold my gaze.

He puffed on his cigarette and looked over to Conway for a lifeline. But Conway looked at the ground. Both of these guys were years older than me, Conway over a decade, however they acted like they were having to come clean to their father about burning down the barn or something. It was almost funny.

"You didn't have the tag on it did you?" I finally asked.

"No," Bubba admitted. "We smoked a doobie before we left, of that shit my buddy Bill grows in his closet. Remember, you and I smoked some the other day?"

I nodded. "It was good shit. Couldn't get off the couch for hours."

"Yeah," Conway jumped in, "we got lost leaving town. No shit!"

"Pipe down, Hogwash, I'm fuckin' this chicken."

"Well," I said, "get to fuckin' it then and tell us what happened!" I liked these guys they were down to earth and funny, but I had intended for the Jeep to be found in another town, in another county. Not, the little-bitty one I was hiding out in.

"Okay, we were so high we forgot to go by and get Hogwash's tag. Didn't think about it until we were at Joker's place loading up the whiskey. Five gallons of damn fine spirits I might add. Me and Conway split most of a Mason jar."

"Lit the curly hairs on my testicles, it did," the older brother interjected.

"An-y-way"—Bubba gave Conway the *Get out of my story look,* again— "we had burned up most of the gas. We knew you planned on drivin' yer wheels over to Sharon Springs to drop it off. Which was a good idea, by the way…"

I held my hands palms open. "Quit stalling. What happened?"

Bubba looked sheepish. "We pulled in to put a couple dollars into the gas tank for ya, and just like you said, a cop drove by, and saw weren't no tag. When we saw him hit his brake lights we shot out of the station like a pro-mod from the starting line and tried get a jump on him down Main.

"We hit Highway 27 aimin' to get up into Wallace County at least away from here. But they was on us man. Pretty quick there were two of 'em flashin' their red and blues makin' me dizzy.

"Hogwash was tryin' to climb in the back and throw the whiskey out when I swung onto Dixon Road. It's not paved, and I thought I could lose them in the dust."

"Plus we got friends out that way," Conway said, bouncing around in his seat, excited just by the retelling.

"Yeah, but we never made it that far. Hogwash was flopping around in the back and distracted me. Instead of makin' the turn onto Dixon Bridge I slid off the embankment and rolled the Jeep down the ravine into the creek."

Conway gingerly touched the Tampax bandage on his head. "It fucked us up pretty bad. And, busted open the bucket of whiskey we had. It splashed all over the place, and us."

Bubba picked the story back up, "We had to kick the windshield out of the frame cause the roof caved in, jammin' the doors.

"The cops showed up about the time we were crawlin' over the hood. They was yellin' and shinin' their flashlights down at us. My heart was thunderin' in my chest like a stampeding herd of wild horses. Just knew we were fixn'ta get caught. Lucky it took'em a minute to get down the gully. By then we was splashin' up the creek."

"I lost my god danged boot in the mud, too," Conway griped.

Bubba wiped his hand across his forehead. "We made it though. It took us two hours of hidin' and creepin' to get back to ma's so we could patch ourselves up enough to come tell you about it." Gene handed Bubba a beer. He popped the top and took a long drink, then said, "but that's not the worst of it."

"How the hell could it be much worse?" I asked, "Short of you two being in jail or dead."

"When we was walkin' back over here we saw the wrecker unhookin' the Jeep in front of Bryson's Garage. I imagine that's where they will go over it for prints and run its numbers. We started to set it on fire but thought we had better tell you about it first."

"Fuck me a'runnin'!" Gene cursed his favorite curse. "You guys are some real fuck-ups! What's Jimmy supposed to do now. This town is too small for him to hide in if they know he's here." Gene looked at me and shook his bend. "I'm sorry little brother."

"Well," I said, "what's done is done, at least y'all are still walking." I killed my beer and crushed the can. "Let's go look at the fucking thing. If it's as trashed as you say it is I may as well let you burn it too. It will get rid of the whiskey, your prints—if they even do that here—and hopefully it will take a little longer for the cops to find out where the Jeep came from."

"Well, it won't matter if Rhonda tells them where you are," Conway said.

I shook my head. "She might be mad at me, but she would never tell on me, or anyone."

Julie stayed at the house while the three brothers and me piled into Gene's Nova and took a cruise down Main Street. There were no red-brick pavers here. No covered sidewalks, or even any stoplights. The whole street wasn't a mile long from highway to highway. Nevertheless, right there under a sign that said: Bryson's Auto Repair and Salvage, was the golden brown mashed tin can of my uncle's windowless Jeep.

There was no need to look at it twice. It was totaled. I shook my head. "Burn it."

They got out and Gene and me drove to the end of the block and around the corner. Bubba Luke and Hogwash gathered some big pieces of cardboard and a few chunks of wood from a nearby alley. They jammed it all in through the shattered windows. Then took some discarded grease rags and other trash they found to light it, and dancing like wild Indians around a wagon train threw the flaming refuse onto the pyre.

The fire started slowly in several areas, then the remnants of the whiskey must have caught. The flames seemed to spread suddenly, filling the interior. Soon the whole Jeep was engulfed, flames were pouring out from all the windows and coming together in an inferno over its roof reaching with orange and yellow fingers tickling the underbelly of the dark heavens above.

As it burned, I turned away. Not for the first time, I thought that Jim and Cheryl deserved a better nephew. And, Rhonda, deserved a better boyfriend, too. I didn't think I was bad. I didn't want to be bad. But...I guess, I was.

We drove off to the sound of approaching sirens.

I took a job the next day after Bubba and Conway torched the Jeep, with a guy and his son who traveled around the neighboring states; Nebraska, Oklahoma, and Colorado erecting Star Buildings. They were big iron and sheet-metal barns and arenas that farmers and ranchers use to store their heavy equipment and train their horses, amongst other things. It worked for me. They covered my meals and motel bills and paid in cash at the end of the week. Plus, they drank almost as much as I did. There were girls, booze, and brawling in every town. By the time the law got onto me for fucking something, or someone up we would be moving on.

Inevitably, me and the son got into it over some sexy blonde, named Karin, up in Nebraska. I quit and stayed with her for a few days before hitchhiking back to Tribune.

Julie had left Gene. He'd hit her, one too many times it seemed. He'd moved back into his mom's house. I stayed the night, fucked Lyda again—how crazy is that—then hitched my way back to Guymon the next day.

CHAPTER 16

JOY RIDE

The trucker I caught a ride from dropped me off at fourteenth and Main. He was turning left to hop over to fifty-four wanting to catch some ZZZs at the truck stop. The hiss of airbrakes and the smell of burnt diesel permeated the cab as Hank, he'd told me his name was, came to a stop by the curb. It was a big, cozy, Peterbuilt with a comfortable wood-grained interior. A little yellow rubber duck hung from the dash, and C.W. McCall played on the tape deck. Hank had been friendly enough and brought me the last ninety miles of my trip from Tribune.

"Thanks for the ride, Hank." I shook his hand.

"No problem, son. You stay out of trouble."

"You got it man. You too."

When I jumped down and shut his door the cool morning air caressed my skin. The smell of fresh cut grass, exhaust, and tree sap, and the sounds of birds chirping at the early morning traffic filled my senses. Hank pulled off shooting twin streams of black smoke into the sky from the standing pipes behind his cab. I smiled. I was home again.

My grandmother's was only a few blocks away. She worried about me, so I hoofed it to her house to let her know I was okay. And maybe get a feel of just how disappointed everyone was with me.

I was a little apprehensive walking across my grandparents' green, well maintained, (exposed) lawn. I'd been gone almost two months; no one was staking out my Mema waiting to nab me, if and when, I eventually showed up. However, being in a state of constant apprehension is one of the by-products of stealing cars and breaking parole.

As I knew she would be, my grandmother was happy and relieved to see me. She gave me the 411. Apparently, my uncle declined to press charges over the Jeep, but the insurance company on the other hand was out for blood. Also, when Rhonda came back the cops and her parents both tried to pry where I was out of her, but she refused to give me up. They even incorporated Cassie the dispatcher, who called Rhonda out of some sense of guilt and admitted her affair with me— sure that the pressure of sleeping with an "older woman" had been too much—and that Rhonda should tell her where I was so she could talk to me. My grandma said Uncle Jim was on the other line when this went down. P-a-lease. What pressure are we talking about other than the cops breathing down my neck. I was a sixteen year old rebellious delinquent just out to get laid. Oh...but thanks for telling my girlfriend—who was already mad at me—that I had cheated on her, again. Cops, go figure.

From there I went and checked on Arley Larson. A gorgeous slim-built blonde let me in. I walked down to Arley's room passing his little sister, who waved at me, and a couple other small children playing in the living room.

"Damn Jimmy, it's good to see you!" Arley's enthusiasm at seeing me always lifted my spirits. "Been worried the fuzz was going to get you." He went on to tell me that David and Lisa had moved to Liberal, Kansas, while I was gone, and that Robert had gotten out of Helena.

I was pretty bummed about David and Lisa, until he told me that Dave was planning on driving down when I got back so he could tell me where they ended up. On the other hand, I was overjoyed about Robert.

"Yeah, Robert has been asking about you," Arley went on, "He's not even on parole no more. Done turned eighteen. Free and clear, he says." Arley looked over my shoulder as the blonde girl came down the steps carrying three bottles of breakfast Budweiser with her.

"This is Joyce, my cousin." He stopped while she handed us our beers. I looked at my watch, it was 9:30, *My kind of girl*, I thought. "Joyce and her husband split up so she and the kids are staying with us for now. Joyce this is Jimmy Maxwell."

She flipped her blonde bangs out of her face and looked up at me. "You're the guy Arley helped out of the handcuffs, aren't you?" Her green eyes seemed to glow from the inside, but it was the saucy way the corners of her mouth lifted in a fleeting 'come and get me' smirk, that made me want to take her for a test drive.

I nodded.

"You can call me Joy, if you'd like."

With my most rakish smile plastered across my face, I said, "I was arrested one time for joy riding. For you I would be willing to commit a second offense."

She laughed at my stupid line.

Joyce was a hottie for sure, but she was a decade older than me, was still embroiled in exiting the relationship with her ex, and had three kids. A little much for my circumstances. So after another beer and a little more conversation I wrapped up my visit with them. Putting Joy out of my mind, I went in search of Robert.

He was at his parents' house. When he saw me he broke out in a humongous grin and shouted: "Damn brother I was afraid you were going back to the slammer before we ever got to hang out and get drunk!"

I was happy to see him too. Prisons, jails, reform schools, war, those things bond people together in a way normal circumstance can't. Sometimes for better, and sometimes for worse. We gave each other a bear hug then went up into the attic to his room. He lit a joint and gave me a beer and we spent a couple hours catching each other up on what had happened in our lives during the months since we had parted back in Helena.

They moved Cecil Drake in with him after Cecil got out of the Dodge House where he told him all about what had happened to him on his escape. I had known he must have went through some hell to wind up back at the gate tore up the way he was.

Apparently, the powers that be didn't let go of as many kids as was first thought they would. Robert, however, still made it a month before he turned eighteen, just missing mine and Rhonda's exodus by a week.

We smoked another joint and drank a few more beers, from there we proceeded to get shit-faced drunk. Stephanie and Michele, a couple of promiscuous sisters who could have been twins, we referred to them as twins, except one was naturally blonde and the other brunette (we checked), kidnapped us somewhere in the kaleidoscope of my drunken memories. Since we were all in the same bed, it was only a matter of getting up and switching girls to make it a two-for. Yee-Haw, Slam, Pow.

Robert was already working on a rig, within a week I was working in the oil-field again myself. With our first checks we rented one side of a duplex a block off Main Street. The living room was big and stretched across the whole front of the house. The one bedroom it had wasn't bad either. And like we'd done back in our cell in Camaro, we bisected the room with the dresser and mirror into two halves, a side for each of us.

The house was right across the street from a Methodist church, and to its right was the parking lot behind Guymon's only five-story apartment building. The irony was you could look across the parking lot and see the car lot on the other side of the alley where my odyssey with the law in Guymon began. We were just a half block from the convenience store where I'd been caught.

Since Robert hadn't had a chance to properly celebrate his birthday, and mine was only a couple weeks away, we threw a party, to the chagrin of the church across the street.

Half the town showed up, at least the undesirable half. The Hood lot was in our front yard that night. I sent word to Rhonda through one of the "twin" sisters and asked her to come. But she didn't.

"Damn it looks like a salvage out here," Robert commented when he saw the cars and trucks parked all over our front yard. "Oh well, it's all dirt anyway."

Smiling like it was the most beautiful sight ever, I said, "Ain't it great?"

The party was a blast. The music was blaring, people were drunk. Arley showed up with his cousin. "What's a party without a little Joy in it," I said. She laughed and punched my shoulder. I grabbed her and kissed her....

Joyce was next to me when I woke up the next day. Some unknown female body was curled up with Robert in his bed. He had his head thrown back snoring with his mouth open. I thought about dropping a sock in it but decided to have mercy on him. Picking my way through the living room was like running tires in football practice; people were crashed out everywhere. I made it to the kitchen, where I found the open half can of beer I'd left in the crisper of the refrigerator. Flat, stale beer was my hangover cure.

From the kitchen I surveyed the remnants of our birthday party and smiled. Not only were there passed out and sleeping people filling most of the floor space, but they were also draped over every piece of furniture. I killed my beer and felt better.

Somehow, or another, our little piece of party heaven was invaded. Joyce moved in—along with her three kids. Don't get me wrong her kids were awesome—two girls and a boy—the little tow-headed brats. They liked me and I liked them. But they put a real wrinkle in party central. Joy liked to drink, but now the house was supposed to be a home. Everybody had to go. What was even worse, she wanted me to act like a parent and discipline the kids. "Not good."

"Alright kids, your mother wants me to ground you while she is at work. I want each of you to sit in a different chair." When I had them separated across the living room from each other, in my sternest no nonsense voice, I said, "Now me and Robert are going to walk to the store for some smokes. Don't move! Not a muscle! I mean it! If y'all have been good and minded me, when I get back you'll be ungrounded."

Robert and I went out and watched them through the window. They laughed with glee as they dared each other to run around the living room and back to their places like a scary version of musical chairs.

Robert elbowed me in the ribs. "Damn Jimmy, are you sure those aren't *your* kids? They act just like you."

I laughed. "Come on."

We stomped our way up the steps. Low and behold, the kids were exactly where I'd left them.

"Did you move?" I asked.

"No...no..." they all answered. Pure innocence and smiles.

"You wouldn't lie to me would you?"

"No... no..." Not a shred of guilt among them.

I shook my head. "Well then...go play."

Needless to say, Joyce didn't like my parenting style. But I would be damned if I would ever be like my stepdad. She was starting to get on my nerves with all of that, "You need to be stricter," shit.

The next time the boy, Dillon, got into trouble—him and his friend held Rufus, Arley's parents' cat, up to their fish aquarium while Rufus pawed little fishes out onto the floor where he promptly ate them—Joyce wanted me to whip him with my belt. I took Dillon in the bathroom and locked her out.

"You'd better scream like I'm peeling the hide off you," I said, then commenced to slapping the walls, the toilet, and the sink with my folded metal studded belt.

You would have thought I was killing him the way he howled.

"Make your eyes red and leave crying. And don't rat me out."

"I won't," he said with a smile, right before he broke out in a crying fit that could have won him an Oscar had he been an actor.

That was the end of her harping on me to discipline the kids, and probably when I decided that her and I were not going to work out.

When I told Robert my feelings about my domestic lifestyle issues he sighed with relief. "About time," was all he had to say before he headed off to work the evening tower.

Joyce went ballistic when I told her a couple days later that she needed to move out. She screamed at me about how juvenile I was, and how I didn't know anything...it went on...and on.

I held my hands up. "You are the one chasing your lost youth by playing house with a buck-wild sixteen year old in the first place."

"Aaaagggh! You said you were turning eighteen!" She growled between gritted teeth. Her arms straight down by her sides, fists balled so tight her knuckles were white. Her eyes flicked to a beer bottle on the nightstand...

I ducked as it flew over my head and stuck in the plaster wall behind me.

Laughing I said, "Ooooh, must have struck a nerve."

Next came makeup bottles, an ashtray, and I don't know what else because as deftly as a professional dodge-ball player, I ducked out the door.

Dillon was sitting on the front porch steps. He had his elbows on his knees and his face cupped in his hands. I'd forgotten he was there. His little sisters were at Arley's folks' place.

"Does this mean we have to leave?" He looked up at me. "Me and my sisters like it here with you."

My heart almost broke. I sat down beside him. "I like you and your sisters, too, Dillon. But, this isn't a good house for you to live in. More often than not there are people you don't even know sleeping on the living room floor." I ruffled his short, shaggy blond hair. "Besides, your mom wants me to be something I'm not. Or at least, not ready for yet. Let's face it I'm not a good dad.

"But you aaaare," he said, dragging the word out in a pout. "Almost as good as my real dad."

"Well thanks. But you only think that because I let you do whatever you want. That might make a pretty good friend; but I am realizing, not much of a father figure. Hey, we'll always be friends, okay?" I held my hand out to shake his, "Pals?"

"Pals," he said, then he wrapped his arms around my neck and hugged me. This was hard. I was just another squeeze and a tear away from changing my mind and making up with Joyce, when she came out the door with two big bags in her hands—snapping for Dillon to follow her. *It's for the best*, I thought.

For the first time I realized that my age limited me. I didn't want to be that grown up. Not just yet.

Joyce tried to run me over that night in her ex's Lincoln Continental. I was coming out of the convenience store with a sixer of beer and a pack of Marlboros, when she came screeching up in that big hunk of metal. Her brother, Jimmy Brock, was sitting in the passenger seat. Joyce had been drinking and was yelling at me—calling me everything but a white man. With my middle finger extended in the air, I started to walk past. When she blocked me in and bumped my hip with the passenger side fender, I got pissed.

"What the fuck are you doing, you crazy bitch!?"

"You can't just walk away from me like this!"

"Watch me."

She did her teeth gritting thing again and jerked the car into Reverse, hitting the gas and spinning the wheel to the left. Effectively swinging the front of the car into me and knocking my sack of beer bottles out of my hand. I latched onto the passenger window to keep from being dragged under the wheels. When her brother tried to push me off, I jerked my body halfway through the window and started beating him in the face with my free fist.

Joyce slammed on the brakes so she could turn in her seat and try to get me off her brother. She pummeled me with her fists. However, as soon as I got my feet back under me I let him have it with both guns right through the open window. He laid over on the seat and she tried to crawl on top of him to protect him.

She was catching a lot of abuse herself so she gave up and threw the car in Reverse again. This time she backed halfway across the parking lot. She sat there staring at me through the windshield, revving her engine. *What the hell did I get myself into with her?* I'd just figured out where the saying: *Hell hath no fury like a woman scorned,* came from. I was having some bad luck with girls lately. I heard her shift gears.

When she hit the gas pedal I snatched one of the unbroken bottles from the ripped, wet paper-sack laying on the ground. The bottle hit the windshield right before the car hit me, exploding directly in front of the steering wheel into jagged shards of brown beer-bottle glass and foam. The windshield spider-webbed into a million little crystal-sized pieces.

From the impact of the car I rolled over the long gold-colored hood, gouging my side on the ornament sticking up from the grille. Joyce took off down the street with me hanging onto the wiper-blades. She tried slinging me off by spinning doughnuts at the cross-street intersection, but I held on as if my life depended on it. She gave up and roared back into the store's parking lot, with me taking every opportunity I had to cave the windshield in even further with my forearm and elbow. By the time we got back to the store it was sagging in its frame only held together by its plastic safety fiber.

She found herself blocked in and had to stop to reverse out. When she did, I pulled myself around to the driver side so fast a stunt man would have been proud.

I slapped her, hard; reached across her while she was sitting back stunned with an outraged look on her face; turned the engine off and took the car keys. "You crazy cunt," I growled, then turned and threw her keys into the Jock lot across the street.

Afterward, I limped to my bag and plucked my soggy pack of smokes out of it. Several bottles were broken. I was toeing through the foam and cardboard looking for—hoping for—another undamaged bottle, when someone yelled, "Look out Jimmy!" just in time to see Joyce's brother swinging a three-foot-long steel pipe at me.

I rolled away from the swing and heard the air whistle as it skimmed by an inch from my head.

He swung again, and again I evaded it. I crouched facing him, all my senses running at peak efficiency. This was even more dangerous and intense than the battle with the Lincoln. I was alive and watching this loser swing in slow motion. It seemed as if I could anticipate his every move—he was going in for the kill, a total horizontal head shot. I ducked under it and stepped into him, locking the pipe and his elbow into the extended stretch of their arc.

I had him.

His back was pressed against my chest and I had a hand on each end of the piece of steel now. He was trapped between me and the pipe. I tried to pry it from his grip. As soon as I got it out of his hands I was going to beat his head mushy with it. I was there, in that dead zone. No other thoughts. Kill or be killed.

Brock tried to throw his head back into my face. I caught his ear with my teeth and bit the back edge of it off. It felt strange to spit out a piece of someone's flesh.

He screamed, and the blood flowed. And I roared like a crazed beast.

Arley came out of nowhere and started trying to wrestle the pipe away from both of us. He was right in the way when I took Jimmy Brock to the ground.

They let go of the length of steel for a second and I realized that Joyce's brother was rolling across the pavement trying to get away. I was up and on him.

Arley jumped in front of me. "No Jimmy. No...you will kill him with that!"

"Out of my way Arley."

Sccreeeeech!—was the sound the Lincoln made as Joyce dropped it in first gear and burned rubber out of the parking lot. Her blonde head hanging out of the driver's side window so she could see past the shattered windshield. Her brother was slumped over in the passenger seat.

Arley stopped and looked after them. Robert's sister, Angela, appeared from among the spectators; running towards me. I remember thinking how amazing it was that bitch-ass Brock hadn't been able to land that piece of steel on me, not one time. And, how fast I must of been to avoid it. I was processing these thoughts as I took

...one...two...steps and collapsed.

Angela reached me about then, all concern and worry. "Where did you come from?" I asked, then the light dimmed and the curtain dropped...and all was black.

I woke up the next morning on Angela's couch. Beat to shit. Bright sunlight was coming in through the living room window, making me squint. Stiff from my knees to my neck, I'd been sleeping sitting up leant against the arm and back rests. I might have woke up swinging, but I was so battered and sore, all I could do was groan.

There was movement in the other room Angie must have heard me moaning as I took inventory of my injuries: A huge bruise along my left ribcage that ended in a deep scratch. Several more bone deep aches across my back and shoulders that I was sure would be black and blue, too. My legs and hip-joints were banged-up, and I had a cut on my forehead. I had obviously not been the floating untouchable ninja that I'd thought I had been. I could count at least four long welts and contusions which could only have come from that damn pipe. Angie came out of her bedroom while I was trying to lay down on the couch.

"Well look at you. Back in the land of the living?" She lit a cigarette and leant against her bedroom door. She was wearing a long t-shirt that hung down to the middle of her tanned thighs. It was a nice look.

"I'll have to get back with you on the living part."

Flipping her dark shoulder-length hair out of her eyes, she went on, "It took me and Arley both to get you into the house and onto that couch. And he is pretty banged up too."

Another moan. "Why didn't you take me to my place, it was closer?"

"We'd barely got you in the car before the cops showed up. After not finding anything going on at the store they made a point to drive by yours and Robert's house *real slow*. We watched the whole thing from where we were sitting and thought you would be safer at my place. Plus," she said with a devilish smile, "I figured I might get you over here and take advantage of you. But I can see that ain't happening." She blew smoke in the air and rolled her eyes.

I laughed and groaned again when a sharp pain shot through my ribs. "Thanks, I'd probably be in jail if it wasn't for you."

"Arley too, he was trying to look out for you. I didn't realize how much I liked that boy until I saw him helping you. He thinks you are mad at him."

She stepped around the coffee table and helped me to lay down. Sticking pillows where they would help most. She handed me a couple Tylenol that I took dry and I fell back asleep before my head even hit the pillow. It was a fitful sleep, however, bouts of pain wracked through me when I moved wrong.

At noon I woke up and could move. Albeit, slowly, and stiffly, but much of the pain had subsided. With considerable care I stood and made my way to the refrigerator to retrieve a beer. I slammed it like Popeye with a can of spinach, and felt some of my strength return. Not enough to go wrestle around with Angela, but enough to walk in and wake her up.

When I stepped in it dawned on me that I had never been in Angie's house before. It was nice and clean and girly—her bedroom was more of the same.

"Here, Ang."

She looked up and smiled at the cold can of beer I was holding out to her. "Do you want to lay down with me? It is more comfortable than the couch," she asked.

"No. I mean I'd like to, but it seems the longer I am up moving around the better I feel. I don't want to get stiff again."

"And to think, that's exactly what I was hoping for." She laughed. "Just kidding. I couldn't resist. So what are you going to do now?"

"Well it seems to me that I need to find out what is going on with the cops. I don't see how Joyce, her ex, or Jimmy Brock could press charges on me. The car was beat to hell, but Joyce would have to explain how all that happened. And I'm pretty sure there are laws against running someone over then attacking them with an iron pipe. Anyway, I have to check on Arley, and let him know I'm not mad at him. Joyce is his cousin so he will probably know the answers to my questions."

When I got to Arley's his mom let me in. She frowned at my limp. "You, too? You and Arley weren't fighting each other, were you?"

"Huh? What...no...Mrs. L. What makes you think that?"

"Well, he's been beat all to hell, and it doesn't look like you are getting around much better."

"He was trying to stop a fight between me and someone else. I would never purposely hurt Arley, Mrs. L. Y'all are like family to me."

"Well, I would hope not. You had better go check on him, he's downstairs."

When I saw him, I understood why his mom was upset. He had a goose-egg under one eye and laid in bed as stiff as if he were in traction. My memories of him the night before were spotty at best. "I didn't do that to you, did I?"

"Not directly." He grimaced and adjusted himself so he could look at me. "This all happened while I was trying to get that pipe away from you and Brock. He head-butted me in the face"—he touched his eye and winced—"I caught several shots to the ribs while you were trying to wrench the thing away from him. I really didn't know how messed up I was until I got home last night."

"Yeah, I know the feeling. I didn't think I'd even been hit till I woke up. Crazy ain't it?" I looked around the room. "You gotta get your ass outta that bed, drink a beer and get back on the horse. It only gets worse the longer you lay there."

He flipped me off. "Fuck you *and the horse*, too. The beer is in the garage. Bring me a couple of them while you're at it."

Like the good friend I am, I retrieved the beer and even popped the top for him. When he'd had a good long drink, I asked him if he thought Joyce had went to the cops.

"Don't know. I doubt Joy or Jimmy Brock will, considering what *they* did, but Joyce's ex—that's another story. His car is demolished. I got the impression last night that the police had been called by a by-stander, or maybe the store. But the way they were eyeballing your place there is no telling. And really, all it would take for the cops to get after you again is just letting them know you were back in town."

"That is true. I may as well assume that they know where I live, too."

Sure enough, when I got back to the house, Robert told me the po-po had been by looking for me. He told them I didn't live there—it was his place, and as far as he knew, I was up in Kansas somewhere.

Here we go again, I thought. I'd gotten lax. I glanced over at Little Joe, a short Mexican friend of ours, who had been sleeping on our couch for the past week. He shook his head in sympathy, we all knew where this was going.

"Rhonda came by here, too," Robert said. He blew a shotgun stream of pot smoke into Tom's face, a big yellow cat that adopted us not long after we'd moved in, while Tom laid back and gently pawed at the floating tendrils of smoke.

"That cat likes to get high more than I do," I commented. I wasn't sure what to say about Rhonda coming by. "What did she say she wanted?" I finally asked, afraid to hope it was because she wanted to see me.

"She heard that you were hurt and was worried." He looked at me with a sarcastic half-smile on his face. "She was particularly interested to find out that the fight stemmed from you kicking Joyce out."

"Oh yeah?"

"Oh yeah. She said she would be back to check on you and that she'd been staying at Shelly Woods's house."

Little Joe popped off. "When Rhonda was leaving, she said, it was a good thing you ran Joy off when you did because she was about to do it if you didn't."

I shook my head my head. *Girls. I will never figure them out.*

CHAPTER 17

BUDWEISER DAZE

The cops picking up my scent definitely changed the game. They led Robert to believe that the tip they had received stating I was living at his residence was flimsy at best, but they were required to follow up on it. Regardless of what they told him the police did start cruising by our place a lot more than they previously had. So, I kept my eyes open and stayed wary.

Robert was wanting a little speed for work, I told him I would drop by Shelly Woods's and pick some up for him. Neither Robert nor I had a car at the time, so I took the few dollars he had to spend on it and started walking towards her house. I hadn't seen Shelly since buying the weed from her that I put in my toothpaste and smuggled into Helena. I wasn't necessarily going after Rhonda, however, if I should happen to run into her... I smiled to myself thinking about the possibility.

I hoofed it down Main Street until it turned into Highway 67, then cut diagonally a couple blocks where I could walk through the park and pass by the swimming pool. I've always liked the smell of chlorine, water, and suntan lotion. Of course, even though it was a nice day, this late in the year it was probably closed. Still, it was the quickest way to Shelly's on foot since she lived right across the street from it.

Shelly seemed happy to see me and flipped her shoulder-length blonde hair out of her face as she introduced me to Louis Muller, her daughter Jennifer's father, and her on and off ol' man. Louis was tall and lanky, and sandy blond himself. He was ten or twelve years older than me, had a nice chopped Harley Davidson (amongst a few other vehicles), and had a reputation around town as a drinking, fighting, wild biker. *Just my kind of people*, I thought.

"Good to meet ya," I said to him.

Shelly went on to tell Louis that I was Rhonda's boyfriend.

He shook my hand then handed me a beer. "So, you're the guy she's always talking about?"

I grunted. "Good or bad?"

"Well, she is, or was mad at you," Louis said. "Mostly for not coming to get her sooner would be my guess. She is definitely in love with you. There ain't a couple two or three hours goes by that you don't become a part of the conversation."

"She could have fooled me," I said. "I invited her to a party we threw when me and Robert first rented our place."

Shelly laughed. "You still don't know anything about girls. *You* didn't invite her. You told someone, who told someone to tell someone to invite her. I heard all about it. She was about ready to come over there and beat the shit out of that girl you had shacking up with you."

"I heard. Where is she by the way?"

"She has been floating between her parents, here, or my sister Jan's apartment across from the hospital. My guess is she's probably over there right now. But she will show up here later if you want to hang out."

"No, I've got to pick up a half-gram for Robert and hike back home."

Louis put his hand on my shoulder. "Hell, you don't have to walk. I'll give you a ride."

"Thanks, I'd appreciate it."

I concluded my business with Shelly. She gave me a peck on the cheek, and Louis and I headed out.

"I know where Jan lives if you want to swing by and see if Rhonda's there before you go home."

"Yeah, why not." I flipped my cigarette butt out the passenger window of Louis's Chevy Silverado.

When we pulled into the rear parking lot I saw a stocky man a couple inches shorter than me trotting up the back stairs. He was in his late twenties and had a prematurely receding hairline. Something was familiar about him, like he'd been described to me before. I couldn't put my finger on it. Then it hit me.

"Hey, I think that is Chris Parker. The freaking weirdo who married Rhonda while I was gone to juvy."

Louis squinted his eyes staring at him through the windshield. "Shit that guy's got to be as old as I am. What's Rhonda, fifteen, sixteen years old?"

"She was barely fourteen at the time. It didn't last. He couldn't keep her drunk enough to stay home, and when that didn't work he started beating on her. I have been waiting to run into the twisted prick for a long time. You can take off if you want to. I will completely understand."

"Hell no... I want to see this."

We bailed out of the truck, and I jogged up the stairs. When I got to the top Chris was just turning away from an unanswered knock.

"Are you looking for Jan or Rhonda?" I stopped in front of another door like I lived there. Still not a hundred percent sure he was who I thought he was. Almost hoping it wasn't, because I was going to be more than a little disappointed if Rhonda was seeing this freak again.

"Rhonda. I heard she might be staying over here these days. Been trying to get a chance to talk to her for a long time. Do you know where they might be?"

"She's a little young for you ain't she?" I stepped up to him, blocking him from the stairs. I could see in his eyes that he realized I wasn't a friendly neighbor.

"She's my wi—"

He didn't get the rest of the word out of his mouth before I dropped him in Jan's doorwell. I gunned him like I was working a heavy-bag all the way to the ground, and kept gunning him after he was down. He couldn't get away with the closed door at his back and I took advantage of it, unloading one eyebrow-splitting, nose-bone breaking blow after another. I didn't stop until my fists were busted-up and bloody from his teeth, then I stomped and kicked him until Louis finally pulled me off. Up to this point I hadn't realized how much I despised this guy.

"Come on let's get the hell out of here. You could go to jail if someone is looking out their peep-hole and calls the law."

We were just starting for the stairs when Rhonda came around the corner.

"What the hell?!" She stared at my gore-covered hands and red-spattered face.

I stared back at her like I'd just got caught drinking milk from the container.

She looked down at the bloody bald-guy beat to shit in her doorway. "What the fuck are you doing here Chris? I told you to *never* come near me again.

"I-I-I jus wan ta tauk," he mumbled through broken lips.

"There is nothing to talk about. I see you've met my boyfriend." He looked up at me and groaned, realizing that I'd played him into this trap. Rhonda turned back to me, "We have to get out of here before someone calls the police on you."

"That's what Louis said. We were leaving when you showed up."

"One second," she said, and ran over and kicked Chris right in the face. "Ain't no fun when the shoe's on the other foot, is it Chris?" Rhonda turned around and flipped her brown hair over her shoulder. "I'm ready now."

Louis was grinning as he trotted down the stairs. "I *really* like you two."

With that a lifetime friendship was born. He told Shelly, Norman, and Gary Dale (GD for short) what happened, and they adopted me and Rhonda into Guymon's little family of bikers. But, that is another book.

Rhonda and I went to my house and spent the rest of the day talking and making love. She told me about hitchhiking home from Tribune and the pervert trying to molest her on the road, and how she ended up over at Shelly's. She told me about how her parents, and the police messed with her when she got back, even about Cassie, which she didn't seem that mad about. As well as what she'd been doing since then. I told her I was sorry, and I'd never meant to hurt her. Somehow, she forgave me.

When Rhonda came back into my life, she walked in like she'd never left. The only difference was now I was determined not to hurt her again.

Bubba Luke came down from Tribune to visit us. Gene was busy working. Bubba had picked up an Oldsmobile 442 that would run like a banshee out of Hell. We'd become pretty good friends when I'd been up there, and it was good to see him—wrecking my uncles Jeep notwithstanding. Rhonda didn't seem to hold any grudges toward him, Gene, or Conway just because their sister was a "psycho slut". Rhonda's words.

Bubba was driving me, Rhonda, Robert, and Little Joe around the back streets showing off his ride, when we passed by the Motel 6 out on the southeast corner of town. It served truckers and commuters who were traveling down fifty-four or coming in off of Highway 3 from Woodward. As we drove by the back parking lot Robert pointed out a Budweiser truck pulled lengthwise through the far parking spaces. It was one of those long trucks with a rear compartment half as long as a short semi-trailer. It had five or six sliding jointed doors down the sides so the driver would have easy access to unload cases of beer at his various stops. The whole thing had the Budweiser logo stretched from one end of the truck/trailer combo to the other, super-imposed over huge pictures of cans and bottles of Bud dripping with enticing ice cold looking drops of dew running down their sides. To obsessive drinkers like us, it was a Heavenly sight, and appeared to have a divine light shining down upon it from above. Could have been a streetlight, I suppose, but...I swear I even heard a soft chorus of angels singing in the background. Okay, I'm jerking your chain now, but to a bunch of party minded teenage alcoholics the truck sitting in the middle of the parking lot unattended seemed like a genuine blessing from the beer gods to us.

"I'd like to drive that whole truck off," I said. "We'd have Budweiser for weeks, maybe even months! Not to mention how much we could sell to the bars around here."

Bubba turned into the parking lot and drove along the far side of it. The truck was pulled in parallel to the motel, twenty yards from the line of doors. As we drove past the trailer blocked us from the room's windows, however the beer truck itself was the biggest thing on the asphalt.

"It would draw too much attention to start it up and pull off with it," Bubba said. "You'd have to let the air-pressure build-up first. The brakes won't unlock until you do. But..." he raised his eyebrow at me.

"If we stayed on this side of the trailer and got one of those side doors up, we could unload it where it sat. With no one able to see us," I finished.

Bubba nodded. "Exactly."

Me, Little Joe, and. Rhonda got out, while Bubba Luke pulled the car around the corner of a building that abutted the other side of the parking lot. The night was dark with just a little chill to it. And although it was only nine o'clock and the back area was fairly well illuminated by the lot's lights, no one seemed to be around. The three of us were hidden by the trailer while we examined the sliding doors. They were rollups, but there was a locking mechanism at the bottom. Bubba Luke and Robert joined us. Bubba had his car's tire iron. I took it and jammed it under the nearest door and pried up with the cheater-bar. When it lifted enough for us to get our fingers under, Robert, Bubba, and I yanked it two feet up before it jammed. Little Joe started to work on the next slider over.

Immediately, I leaned in the half-open door and started pulling cases of beer down and handing them out to Rhonda, who headed for the car with two of them in her arms. Soon I was pulling them out and handing cases to whomever was there.

Little Joe pushed his shoulder-length black hair out of his face and cursed, "Dammit! I bent the door. It won't move."

"Hell, with it just load what I hand you. We only have so much room in the car anyway," I said.

Panicked and expecting someone to pop around the corner at any second brandishing a shotgun, or some other weapon, we stayed tense and alert. But no one came.

I was pulling out boxes of beer as fast as I could without crawling inside the trailer where I would be vulnerable if someone did come. Even though the air was cool we were all sweating. The harder it got to reach, the more beer fell and hit the ground. There was a half dozen dented and busted cans foaming around my feet. I was glad it wasn't bottles.

Robert ran up. "Bubba told me to let you know the trunk and floorboards are full. Anything else we will have to hold in our laps."

After handing three more cases to Rob, I pulled a couple down for myself and we ran around to the car where the others were waiting. Rhonda's eyes were sparkling, it was obvious that she was having fun. We drove off without any problems, never seeing a soul.

At home I pulled all the shelves except one out of the refrigerator and stacked cases of beer from the bottom to the top. The rest we unloaded in the middle of the living room, five stacks waist high.

All of us were laughing and excited that we'd gotten away with such a nice little beer run. It wasn't enough to sell and make any real money, but it would keep the party going for a while.

When the car was cleaned out Bubba suggested we drive by the motel and see what the cops were doing. From a distance of course. Me and Rhonda were game. We left Little Joe and Robert to rearrange all the cases of beer we'd carried into the house.

When we neared the motel Bubba drove down a side street not wanting to get too close. We assumed the parking lot would be awash with red and blues by now; crime-scene tape, and gold-badge detectives all investigating the big Budweiser heist. As we came in sight of the truck, however, we were surprised to see...nothing. No one was around. There was still cans laying under the trailer leaking suds into the same wet and foamy puddle that I'd left them in earlier.

"Pull back in," I told Bubba.

He glanced at me sideways, then nodded.

This time he pulled the Olds right alongside the trailer and popped the trunk. The car was blocked from the motel the same as we were earlier.

Not wasting a moment I climbed through the sprung slider and all the way inside the trailer, where I began handing boxes down two at a time to Rhonda and Bubba Luke. They loaded the trunk, the back seat, and the floorboards. When the car was packed full we drove off without so much as a fare-thee-well.

We had more beer than we knew what to do with, even minus the trunk load we sent home with Bubba.

Robert and Little Joe had already started building furniture out of the cases we'd had before we unloaded the second load. Now they got creative. They made a big coffee table, end tables, and a couple night stands for the bedroom and we still had cases stacked against the wall almost to the ceiling. If the cops were to walk into our house for any reason, we would be busted.

We drank it and sold it as fast as we could.

With Joyce gone and the duplex fully stocked, the party kicked into high gear. The crowd of people who Joy had me run off—trying to make mine and Robert's party pad into a responsible home for the kids—came pouring back in. Not only was Little Joe crashing in our living room, but now there were five or six other regulars. We'd picked up Stephanie, one of the "twins", who had somehow became Rhonda's bestie, and Bryan, Rhonda's brother—he didn't sleep there often but he seemed to always be around. Along with a constant flow of revelers and Hoods from the lot coming and going.

The place rocked pretty much 24/7. Oil rigs worked three towers around the clock so when each shift got off we would have an influx of people stopping by. Besides selling beer, Robert and I would hire out to work a shift in place of someone who wasn't feeling up to it for a crisp C-note. We made enough money to keep the lights on and not have to be on any company payroll.

With the continuous party came a constant flow of drugs through our door. For the most part Rhonda and I, even though we would partake in just about anything that came along (acid, weed, or speed) we never found anything to replace our first love of alcohol. Not at that time in our lives, anyway. Still, I turned seventeen in a chemical induced fugue.

One day we came home to find Tom, the cat, dead on the porch. He'd dragged himself up to the door after being struck by a car.

"The poor little dude, we were his family. He was a lost stray just like the rest of us," Rhonda said, wiping a tear from her eye.

I picked him up and gently wrapped him in a towel. "He was probably too high to get out of the road in time. Tom was the most laid-back cat I have ever seen."

Everybody loved Tom, he was a misfit thug like the rest of us. All were sad at his passing. There were about ten of us who attended Tom's funeral on the side of the duplex where we buried him. After, we got good and drunk and smoked a number of doobies in his honor.

By two in the morning we were all totally messed up. Someone came up with the idea to break all the animals out of the pound. A final tribute to Tom. How releasing a bunch of dogs would make Tom happy up in cat Heaven I'm not sure, but freeing living things from cages? I'm all in. The ten of us piled into the few cars and trucks available and swerved our way the half-mile out of town where the municipal dog pound was located.

It was as if the dogs—I didn't see any cats—knew we were there to liberate them. One side of the long building was lined with outside kennels. There were dogs of all breeds, jumping and barking with excitement as three or four of us would grab the bottom of the gates and bend them up, one after another. It was surprising how easily the galvanized tubing folded with all of our backs into it.

Many of the dogs ran off into the night, presumably to find their way home. Five or six ran straight for the cars and jumped in. Tongues hanging out and tails wagging. If I could read a dogs mind, I would swear one little gray schnauzer that had jumped in, and was standing in the seat with his front paws on the dash, was looking at me thinking, *Hurry up dude before the cops get here!*

A couple of the dogs went home with a girl from the rescue brigade. The rest had tags, and over the course of the next few days we found the owners. For all of them except my buddy the schnauzer. As easy as it had been for us to locate the animals' owners and return them, made me wonder why the pound people hadn't already done that. Anyway, just as I was getting attached to the schnauzer, who we'd started calling Luke—in remembrance of the escaped convict in the movie *Cool Hand Luke*—Rhonda got a hold of his owners and they came and got him.

The never-ending party died down when the police started knocking on our door. The Methodist Church complained to the law about beer cans and bottles, along with other miscellaneous trash ending up on their side of the street. So, with an excuse to come onto our property the police started making their presence known. Luckily our beer supply had dwindled so we weren't in possession of a wall of stolen goods anymore. Law enforcement was still looking for me and never failed to ask anyone and everyone where I was. They even hit-up people on the lots but reports of my whereabouts were scattered. Tina had gotten in some legal trouble with a new boyfriend and was on the run somewhere herself, so I didn't have to worry about *her* ratting me out again. My trail it seemed had cooled, and of course there were other crimes going on and the police had bigger problems than just some parole skipping, Jeep stealing, teenage hot head. However, a few of their tips like from Joyce and her ex—and probably a few others—did point toward the duplex. The cops told Robert and Rhonda about the church complaints, also letting them know the district attorney was wanting me found, inquiring if either of them had seen me. A couple of the city cops seemed particularly persistent, but without any evidence to the contrary they had no reason to push them when they said they hadn't. Although, the head dick in charge still threatened to cause either, or both of them problems if they were found to be lying. With the added pressure of the occasional county or city cop drive-by, or stop and knock; and, the lack of free brewskie, the endless-party ended.

It was just me, Rhonda, and Stephanie at the house. One of the rare times it was quiet. Rhonda and I were laying on the couch and teasing Stephanie about being such a hooch when Robert, Little Joe, and Bryan, Rhonda's brother came bursting through the front door.

Robert breathing hard, blurted out, "Jimmy we need your help. Some drunk-ass rednecks over at the Stage Coach Bar threw a beer bottle at me and threatened to fuck us up if they caught us cutting through the alley again."

The Stage Coach Bar was a small hole in the wall, on the ground floor of the apartment high-rise building across the parking lot from the church. You entered it from the back side, and it had another door that opened into the alley that they left open when it wasn't too cold outside. It was this door the drunk wanna-be regulators were harassing innocent passers-by from.

"Oh yeah?" I said, instantly angry. "We'll see who's fucking alley that is. Let's go."

We emptied out of the house. There were four guys and two girls to our little army. Having the regular house-load of people at a time like this would have been nice. Fate, however, never seems to give me an easy row-to-hoe. Regardless, we were going over there and making a statement win, lose, or draw.

"Have you got a plan, Jimmy?" Robert asked.

"Do I look like I have a plan? The best I can do is suggest we come down the alley from 6th Street. The girls should go all the way to the parking lot where they can get away if they have to. Little Joe needs to pick up some rocks or pieces of brick and station himself between them and us. And me, you, and Bryan will give the pricks a dose of their own medicine."

"A couple of them are pretty big," Bryan said.

"Well even if they get the better of us, they will know we were there.

We're not going to let them get away with doing you guys like that without costing them *something*."

At the corner of the building Little Joe stepped up hefting a couple good-sized pieces of masonry. "I am ready amigo."

I laughed, we all knew that Joe, Mexican that he may be, did not know a lick of Spanish. "Oh so now you're Zorro and I am your amigo, huh?"

"You damn straight," he said. "A friend is a friend, in any language." I grinned, Little Joe was a pretty good dude.

It was a cool night and I hadn't taken time to grab a jacket or even a long-sleeved shirt. I was surprised the juke-joint had the alley door open. But I supposed it was hot and stuffy inside the bar.

Rhonda gave me a quick kiss. Her eyes were twinkling from the street lights, dancing the way they always did when the shit was going down.

As we walked down the alley we came upon a trash dumpster that smelled like stale beer and bad meat. I opened it and found what I was looking for. Robert grinned knowing what I was up to. Bryan hung back near the corner of the high-rise and Little Joe and the girls moved on past the open door. As Robert and I neared the rectangle of dim, smokey light, I could hear music, laughter, and clinking bottles.

When the girls were at the end of the building where they would have a straight shot to the house if something went wrong I stepped into the door. Robert pointed at a tall lanky man standing at the bar. There was a woman and a couple of men pulled up near him. The lighting outside was only a little darker than the interior of the murky club. I now recognized Waylon Jennings singing about a good hearted woman on the jukebox. I threw the bottle I'd dug out of the trash at the vacant end of the bar. It had the desired effect when it exploded in a rain of flying brown bits of glass. All went quiet, except for Waylon crooning about being a good timin' man. "Somebody in here threw a beer bottle at my friends. We want them outside."

The lanky guy immediately bowed up, followed by four or five other patrons. Even the bartender was up in arms over the bottle I'd thrown.

All I could say was he shouldn't have let his customers throw them at my friends. The whole lot were cut from the same urban cowboy cloth—who knows, maybe one or two of them had actually rode a bull or roped a steer, and had some grit—but for my money I'm guessing they were just field hands dressing the part, and drinking enough to be rude, dip snuff, and think they were tough. Yee Haw.

"I did," said the tall lanky man Robert had pointed out. Poking his chest out, he stormed towards me. "We are tired of you punk-ass kids cutting through back here. Scratching our cars and trucks up and shit!"

We'd never done anything like that, but that wasn't the point here. I stepped back as he and the others converged on the door, letting him have room to strut out first. He was focused on me. The others, were just coming across the threshold heading toward Robert and Little Joe when I struck, shooting forward and head butting the tall man across the bridge of his nose.

The others came pouring out of the bar. From the corner of my eye I saw Robert lay into a beefy man and knock his hat off his head. Unfortunately the guy didn't even stumble, and the last glimpse I had of him he was swinging at Robert. There seemed to be a lot of movement all around, but I got lost in a red haze that fell over me as I pummeled my opponent into the wall and down to the ground.

He still had hold of his beer bottle and blindly swung it, hitting me in the shoulder. I grabbed his wrist and broke the bottle in his hand against a metal gas meter he was laying next to. His hand was bleeding but he held onto a broken shard of glass and tried to swing at my face. I recaptured his arm and pinned it to his side and then reared back and hammered my forehead into his ugly mug. If his nose wasn't broken before, it was now. Again and again I smashed my hard-ass melon into his face. Then I lost myself, hitting him over and over with my fists and elbows.... He had taken us to a savage place, and now I was consumed in it.

How long I was there battering the dude is a mystery to me. At one point I could hear someone yelling for me to stop. When my senses cleared, I looked down at a totally limp, unconscious, beaten bloody mess. My peripheral vision told me I was surrounded by denim covered legs, cowboy boots, and several knee-length skirts and high-heels. My hand closed on a fist-sized rock. A woman pleaded with me to stop.

"Get off of him!" It was a man speaking now, although he sounded panicked and his voice cracked. From getting a good look at what was left of his buddy, would be my guess. I was pretty shocked myself.

"I said get—offff!" This time he screamed it and ran behind me grabbing a handful of my semi-long brown hair. His momentum yanked me up and off of his friend—where the head goes the body follows. He let go and kept running trying to stay out of my reach, but I'd come up with the rock still in my hand and fast pitched it right into the back of the guys shaggy-blond head before he was three steps away.

Confusion washed over me—I was surrounded by enemies all yelling at me. Some women were crying. *Where are my friends?* The end of the alley facing the parking lot cleared and people moved back like ripples in a pond when the guy I'd hit with the rock, face-planted in the asphalt like a felled tree.

What I could see now was Rhonda with a beer bottle in her hand threatening a tall, broad man who had both hands on the roof of a car and was kicking something underneath it. Robert was being backed off by two other drunks as he was trying to get through the crowd to me.

Stepping right over the lifeless prone body of the dude who had pulled my hair. I could now see that the big redneck had Little Joe trapped under the car and was rearing back kicking him repeatedly with all he had. Rhonda tried swinging the bottle at the man, but he grabbed for her and she had to back off to evade his grasp.

"Get off of him and fight me," I bellowed and headed towards them.

An older man with a bad comb-over in his mid-forties or early fifties stepped between us opening his pocket knife. My Buck was in my hand in a flash. The man took one swipe at me and I sliced his forearm as it went by. He grabbed his wound and dropped out of the fight.

Robert and Rhonda ran up beside me—Stephanie was even halfway across the parking lot wielding rocks in each hand. Armed with a knife, Rhonda's bottle, and my friends, the crowd cleared out of our way leaving the jack-ass kicking Little Joe on his own. He saw us coming and broke off his assault and ran back into the line of spectators. The whole pub was outside now. They were, however, all keeping their distance.

Stephanie and Rhonda threw down their weapons and helped Little Joe out from under the sedan. They got him headed toward the house, while me and Robert stood facing the mob. We walked backwards until we were confident no one was going to follow us, then crossed the parking lot and jogged to our house on the other side of the street.

When we rolled up into the duplex Bryan was already there. Not looking any worse for wear. Rhonda and Stephanie were helping Joe lay on the couch, he groaned with every movement. It was apparent he'd gotten the blunt end of the stick. Robert had a pretty good-sized lump growing under his left eye.

Rhonda gasped, staring at my hands and arms. "God? It looks like you dipped your arms up to the elbows in red paint! Are you cut?"

It was the first time I'd had a chance to notice, they were ghastly, but none of it was my blood. With the heat of the moment past I went to wash my face and arms off in the kitchen sink while everyone started reliving their parts of the fight.

Robert held a cold beer to his cheekbone while he told about the big cowboy who hit like a horse kicked. He relayed how when he would punch the man—other than knocking his hat off—it didn't seem to even phase the guy.

Little Joe drew two of the drunken assholes to him. He threw his bricks at them catching one in the shoulder but the other one got by them and knocked him down where they started kicking him like he was a soccer ball. He had to crawl under the car to narrow their range, he said.

Rhonda and Stephanie were watching until they got Little Joe down, then Rhonda grabbed a beer bottle and ran over and hit one right behind the ear. The guy chased her and Stephanie ten or twelve steps but couldn't catch them. He gave up on Little Joe though and went after Robert.

I told them what I could remember of my ordeal, parts were lost in a black and red battle haze....

Bryan hadn't said anything.

When I noticed, I looked at him. "Where were you, Red? How come you ain't got any blood on you? The last time I saw you, you were at the end of the alley."

"I-I-I ran. I thought you were going to unload some bottles on them and then run."

Leaping over the couch in a single bound I hit him with both fists right in the center of his chest. He flew back into the wall leaving dents in our sheetrock. I brandished my knuckles at him but refrained from lighting him up. "You thought we were going to run!?" I snarled. "When have we ever run?" I was so mad I was shaking. "Look at Little Joe. Does it look like he ran? Your little sister has more balls than you do!"

Rhonda stepped up beside me and wrapped her hands over the fist she knew I was about to hit her brother in the face with. She was the only reason I hadn't already smoked his chicken-shit ass. "Bryan, you'd better leave. You're not one of us, and you need to quit trying to be."

He gathered himself, and hugging the wall, made a wide path around me and Robert. "We're really just kids, they were grown men. I didn't know what to do. I'm sorry."

"Save it Red, and just get out of here," I said.

He opened the door—then slammed it back shut.

"There's cops and an ambulance over at the bar!"

We killed the lights, and all ran to a different window. From my vantage point I could see the main entrance of the Stage Coach, sure enough a squad car and meat-wagon were pulled up to the front doors. The cops and EMTs must have been inside, they were nowhere to be seen. Although at the corner of the building we observed four or five people, at least one was a woman, carrying the limp figure of what looked like the first redneck I'd fought and laying him in the back seat of a car. When they had him loaded, two of the men and the woman climbed into the sedan and drove off, obviously not wanting to get caught up by the law. They were still going to have some explaining to do at the emergency room I thought.

Ten minutes later the EMTs came out the front doors wheeling someone on a gurney. Presumably the man I'd hit in the head with a rock, but it was hard to see him from where we were. Within a few minutes of loading him in the back they left. The police remained twenty more minutes talking to people before finally pulling off too. It looked like they made a point to drive by our house since they turned back toward the hospital at the next block.

For the first time I had to make myself feel concern for the well-being of the men we had put down. It was never my *intent* to do so much damage, but it seemed like I was getting more vicious as I got older. I wasn't sure if it was because I was growing bigger and more capable, or if it was a by-product of some of the horrific, violent, and frightening encounters that I had been faced with over the last few years. Don't get me wrong, I didn't have much sympathy for people who tried to hurt me, or the people I cared about, but I didn't want to become a soul-less animal either—and I could sense my empathy for these men becoming harder to hold onto.

The police raided our place three times after the bar fight. I don't know who told them what, but they were now on fire for me. And they seemed pretty angry with anyone and everyone who stayed in our house. Feeling now that they were covering for me and hiding me out all along.

The first time the cops came I was next door at the other duplex, There was a small group of people who lived over there. Although it was Naomi's place, a very pretty half-Indian girl; her boyfriend, Chad, who had been discharged from the military for mental issues and drug use, and a couple of their mutual friends lived with her. The first time I'd met Chad, he was rocking back and forth on the couch holding his head in both hands. "Don't ever shoot-up a green Placidil!" he said. "It's bad; it's no good!" Right then and there I marked that down on my lists of things not to do.

I was in their bathroom when I heard an official sounding knock at their front door. Naomi answered it. I listened as a police officer identified himself and asked her if there was a James, or a Jimmy Maxwell there. She told him there was a Jimmy in the restroom although she didn't know his last name. He asked to speak to him.

I came out of the lavatory then. "Jimmy this officer is looking for someone named James Maxwell. He asked to talk to you."

"Sure, though I don't know how much help I can be. I've only heard of him, don't even know him," I said as I passed her heading for the door. As far as I knew she didn't know my last name, but I knew the cop at the door was listening to what I was saying to her. So, I laid the groundwork for how I planned to handle the situation before I ever stepped into the doorway, and said "Hello, my name is Jimmy Brock. I hear you are looking for Maxwell?"

"Yes I am. We just searched the house next door for him. Do you by chance have any identification?"

"No, I am afraid I've never had a license and don't drive. As far as Jimmy Maxwell is concerned, I really don't know the guy, just heard of him. Why are you looking for him? Should we be concerned?"

He went on to tell me that that was none of my business. Following up with a line of questioning designed to determine whether I was lying to him of not.

I stayed as calm and aloof as I could, with my heart pounding in my chest like the Los Angeles Times printing press. When the officer finally seemed satisfied I wasn't who they were looking for, and we weren't hiding him out at Naomi's little pad either, he left. While the knots in my stomach untied themselves, I breathed a sigh of relief and counted myself lucky that I did not look much like my year-and-a-half old mug-shot. I had obviously been through some changes and aged since then.

The second time the cops came barging in I was laying right on the couch. I got up acting groggy—too groggy to make up a seamless lie about being Jimmy Brock, at least I hoped they would think that, still I acted unafraid and with Rhonda backing up my story they were hesitant to jump to conclusions. One of the officers was the same as before. Finally Robert woke-up in the other room and flew off the handle. He demanded their search warrant, which they didn't have. The policemen were digging through drawers in the kitchen, and pilfering through the medicine cabinet in the bathroom.

"Get the fuck out of my house! For the hundredth time, Jimmy Maxwell does not live here. And if he did, he wouldn't be in the fucking medicine cabinet!"

The police didn't like it, but they herded out the door. Before the officer who I'd had my exchange with over at Naomi's stepped out, he looked at Robert, but pointed his thumb at me, "One last thing. What is *his* name?"

"Jimmy Fucking Brock. Why, you after him, too?"

"No. I was just checking." He turned and left.

When we were sure they were gone, Robert laughed. "Damn, it's a good thing you told me what had happened next door. I just put two and two together."

Two days later, and a week-and-a-half since the bar fight someone drove by the house and fired four or five rounds into it. They went high and straight through the walls, lodging in the rafters on the other side of the duplex. We looked but found no exit holes. After that Louis gave me a Saturday Night Special to carry with me.

The cops were not called and not involved in the shooting, but apparently they got wind of it. Within the week they came busting through our door like gang-busters. In the middle of the day. Warrant in hand.

Sleeping one off in the bedroom, I had the small .32 caliber pistol laying on my stomach in a purple Crown Royal bag. Rhonda running into the bedroom caused me to open my eyes. She came straight to me, keeping her back to the bedroom door she grabbed the bag and shoved it down her pants. Before Rhonda had the string from the Crown Royal sack tucked all the way in, three officers all trying to fit through the doorway at once, sprang in guns drawn.

"Do not move! Jimmy Maxwell, you are under arrest. And don't bother trying to tell us you are not him. We have a positive ID this time!"

Rhonda leant down and kissed me before the cops pulled her back and shoved her to the side, out of the way.

There was no point in fighting it. They had me. Hell, they had me cuffed before I could even formulate any words.

Rhonda tried to come to me again, but they pushed her back. "They just rushed in, Jimmy. And went straight for the room. I love you. I'll wait for you."

When I was shoved into the living room there were at least ten people, including Bryan who we 'd let come back, all herded to the far end of the den. They all looked ashamed for letting the law-dogs sneak up on us like this. Robert looked especially abashed, he shook his head and dropped his shoulders.

"Don't worry about it bro, I'll be back." With those last words I was escorted out the door. Well-armed officers came from both sides of the house. They were not playing around this time. They may have even planned on shooting me given an excuse. And if Rhonda hadn't gotten to that gun when she did, I very likely would have been. I looked back and saw her standing on the porch. Her face was sad. I winked at her...she smiled, and waved a half-wave, then I was pushed into the back of the squad car.

My charges included: assault and battery with a dangerous weapon— several regular assaults, one count of burglary which was a complete fabrication, theft of a motor vehicle, and vandalism (Joy's hot-rod Lincoln). Not to mention, a half-dozen parole violations. The powers-that-were considered adjudicating me as an adult since I was now seventeen, but in the end the burglary, vandalism, and a couple of the assaults were dropped. There was still, however, more than enough to wrap me up and send me back to Helena.

The jail was a barred box with several celled tanks, perched on top of Guymon's four-story Victorian court house. From the window, where they kept the juveniles, I could see the flat tops of the one- and two-story buildings on the other side of Main Street and the alley behind them. Rhonda would climb up the back walls and hang out on the roof-tops, where without too much effort we could holler I love you's and other short messages to each other. She wanted to take her clothes off for me—the guys in the next tank over almost cried, when I nixed the idea. Even if it wasn't for the perverts on the other side of the wall, it was getting too cold, and I didn't want her suffering just for the idiots next door's entertainment. It even snowed a couple days later and she was up there walking out the shape of a building-sized heart in the white fluff.

Before I left to go back to the reformatory she told me she loved me and would always be mine. I told her that they could only keep me until the end of the year. But to be watching for me, because I would be back the first time "the man" took his eyes off of me.

"I'll be waiting," she said.

CHAPTER 18

MUSTANG

It was late January before I got my assortment of new felonies and my revocation wrapped up. The Panhandle had just had its worst snow storm in years. Handcuffed and leg-shackled, I rode in the back of the county's only SUV, cold even though the heater was blowing.

I watched out the window as we drove mile after mile through the snow covered landscape. The only disturbance in the roiling blanket of white was the oil and exhaust-stained slush splattered ribbon of highway we traveled, which seemed as offensive to the countryside's clean pristine beauty as a long brown skid-mark in a pair of brand new tighty-whities.

When the reformatory came into sight I noted how the vista of cottony snow-drifts covering the grounds, trees, and rooftops softened the eerie and malevolent impression I'd gotten from my first look at the reform school over a year before. Or maybe it was that I now knew what to expect, and the mystery of the unknown no longer haunted the inner passageways of my mind with anxiety and trepidation. Thereby allowing me a less exaggerated point of view. Either way, it was not as intimidating the second time around.

Many of the guards now knew me by name. So, when the deputy duo from Guymon hustled me through the gate-shack's door, stomping ice and snow from their boots, I was met with, "Well look at this Bob, Santa brought us a late Christmas present. It's Jimmy Maxwell, all wrapped up in holiday tinsel."

It was Phillips, the Sergeant Carter look-a-like. He had replaced the *Hills Have Eyes* desk-jockey with bad teeth. I can't say that I was happy to see him. I'd disliked him ever since he'd crimped my cuffs on my wrist as tight as he could make them and left me in that Dodge House cell so long ago. And although he hadn't played a major role in the beatings I took up in LTD, he had been there, and was a part of the rat pack they had here.

The one thing which hadn't changed was Bob. Bob Bowers, I'd learned his full name was. He didn't always work the gate-house, but it was a strange sense of Deja vu that he happened to be there to see me processed in again. He stood there, for the second time, frowning at me with his leathery, weather-beaten face.

"What's the matter Maxwell, you miss our cookin' or somethin'? Or maybe you are just one of those guys who are going to make coming to jail a lifetime habit." He looked disappointed.

The Guymon deputies removed their hardware from my wrists and ankles, signed me over to Phillips, and left.

Then Bob said, "Come on Fuck-up, I'll take you up the hill. We were expecting you."

There was a certain breed of officers like Phillips, Carver, Walter, and many others that would always enjoy seeing my failure. Or anyone's they deemed beneath them. I'd come to expect it. The funny thing was, Bob being disappointed in my return, oddly made me see him in a different light than I had before. *He must actually give a damn*, I thought. *Old hard-ass. Go figure.*

After we got inside the grounds and were making our way up the snow covered sidewalk, I said, "Mr. Bowers, you are right, I am a screw-up. I make the worst decisions. Seems like I just do things before I think them through. I don't intend to let people down. It just happens."

"Well Maxwell, things probably won't change for you until you decide that you don't want to let *yourself* down anymore. Like they say in AA, You can't get sober for someone else. I reckon you can't change other bad habits for anyone else either." He paused as he thought about what pearl of wisdom he was going to drop next. "At some point you'll want to get ahead in life, and you can't move forward if you are always going backwards." The old man didn't go as far as smile at me, but he did soften a bit. I could see it in the set of his shoulders.

When we got to the top of the ice-covered steps leading to Impala, Mr. Bowers hesitated before bringing us to the barred, glass front door. "Word to the wise. Since Maxine's death, there has been a more punitive and even vindictive attitude building among some of the officers here. People are still hurting, and still very angry. I suggest you do your time and get on through this. And while you are here stay off of their radar."

I nodded my thanks, and my understanding, then walked through Impala's door.

It looked the same, it smelled the same, and it felt the same, but it was totally different. There was a new person sitting behind Mr. Green's desk. Green had retired. It was said that after what happened to Mrs. Fullerton he just couldn't stand being there anymore. It was strange, but his absence changed the whole atmosphere of Impala. It didn't help that I didn't know any of the kids who were now there either. When I got out of orientation I hoped to find out what had become of all the friends I'd left behind. It seemed I was alone. I was beginning to wonder if I was going to have to start over carving out a new reputation for myself.

However, my cavalier, *Been there done that*, attitude carried me through Impala, this round, without any of the problems or issues I'd had the first time. Hell, if anything it was the opposite, being considered a veteran of the worst this place had to dish-out gave me a bit of celebrity among the newbies in orientation. Regardless, I wasn't there long. Two weeks into it, a case manager informed me since they already had my test scores and I didn't need to be indoctrinated again. I was to be moved to Mustang the following day.

I was happy enough to hear that, even with my *Walk on water* status, being back in Impala was depressing. Or maybe it was Bob's less than hopeful insights into my life that had me chagrined. Either way, stuck in limbo with a bunch of first timers feeding me a hundred questions a day was getting me down. Things would be better once I was back in general population. I hoped.

Walking up the sidewalk to Mustang I could see a dozen faces staring at me through the front door. I'd heard they started locking the sally-ports of the regular units now. After what happened you now had to have an officer key the door before you could leave the unit. The kids were grouped up in the foyer, friends or foes, I could not tell. No sooner had I made it through the door than I was surrounded and accosted by a crowd of teenage thugs.

Nathan Lentz and Shifter led the charge, they were still there! "Hey brother! Man, it's good to see you," Nate said, giving me a hug and a slap on the back that almost knocked the bag of clothes, letters, and books I was carrying, out of my arms. At the same time I was being hugged and pulled on by Wayne Womble, Billy Beasley, Timmy the nose picker, and Curtis Whitesel, who I hadn't seen since LTD. There were others, who I hadn't know as well. They were all around me slapping me on the shoulders and telling me how much they missed me. Along with throwing a barrage of questions my way.

I was stunned, and happy, and confused. "How the hell did all of you end up here on the same unit?"

Wayne stepped to the forefront and told me that a lot of kids got sent home after the incident. Not as many as we'd hoped and obviously not them, but enough to empty out a couple of units. For a few months the staff had consolidated the remaining kids in Mustang and Cadillac. Of course, since then, the reformatory had filled back up.

"Damn Wayne. I thought you would have aged out of this bitch by now," I said shoving him back as he was trying to hug me again.

"Three more weeks. I ain't glad you are back here, but I am glad I got to see you before I go home. We were just talkin' about you the other day."

The genuine friendship and enthusiasm these guys expressed toward me felt good. I looked over the heads of the kids who were around me and saw Kilo standing by one of the dinner tables. Watching us. I could tell he wanted to come over and say something, but he didn't.

I spent the next two hours catching up with everyone and settling back into Mustang life. It hadn't changed much—still had the same foosball table. I was even given a single cubicle on the same side and section, three beds down from where I bunked the last time I was there. Only the faces had changed and not as many of them as I would have expected.

Mr. Bob was right about a shift in attitude around there, soon as I got back in general population it was very clear to me that while I'd been gone the "Hatchet Crew", "Rat Pack", "Goon Squad" whatever you wanted to call them, had stepped up and taken a more active and visible role in the day to day operations of the institution. They trolled around picking on everyone just like they did in LTD. If anything they were even worse. Now that they seemed to have the backing of the administration and public sentiment, they were true tyrants. They would make kids stand in the snow and hold buckets half-full of water out to their sides until it froze, which it never really did. It was just torture, plain and simple. Or run laps around the unit without a coat or shoes. Randomly inspecting or shaking down a kids cube while they made him stand at attention in front of it. If it wasn't to their satisfaction he stood there for hours. The kid would be shaking and ready to collapse before the dick-wads would release him. If you bucked them, or fought back, then you went to Dodge House. A few days later you came back with black eyes and bruises—and a different attitude.

For some reason, other than making me shovel snow, do PT, go to school, and all the normal daily shit, the staff generally avoided confronting me. I assumed that since they had already taken me as far down the road of pain as they could get away with—and I survived—that maybe I was exempt or something. Maybe me attacking them the way I did gave them some weird respect for me, I didn't know. Regardless of the reason, I was happy for it, though I still despised Walter and the rest of them. Lieutenant Carver on the other hand, had a different, almost apologetic attitude towards me, like we had weathered a storm together. Maxine had helped me, even got him chewed-out over his abusive nature, it was possible I suppose that out of respect for her he'd had a change of heart, at least in my case.

To be honest I noticed that the guards who either made up the goon squad, or were cast from the same mold seemed to concentrate their aggression and hatefulness more toward the African American population than anyone else. I don't know if it was racism, as the black kids all claimed. They were sure all the cops were Klan members, or some such shit. Maybe that was some of it, but they sure didn't discriminate when they were beating me senseless up in LTD. And, the couple of black guards who worked there were just as bad. Myself, I thought it had to do more with the fact that Armstrong was black, and they were mad at anyone who looked like him for what he did to Mrs. Fullerton. If Keith were white, or Mexican, I was pretty sure their focus would have been pin-pointed in those directions. But, what the hell do I know.

Either way, it wasn't fair to blame everyone for what one sick sack of shit did. Although what could you really expect from a small-minded pack of bullies, who believed it was alright to stomp-out teenage kids in the first place. You would think their mommas would have raised them better.

They went after Kilo.

We had talked a few times since I'd been back. Enough to understand that when Tracy, Niegro, and I escaped without even giving him the chance to come, instead leaving him behind to get jumped by the very people he rode against with us, it felt like a huge betrayal to him.

I wanted to defend our motives, but the truth was no one even thought to ask Kilo—or about the repercussions of leaving him behind. We trusted him. He could have come with us as far as I was concerned. It never even crossed our minds. He was right we had let him down in a big way. I wasn't sure if it was enough for me to forgive him for riding against me in Impala...but it was a start.

All I could say was: "I didn't mean for it to be like that. We were just caught up in the moment and didn't think..."

He looked solemnly at me, "Would you have asked me to go if I was white? We were friends. I thought."

"I don't know Kilo. We asked Niegro, he's not white. The three of us always sat around day dreaming about running off. You never mentioned it.... I just don't know the answer." His line of interrogation caused me to look at the whole thing from a different perspective. I didn't think that was the reason. However, now that he put it to me like that, I wasn't sure.

Our few talks went a long way toward at least making us not hate one another, but we'd both erected too many barriers between us to get back to where we were. We did start acknowledging each other when we passed again. So I guess it was an improvement.

Kilo got into it with Sergeant Phillips. Phillips wasn't as big an asshole as the rest of the Hatchet Crew were, he was a little older, maybe a little wiser. Nevertheless he was still a prick; as I well knew. He caught Kilo smoking in the bathroom.

"Give me a hundred push-ups. Right here. Right now," Sarge ordered Kilo.

"In the dayroom, but no way am I doing push-ups on this nasty-ass floor."

"Oh yes, that's exactly why you are doing them *in here*. At the scene of the crime. Maybe you'll learn not to smoke in here. Now get down there and hug the fucking floor."

"Fuck you, you fat-headed cracker!"

Kilo tried to leave the bathroom past the heavy-set older man, but Phillips stepped in front of him and pushed him back. Faster than his good sense could keep up Kilo planted both palms in the middle of the sergeant's chest, slamming him into the door frame. Kilo then stormed out of the lavatory and went to his cubicle.

The sergeant turned red as a stop sign. His hat had fallen off and the thin patchy flat-top he had on his head could not hide his flaming fury as his blood pressure boiled over. "You're going to regret that Mr. Washington. You just wait!" he shouted at Kilo on his way to the phone. Before the sarge picked up the receiver he bellowed, "Everyone to your cubicles, NOW!"

There was no doubt about what was going to happen to Kilo from there. The Rat Pack had put kids in the hospital for less.

Soon another officer came in and relieved Phillips. Kilo knew what to expect when the man left and was pacing in front of his cubicle. He had always been more of a loner and didn't have many friends on the unit. The few homeboys he did have had already been cowed by the rough-shod manner they'd been treated by the guards since Mrs. Fullerton's murder and were keeping their distance from him. As sure as if he had the plague.

I was standing across the unit at the end of my cubicle, watching him circle his area by the bathroom like a caged panther. Fear was etched in every line of his face. He appeared deep in thought. Suddenly he turned and walked over to me. Billy, Wayne, and Nate all lived on the east side across from me too. They were watching to see what Kilo was doing.

"Jimmy, you know I don't got nobody gonna help if they jump me. I know we has our problems. Me sidin' against you with Leroy wuz just as big a mistake as y'all leaving me behind, maybe more so since I knew what I wuz doin' when I did it. But we were friends. Will you help me if them jack-straws start to hurt me too bad?"

It was a good speech, and honestly I didn't know what my answer was.... He'd stood against me and I was under no illusions that he probably would have put the boots to me right along with Leroy and the others if it had went that way. I stared at him un-committed while I ran every moment I'd known him through my head. With everything we both now knew thrown in with it. Fighting the police, regardless how righteous the cause, or how badly we might beat their asses in this moment, was a lot to ask, especially with the baggage Kilo and I had between us. Because they eventually would have me isolated in a cell again where I would be at the Rat Pack's mercy. It would not end well—*could not* end well. They had hurt me worse the last time than I had ever let on.

He could see the distrust on my face and he didn't have time to try and convince me—or even wait for an answer; because right then six hard-core squad members came stomping through the door with Sergeant Phillips straggling in behind. Resigning himself to his fate Kilo ran back over to his side of the building.

The crew was led in by Walter, my big, corn-fed, sadistic nemesis. Lieutenant Carver wasn't among them. The rest of the gang were all there; Chett, Bill, Jones, from the Torino, and two newbies to the Rat Pack that I had never seen before. And of course there was Sergeant Phillips, but he stood aside and pointed Kilo out to Walter, who immediately took charge.

At that moment I still was not sure what I was going to do. What I *was sure of*, seeing the big-ass hateful hayseed of a child abusing piece of shit Walter storming by in his calve-high army boots with the legs of his pants stuck down in them and laced up like he was going to war, was that if something or someone didn't interfere here, Kilo was going to be seriously injured.

They were all big men. Even Chett, though he was slim, was tall and lanky, and had big gnarled knuckled hands. And the two new guys looked like they could have played college ball. They didn't even wait to see if Kilo would comply. They struck as soon as he was surrounded. I saw Kilo swinging, but he was soon lost in a sea of rednecks.

God how I hated Walter, and that whole bunch. They had hurt me pretty bad. And you know what? Regardless of what Kilo did or didn't do with Leroy, he had rode with me against him too, and I for whatever lame-ass reason had left him behind. I could hear him in my head asking me, "*Would you help me if I were white?*" And I could hear me telling Nathan, "*I would have helped him, and you should have too.*"

Kilo yelled as he went down. My indecision evaporated like a drop of water on a hot griddle, and suddenly I was there smoking my way through their ranks. Aimed straight at Walter like a heat-seeking missile. *CRACK!* I heard the bone break. I'd hit him from the side right behind his jawbone. When he went down I turned on Jones and gunned him down. Kilo got to his feet. With new hope breathing life into him, he went after Phillips, who turned and tried to get away. But Kilo caught him and rode him to the floor. He was hitting him in the back of the head all the way down.

Billy, Wayne, and Nate dove in and within seconds it was a melee. We had the goon-squad so bunched together that as long as you were swinging you were hitting someone.

Shifter, Timmy, Curtis, and the rest of my friends ran over from the other side and together we kicked the Hatchet Crew to pieces.

When I looked up the whole unit was with us. White, black, Mexican—it didn't matter—we rolled the officers up and threw them and the houseparent out the front door. Someone tore the phone off the wall, and a couple other guys pushed the desk into the sally-port effectively barricading the door...and that is when we paused long enough to realize what we had done. We had seized control of the unit. *Man...oh man.*

Kilo came up to me, "Thanks Maxwell. Ain't no doubt them hillbillies would have hurt me bad if you hadn't helped me. I am sorry I doubted you."

"Well don't thank me yet." I nodded to draw his attention through the glass of the barred front door. Outside men were already gathering; holding batons, tire thumpers, ball bats, and more than one ax-handle. At least they looked like ax-handles from where I was. "We just knocked a hornets nest out of the rafters with the barn doors locked. There is nowhere to run and we are about to get stung."

Someone broke a window out and yelled at the gathering crowd: "Fuck you coppers...You'll never take us alive!"

We looked at each other and both cracked up. It was nervous laughter, but laughter nonetheless.

"Yeah well, whatever else happens here, yo-ass helped me when it would'a been easier for ya not to, and I won't never be forgetting it."

He glanced solemnly at me. "So what now?"

Nate, Womble, Billy, and Curtis were crowding around us, along with a couple of Kilo's friends who had joined in. "Yeah, what do we do now?" Wayne asked.

A kid guarding the door said some po-pos were coming to the door. Lieutenant Carver knocked on the glass, coach Schwab was standing beside him.

"I don't know," I said, "I didn't plan this it just happened. But let's find out what they have to say."

When I got to the door I could see Mr. Bowers, from the gatehouse, standing behind Carver and the coach. And behind him out on the sidewalk was a line of men: police, guards, school teachers, even farmers and men from town. They had to be volunteers, it's the only thing that could explain where all of them had come from so quickly. The line of club wielding men stretched around the building out of sight. A kid looking between the slats of the north side windows confirmed that the whole building was surrounded. They were all armed with some type of weapon and they didn't appear too happy to be standing out in the cold.

"Let those three in," I told the four or five kids guarding the door.

They pulled the desk back and the three men I had probably come to know best in my time there at Helena entered the foyer. Directing his attention to me, the Lieutenant spoke: "Maxwell, are you the one leading this little insurrection?"

"No one is leading anything," I said squaring myself. "Everybody is just tired of the abuse that Walter and his crew have been handing out. I am surprised you weren't with them."

"A year ago I would have been. A lot has happened since then, and I have had a change of heart, so to speak. But they are saying *you* attacked them. I am trying to help you kids here. Those men outside are wanting to come in here and lay waste to all of you. The town still has a lot of raw nerves when it comes to this place."

"Look LT, there were six of them, seven if you count Phillips. They came straight in here and put the boots to a sixteen-year-old kid. That ain't right. And after what I went through with y'all up in LTD I couldn't stand by and watch it happen to someone else."

Mr. Bowers stepped up with the coach beside him. "I warned you when you got back about these guys. So there are some of us who understand"—he nodded at coach Schwab, who nodded back—"but if you kids don't give this unit up peacefully and come out with us, the people outside are going to use it as an excuse to hurt as many of you as they can."

I looked at Carver. "Most of these guys didn't do nothing wrong. So what exactly is it that you want?"

"Well, a few of you are going to the Dodge House—"

"Oh yeah so you can separate us from our pals where Walter and his bunch can gang up on us one at a time."

"No Maxwell." Carver shook his head then looked over my shoulder. "Walter is in no shape to do anything. You unhinged his jaw. It appears to be causing him some complications, something to do with nerve damage Doc said. He is on his way to the hospital in Enid."

"Tell him everything Kyle," the coach said, glaring at the Lieutenant.

Carver went on, "I'm not going to lie to you. They are talking about putting charges on you and certifying you as an adult over this. Depends on how bad Walt is hurt, I guess. If you come with us and give this up we'll all three try to help you. You will still have to go to the city jail for now. The others will remain here and probably get out of lock-up in a few weeks.

"If you refuse and we have to take the unit back by force; the district attorney is not only going after you, but Washington, Lentz, Whitesel, and Womble—who is almost eighteen anyway. There are a couple other names the sergeant pointed out, but I don't remember them."

I shuffled from foot to foot looking at the floor. *How do I get myself into these things?* I thought. I looked at my friends. Their futures were hanging on my decision. A couple appeared nervous. I glanced at Wayne.

He read my mind. "Don't worry about me bro. I'll ride this horse to Hell and back with my hair on fire with you, if that is what you want to do."

I gave him a bear hug. "That's exactly why I'm not going to take you down that road, Wayne."

"I'll ride, too," Timmy said. I smiled at him, that kid was always surprising me.

Curtis stepped up, "Hell we all will." There were nods all around.

"And I wouldn't do that to any of you for the same reasons I wouldn't Wayne." I sure felt proud that these boys were my friends. Turning to my three escorts, I held my wrists out towards Carver. "Let's go. There is no winning this and I'm not dragging everyone down with me."

Carver nodded, then pulled his cuffs out and took me into custody.

The kids lined both sides of the foyer as the officers were walking me past with my hands chained in front of me. They each patted me on the back as I went by and said something personal.

Kilo was last, waiting at the door. He grabbed one of my cuffed hands and shook it. "I'm sorry about this. But I am damn glad you jumped in, we both know it would have been me going to the hospital. I won't forget what you did for me."

I shook his hand back. "It's the same thing I would have done if you wuz white." Then I winked at him.

He laughed out loud and slapped me on the shoulder. "You's a hell'uva cracker that's for sure."

Carver pushed me on out the door. Coach Schwab got close to my ear, and said, "I wouldn't worry about them charges. I am going to have a talk with the warden. I don't think he would want the DA digging too deep into Walter's background the way he would have to to prepare for a case like this...if you know what I mean."

The city jail sucked. It was small and the only other guy in it was a drunk who wallowed in his own vomit for a day and a half before he was released. However they did feed me food right from the little cafe on the corner. I was only there three days myself before a couple of transport officers came and picked me up.

Apparently the coach knew his business. There were to be no charges, and no certification. And as an added bonus, Walter no longer worked at the reformatory. I always wished I knew what the coach knew about that fat piece of crap, but I never found that out.

Anyway, even though Walter was out of the picture, the warden still wanted me out of his facility. And just so happened there was a brand-new juvenile detention center in Sand Springs, Oklahoma, opening up. It was called ITC, (Intensive Treatment Center), and it had already acquired the nickname "Little Mac". A play on Oklahoma's maximum-security prison in McAlester, which was called "*Big* Mac". ITC was an all-indoor complex with the newest technology and psychological advancements. It was maximum security. Designed to hold the hard-core juvenile offenders: murderers, rapists, psychotics, and now—apparently—me.

ABOUT THE AUTHOR

Jimmy Maxwell currently resides in the state of Oklahoma. A true outlaw, Jimmy has been in and out of lock-up since the age of fifteen. Over the years he fought his way to the top of one of the most feared gangs in Oklahoma. He has been featured on MSNBCs 'Lockup, and on Discovery Channel's 'I Almost Got Away With It,' Jimmy has survived five different riots, and has escaped on multiple occasions from prison, jail, and reform schools, as well as evading capture by the U.S. Marshals and the state's Violent Crimes Fugitive Task Force for months on end. Jimmy Maxwell has narrowly avoided apprehension and death time and again...from which he now writes books and stories.

Although Jimmy has since retired from gang life, he did so with honor and the blessing of those who love and are loyal to him, and he still remains a respected and influential member of the prison community on both the state and federal levels. He now uses his books, stories, and influence to help others avoid the pitfalls of prison and drugs. After all this time he believes through hard work and education—there is a better way.

—Justin Case, editor/admin, Prison from the Inside Out

"My choices have cost me years of family, friends, freedom on the outside—and a lot more. Let the bad choices I made be a chance for you not to follow my path."

—Jimmy Maxwell

JimmyMaxwell.net

OTHER BOOKS BY THIS AUTHOR

American Outlaw Series

American Outlaw: Price of Pride
American Kidd: End of Innocence

Other Books

Tangle Eye

Coming Soon

American Bad Boy: Coming of Age
American Gangster: Making A Name

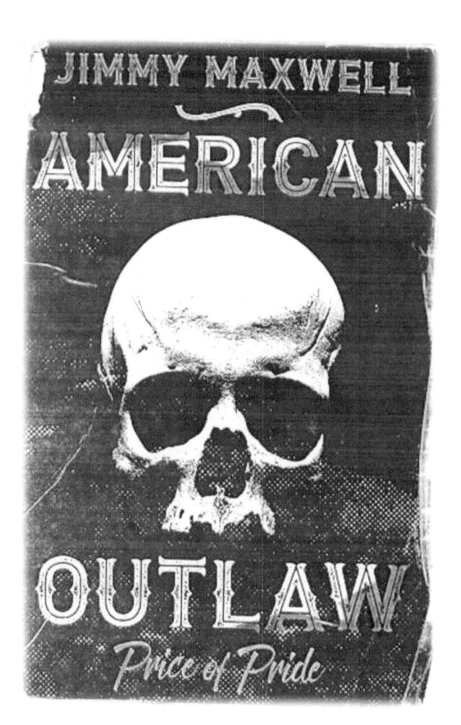

AMERICAN OUTLAW

American Outlaw: Price of Pride is the first book in a non-fictional series based on the life of the modern-day outlaw, Jimmy Maxwell.

American outlaw is an autobiography written around Jimmy's MSNBC Lock Up appearance. This is a galvanizing adventure of nonstop action that will take you on a roller coaster ride through the worlds that most people only see on the big screen.

Peer through the eyes of Jimmy Maxwell as he takes you behind the violent prison walls and to the top of one of Oklahoma's most notorious and feared gangs. Be with him when he finally walks out of those cold institutional gates into the free world for the first time in 16 years! And stand with Jimmy - or against him - as the federal marshals go all out … to get him locked back behind them.

"American outlaw is a raw an unapologetic journey into the world of one of Oklahoma's most notorious inmates. In sincere, and colorful language, Jimmy Maxwell conveys the complex, bewildering - and sometimes terrifying - truth of time spent running from the law."

-Michael Mason, EDITOR THIS LAND MAGAZINE.

AMERICAN KIDD

Turning 15 isn't always easy,
sometimes it's a battle just to reach ten.

"Maxwell's high octane life breaks all the rules along with a few laws. Told with wit and steely confidence. Maxwell's writings feel deeply personal and adventurous."
-Michael Mason, EDITOR THIS LAND MAGAZINE.

This is the second volume in the "American Outlaw" series, a nonfiction, "coming of age" tale of survival, rebellion, love, adventure, violence, and death. In American Kid the modern-day outlaw, Jimmy Maxwell takes us back to his very beginning and carries us with him as he navigates the disturbing memories of his hard-won adolescence. We travel within Jimmy's world, living vicariously through him as we once again find ourselves on the rollercoaster ride that was Mr. Maxwell's life. Experience one youthful pulse pounding adventure after another until it culminates in a truly life changing set of events, which is the End of Innocence. This is the formative years of one of Oklahoma's most infamous inmates, outlaw and author, Jimmy Maxwell

Order Form

Make **Money Orders** PayableTo:

Titles Available For Sell On Amazon.com

QTY	Available Publications	Price
	American Outlaw	
	American Kidd	
	American Teenager	

Ship To:

Name: _____

Address: _____

City: _____ State: _____ Zip: _____

For Shipping and Handling: Add $3.75 for 1st Book. Add $1.75 for each additional book. All books are also available on Amazon and Kindle. All titles coming soon, also can be pre-ordered.

Made in United States
North Haven, CT
14 September 2022

24074222R00163